MAN AND THE BIOSPHERE SERIES

Series Editor J.N.R. Jeffers

VOLUME 17

THE ECOLOGY OF TROPICAL FOREST TREE SEEDLINGS

Edited by M. D. Swaine

Department of Plant & Soil Science
University of Aberdeen
UK

PUBLISHED BY

PARIS

AND

The Parthenon Publishing Group

International Publishers in Science, Technology & Education

Published in 1996 by the United Nations Educational, Scientific and Cultural Organization,
7 Place de Fontenoy, 75700 Paris, France—UNESCO ISBN 92-3-103299-2
and
The Parthenon Publishing Group Limited
Casterton Hall, Carnforth,
Lancs LA6 2LA, UK—ISBN 1-85070-687-5
and
The Parthenon Publishing Group Inc.
One Blue Hill Plaza
PO Box 1564, Pearl River,
New York 10965, USA—ISBN 1-85070-687-5

© Copyright **UNESCO 1996**

Typeset by Martin Lister Publishing Services, Carnforth, Lancs.
Printed by Bookcraft (Bath) Ltd, Midsomer Norton, UK

British Library Cataloguing in Publication Data

Ecology of Tropical Forest Tree Seedlings. – (Man & the Biosphere Series; Vol. 18)
  I. Swaine, M. D. II. Series
  582.16052623

ISBN 1-85070-687-5

Library of Congress Cataloging-in-Publication Data

The ecology of tropical forest tree seedlings / edited by M.D. Swaine.
        p.   cm. – (Man and the biosphere series : v. 18)
    Based on papers from a workshop held by Unesco.
    Includes bibliographical references and index.
    ISBN 1-85070-687-5
    1. Rain forest plants–Ecophysiology–Congresses. 2. Trees–Seedlings–
Ecophysiology–Tropics–Congresses. 3. Rain forest ecology–Congresses. 4. Forests and
forestry–Tropics–Congresses. 5. Forest plants–Ecophysiology–Congresses. 6. Forest
ecology–Congresses. I. Swaine, M. D. (Mike D.) II. Unesco. III. III. Series.
QK938.R34E36   1995
581.5′2642–dc20   95-40788
                                                                              CIP

PREFACE

UNESCO's Man and the Biosphere Programme

Improved scientific understanding of natural and social processes associated with the environment is the focus of UNESCO's Man and the Biosphere Programme. It works towards this aim through the provision of information useful to resource managers and administrators and by promoting the conservation of genetic diversity. Much work is devoted to problem-solving ventures that bring together scientists, policy-makers and local people. In parallel with this, the programme seeks to develop scientific networks and strengthen regional co-operation.

Launched in the early 1970s, the programme is nationally based but internationally co-ordinated. MAB emphasizes problem solving research, training and demonstration. Often interdisciplinary teams are assembled to analyse interactions between ecological and social systems. A systems approach is used to understand relationships between development and the environment.

MAB is a decentralized programme with field projects and training activities in all regions of the world. Universities, academies of sciences, national research laboratories and other research and development institutions are all involved and brought together under the auspices of more than 100 MAB National Committees. Co-operation with a range of international government and non-governmental organizations is characteristic of the MAB Programme.

Man and the Biosphere Book Series

The Man and the Biosphere Series was launched to help communicate results from the MAB Programme. Primarily aimed at upper level university students, scientists and resource managers, the books are not normally suitable as undergraduate textbooks but rather seek to provide additional resource material. Some books are based on primary case studies that involve original data collection. Others provide a synthesis of global and regional research across several sites or countries. In all cases, a state of the art assessment of knowledge and methodological approaches is sought. In some cases, books are commissioned. The series editor is John Jeffers, formerly Director of the Institute of Terrestrial Ecology in the United Kingdom, who has been associated with MAB since its inception.

The Ecology of Tropical Forest Tree Seedlings

Ecosystem functioning and resource use in humid tropical regions has been the focus of several earlier volumes in the Man and the Biosphere Book Series. Case study experience has been reported on the structure and function of a nutrient-stressed rain forest ecosystem in Venezuela, pulpwood logging in Papua New Guinea, shifting agriculture and sustainable development in northeastern India, and Brazilian perspectives on Amazonian development. Multi-authored volumes have focused on such subjects as rain forest regeneration and management, the reproductive ecology of tropical forest plants, and relations between tropical forest, people and food.

The present volume, *Ecology of Tropical Forest Tree Seedlings*, is based on a scientific workshop held at the University of Aberdeen (United Kingdom) in September 1992. The focus is on the young tree, from the vulnerable newly germinated seedling to the well-established plant, and on the factors affecting the high mortality during this stage in tree development. Much selection of individuals occurs at this time, which can have a profound influence on the composition and diversity of the forest.

Following a scene-setting overview and foreword by volume editor M.D. Swaine, the thirteen contributions include wide ranging reviews and more focused research papers. Addressed are such issues as the demography, morphology and physiology of seedlings and their responses to the availability of resources, notably light, nutrients and water. Among the aims of the volume is that of highlighting the importance of seedling ecology in tropical forestry, and of promoting interaction and understanding between forestry and ecology. As such, the intended primary audience of the book is researchers and managers with backgrounds in forestry who are interested in the structure, functioning and management of tropical forest systems, and more particularly the role and characteristics of tree seedlings in those systems.

MAN AND THE BIOSPHERE SERIES

CONTENTS

2. PHOTOSYNTHETIC RESPONSES TO LIGHT IN TROPICAL RAIN FOREST TREE SEEDLINGS

Malcolm C. Press, Nick D. Brown, Martin G. Barker and Simon W. Zipperlen

3. FUNCTIONAL MORPHOLOGY OF TROPICAL TREE SEEDLINGS

Nancy C. Garwood

LIST OF CONTRIBUTORS

P.M.S. Ashton
School of Forestry and
  Environmental Studies
Yale University
New Haven
CT 06511
USA

P.S. Ashton
Arnold Arboretum
Harvard University
Cambridge
MA 02138
USA

Martin G. Barker
School of Biological Sciences
University of Manchester
Manchester M13 9PL
UK
(Jabatan Biologi, Universiti Brunei
Darussalam, Gadong 3188, Brunei)

René G.A. Boot
Tropenbos Programme
Lot 12E Garnett Street
Campbellville
Georgetown
Guyana
(Dept. of Plant Ecology and
  Evolutionary Biology, Utrecht
University, PO Box 80084, 3508
Utrecht, The Netherlands)

Nick D. Brown
Oxford Forestry Institute
University of Oxford
South Parks Road
Oxford OX1 3RB
UK

David F.R.P. Burslem
Department of Plant Sciences
Downing Street
Cambridge CB2 3EA
UK
(Oxford Forestry Institute, South
Parks Road, Oxford OX1 3RB)

Nancy C. Garwood
Department of Botany
The Natural History Museum
Cromwell Road
London SW7 5BD
UK

C.V.S. Gunatilleke
Department of Botany
University of Peradeniya
Peradeniya
Sri Lanka

I.A.U.N. Gunatilleke
Department of Botany
University of Peradeniya
Peradeniya
Sri Lanka

John B. Hall
School of Agricultural and Forest
  Sciences
University College of North Wales
Bangor
Gwynedd LL57 2UW
UK

Annette Hladik
CNRS
Anthropologie et Ecologie de
  l'Alimentation
Muséum National d'Histoire
  Naturelle
4 avenue du Petit Château
91800 Brunoy
France

Kaora Kitajima
Department of Plant Biology
University of Illinois
Urbana
IL 61801
USA
(Dept. Biology, University of
Missouri, St Louis, MO 63121, USA)

Diana Lieberman
Department of Biology
University of North Dakota
Grand Forks
ND 58202-8238
USA

Milton Lieberman
Department of Biology
University of North Dakota
Grand Forks
ND 58202-8238
USA

Mingguang Li
Department of Biology
University of North Dakota
Grand Forks
ND 58202-8238
USA
(Dept. Biology, Zhongshan (Sun
Yat-Sen) University, Guangzhou,
P.R. China)

Danielle Mitja
ORSTOM-INPA Ecologie
C.P. 478
69011 Manaus
AM Brazil

G.A.D. Perera
Department of Botany
University of Peradeniya
Peradeniya
Sri Lanka

Malcolm C. Press
School of Biological Sciences
University of Manchester
Manchester M13 9PL
UK
(Dept Animal and Plant Sciences,
University of Sheffield, Sheffield
S10 2UQ, UK)

Cynthia L. Sagers
Department of Biology
University of Utah
Salt Lake City
Utah 84112
USA
(Dept. Biological Sciences,
University of Arkansas, Fayetteville,
AR 72701, USA)

Margaret J. Still
Department of Biological Sciences
University of Stirling
Stirling FK9 4LA
UK
(MLURI, Craigiebuckler, Aberdeen,
UK)

M.D. Swaine
Department of Plant and Soil Science
University of Aberdeen
Aberdeen AB9 2UD
UK

T.C. Whitmore
Department of Geography
University of Cambridge
Downing Place
Cambridge CB2 3EN
UK

Simon W. Zipperlen
School of Biological Sciences
University of Manchester
Manchester M13 9PL
UK

FOREWORD

M.D. Swaine

INTRODUCTION

Tropical forests hold a fascination for ecologists because of their diversity of life-forms and processes. The apparent complexity of the rain forest ecosystem is a challenge to ecologists and raises questions which might not be apparent to those whose experience is confined to higher latitudes. Many ways of life are found only in the tropics and any one life-form is typically represented by many more species than in higher latitude systems. Thus amongst tropical forest trees there is a wider selection of species for testing hypotheses about functional differences in plant structure and processes than in temperate regions.

In this book we focus on the young tree, from the vulnerable, newly germinated seedling to a well-established plant when its chance of death is substantially reduced (Lieberman, 1996; Li et al., 1996; Still, 1996; Swaine, 1990). This phase in the life of a tree is important because the high mortality seedlings suffer means that much selection of individuals occurs at this time, which can have a profound influence on the composition and diversity of the forest. These plants are the 'regeneration' of foresters who depend on them to supply the future crop of timber in exploited natural forest – still, by far, the greatest producer of tropical hardwoods.

From the Chapters in this volume there emerges a persistent focus on the differences amongst species. These differences (or to some, the lack of them) lie at the centre of efforts to explain the high species richness of tropical forests, how niches are differentiated and how the composition of tropical forests is determined. The Chapters deal with differences in seedling demography, morphology, physiology and their responses to the availability of resources, notably light, nutrients and water. The abundance of different species is both an advantage in providing more points in the sample space (as noted above) and a disadvantage in requiring generalizations to make the diversity comprehensible. In this lies the conflict between useful summary and the recognition of unique differences. The generalizations, or paradigms (Grubb, in press), give us a helpful conceptual framework but the exceptions are subsumed or conveniently ignored. It is hoped that a useful balance of both will be found in this volume.

DIFFERENCES AMONG SPECIES

Differences amongst species will become less confusing if we describe them quantitatively and especially if they are tested experimentally. Species' tolerances of shade have long been known to differ to such a degree that subjective classification is both possible and reasonably functional (Whitmore, 1996). At present we are at the threshold of defining this more precisely than has been possible by the intuitive methods so far adopted. As a result of careful experiments of species' responses to shading, their differences have been quantified, but so far only for small groups of sympatric species.

Recent work in Ghana (Agyeman, 1994) aims to screen all timber species in the country for shade tolerance by such experiments. Agyeman grew a range of species in neutral shade houses at six irradiances, measured seedling leaf, stem and root dry masses, height, leaf area and leaf production and mortality. These measures were combined in a principal components analysis to define an objective gradient of shade tolerance (Agyeman, 1994). The most strongly weighted variables were seedling biomass and stem diameter growth rates in deep shade (2 per cent of ambient light), leaf mortality rates in both deep shade and 65 per cent ambient as well as apparent quantum efficiency (measured as the differences in relative growth rate between 2 and 6 per cent ambient). These results offer the means for a rapid, objective screening of large numbers of different species' responses to light. The correlation of these rankings with results from experiments using artificial gaps in rain forest was strong, as was the correlation with other, independent variables – implying a robust result.

Even slight differences in species' shade tolerance are critical for seedlings in the deep shade of the forest understorey: here species live at or near compensation point and a tiny increase in light may permit a seedling to grow and survive, long enough to take advantage of a later, more substantial opening of the canopy (see Boot, 1996). Processes at the lower limit of plant growth in deep forest shade are thus of critical importance and the relevance of gaps as perceived by humans has been overemphasized (Swaine, 1989). This point has been ably discussed and memorably entitled as 'Forests are not just Swiss cheese' by Lieberman et al. (1989).

The oft-repeated paradigm that 'pioneers' require canopy openings to break seed dormancy is under attack. Li et al. (1996) found that the extreme pioneer *Cecropia obtusifolia* was by far the commonest germinant in the understorey of a Costa Rican forest. It now seems that the apparent absence of pioneers in the understorey may be due to their extreme transience, rather than a requirement for gaps for germination. Kyereh (1994) tested the sensitivity of twenty Ghanaian tree species' germination to light, including eight regarded as 'pioneers'. Only three species, (*Musanga cecropioides, Milicia excelsa* (both Moraceae) and *Nauclea diderrichii* (Rubiaceae)) failed to germinate in darkness. The well-known 'pioneers', *Ceiba pentandra, Terminalia ivorensis, T. superba* and *Ricinodendron heudelotii* germinated equally in total darkness and in light. After germination in deep forest shade, the seedlings of *Ceiba pentandra* lost dry mass for a few weeks before dying, indicating a negative carbon balance (Kyereh, 1994).

Light is the resource which is most commonly limiting to tree seedlings growing in the forest understorey because the great majority of species start life in deep shade. It is the one resource over which foresters have some control. Nevertheless, light limitation is removed in the majority of species in conditions of only slight canopy opening. Of seventeen species tested in Ghana seven achieved maximum growth in 27 per cent of ambient light and five grew fastest at 10 per cent. Under these conditions, nutrient limitation may supervene, especially in the acid, infertile soils which are common in high rainfall areas. It is still unclear whether any one mineral element is most commonly limiting, but phosphorus has been implicated in several studies (see Burslem et al., 1994, Burslem, 1996; Grubb et al., 1994).

Recent experiments in Ghana (E.M. Veenendaal and M.D. Swaine, unpublished data) involved transfers of soil from high rainfall (ca. 2,000 mm year^{-1}) and lower rainfall (1,300 mm year^{-1}) forests to a common site where tree species with different natural distributions were planted in these soils under a range of well-watered shade treatments. The soils differed markedly in fertility from acid (pH 4, total exchangeable bases <5 meq/100 g, available phosphorus <10 ppm) to near neutral (pH 6.5, total exchangeable bases ca. 12 mequiv/100 g, available phosphorus ca. 20 ppm). Of sixteen species tested in this way only two (*Mansonia altissima* and *Triplochiton scleroxylon*, both deciduous Sterculiaceae) showed reduced growth in the infertile soil (at irradiances greater than about 10 per cent of ambient). Despite marked restriction in their natural distribution to particular parts of the rainfall/soil gradient for most of the other species, none showed sensitivity to soil type, and by implication to soil fertility. This result argues against a widespread influence of plant nutrients on establishment and distributional limits of tree species in tropical forest.

A parallel experiment (E.M. Veenendaal and M.D. Swaine, unpublished data) examined the effects of drought on a similar suite of tree species by withholding water from seedlings grown in relatively fertile soil in deep pots until they were permanently wilted throughout the day. Differences amongst the species were assessed by seedling mortality and recovery on rewatering. In contrast with the previous experiment, species showed marked differences in their ability to survive and recover from drought, ranging from 3 to 96 per cent mortality with parallel differences in their ability to regrow after treatment. The pattern of response broadly correlated with the species' natural distribution along the rainfall gradient.

The forests in Ghana span a wide range of annual rainfall, but are floristically and structurally all within the rain forest realm *sensu* Richards (1952). The most drought-sensitive species, confined to high rainfall forest in Ghana, are certainly likely to be affected by the periodic droughts reported for much wetter forests in the tropics, and support the arguments of Burslem (1996) and others that water availability may be an important determinant of seedling establishment in tropical rain forest. Conventional wisdom regards rain forests as ever-wet, but this is another paradigm which must be reconsidered.

These species-specific differences are due to differences in plant physiology, the diversity of which is beginning to be revealed (Press et al., 1996) partly because of improved and more portable equipment and the belated attention of plant physiologists to a wider range of species than formerly. Physiological diversity is a central component of the currently fashionable topic of biodiversity, and deserves far more attention.

Species differences include a fascinating variety of plant form (Bell, 1991) which is no less amongst tree seedlings (Garwood, 1996). A formal scheme was offered for tropical woody plants by Hallé and co-workers (1978), including an attempt to relate these to forest structure, but the scheme has found little application in ecology, despite the naturalness of its principles. Differences in young seedling morphology, however, appear to have more promise (Garwood, 1996) especially when related to physiological function (Kitajima, 1996) or perhaps to later growth and demography in natural forest (Hladik and Mitja, 1996).

The ultimate manifestation of species differences may be seen in the demography of natural seedling populations. Here the intrinsic differences amongst hundreds of species are resolved as differences in recruitment, growth and mortality rates (Lieberman, 1996). Although affected by a wide range of environmental influences these demographic parameters show a measure of consistency within a species or within species groups (Swaine, 1994). The range of maximum growth rates, whether measured in forest or in experiments controlled to varying degrees, is substantial, and can have profound and long-lasting effects on forest composition. Species' mortalities vary over a similarly wide range (Li et al., 1996), with equally important effects. Although these genetically controlled traits may be acknowledged (Lieberman, 1996), we are yet to provide the quantification which would bring powerful models for the forest manager.

HERBIVORES AND OTHER BIOTA

Absent from this volume is a treatment of herbivory, a field of research which has expanded rapidly in recent years (e.g. Coley, 1983). Herbivory is a particularly important biotic influence on seedlings because their size makes them vulnerable, and for young seedlings, the meal available to animals is richer than that of older plants. There are strong links, too, between plant and animal physiology: young leaves function more efficiently than older leaves, and contain much higher concentrations of those resources (water, protein, potassium, nitrogen, soluble carbohydrates etc.) valuable to animals.

The effects of herbivores on seedlings are characterized by their variability. In some seasons, whole cohorts of seedlings may be lost to herbivory, at others herbivores may seem to be unimportant. In forest experiments there is a strong temptation to protect against herbivores when the focus is phytocentric, yet models of plant responses to the abiotic environment may be irrelevant during an invasion of insects. The interactions between insect attack and the abiotic environment are inadequately understood. For example, there is an unresolved connection between illumination and insect damage to plants by shoot-borers, defoliators, miners and sap-suckers: plants benefitting from increased irradiance in canopy openings may suffer greater damage (e.g. Brown, 1990) perhaps because of a larger crop of young, nutrient-rich leaves.

The foregoing presents a case for an holistic approach, or at least for attention to the interfaces between traditional disciplines and different technical expertise. Amongst these we must include studies of mycorrhizae, and other micro-organisms. Although the role of mycorrhizae in plant nutrition is well-known, their involvement with water uptake has been less studied. Infection by mycorrhizae, or lack of it, can profoundly influence the interpretation of many seedling experiments. The importance of damping-off organisms and other plant pathogens to tree seedlings in natural forest has received little attention, but may be a common cause of death in small seedlings (Augspurger, 1984).

SEEDLING ECOLOGY AND FORESTRY

Traditional forestry was firmly grounded in forest ecology, though its tenets pre-date the invention of the word 'ecology'. It used knowledge of tree species and natural processes to manage forest production for sustainable yield. Highly successful systems were developed, particularly in continental Europe, and colonial forest services applied the same principles to natural tropical forests. The more complex nature of tropical forests caused problems, but a number of silvicultural systems were developed and were shown to be effective (Dawkins, 1988). For a variety of reasons, mostly socio-economic, these systems were never widely applied and tropical forestry (and much of temperate forestry, too) drifted from its ecological origins.

Research in natural forest and forestry practice should be complementary, with a two-way flow of ideas and information. Chapter 5 in this book (Hall, 1996) shows the strikingly different focus of modern forestry from ecology:

the diversity of tree species is a problem to be overcome, rather than an opportunity to test new sources of production, and natural tropical forest is seen as too complex to manage for effective timber production, compared to plantations of a few well-known species.

Hall (Chapter 5) concentrates on the need of foresters for ecological information, but ecologists could learn equally from forestry research. Foresters' detailed knowledge of key plantation species such as teak far exceeds ecologists' knowledge of even the best known non-commercial species, and an even stronger contrast exists for agricultural crops such as cocoa and coffee. Intraspecific variation has been intensively studied for many plantation species, but is almost unknown in non-commercial species. Whilst there is a fairly strong experimental tradition in forestry, often associated with practical matters such as spacing trials and nursery methods, it is rare amongst community ecologists. There is also a large body of informal knowledge on species ecology amongst foresters, based on field experience, but this is not widely disseminated, in part due to a fondness for internal reports and publications which fail to penetrate the academic network.

This lack of intercourse between forestry and ecology should be redressed. The renewed importance of environmental concerns, biodiversity and conservation in forestry authorities is beginning the process (Hall, 1996), and ecologists should encourage the interaction by identifying common goals and recognizing the complementary interests and resources of the two groups.

REFERENCES

Agyeman, V.K. (1994). *Environmental influences on tropical tree seedling growth.* Ph.D. Thesis, University of Aberdeen.

Augspurger, C.K. (1984). Seedling survival of tropical tree species: interactions of dispersal distance, light-gaps and pathogens. *Ecology*, **65**, 1705–12.

Bell, A.D. (1991). *Plant Form. An Illustrated Guide to Flowering Plant Morphology.* Oxford University Press, Oxford.

Boot, R.G.A. (1996). The significance of seedling size and growth rate of tropical rain forest tree seedlings for regeneration in canopy openings. In Swaine, M.D. (ed.) *Ecology of Tropical Forest Tree Seedlings*, pp. 267–83. UNESCO/Parthenon, Paris/Carnforth.

Brown, N.D. (1990). Dipterocarp regeneration in tropical rain forest gaps of different sizes. D.Phil. Thesis, University of Oxford.

Burslem, D.F.R.P. (1996). Differential responses to nutrients, shade and drought among tree seedlings of lowland tropical forest in Singapore. In Swaine, M.D. (ed.) *Ecology of Tropical Forest Tree Seedlings*, pp. 211–43. UNESCO/Parthenon, Paris/Carnforth.

Burslem, D.F.R.P., Turner, I.M. and Grubb, P.J. (1994). Mineral nutrient status of coastal hill dipterocarp forest and adinandra belukar in Singapore: bioassays of nutrient limitation. *Journal of Tropical Ecology*, **10**, 579–99.

Coley, P.D. (1983). Herbivory and defensive characteristics of tree species in a low-land tropical rain forest. *Ecological Monographs*, **53**, 209–33.

Dawkins, H.C. (1988). The first century of tropical silviculture: successes forgotten and failures misunderstood. In McDermott, M.J. (ed.) *The Future of the Tropical Rain Forest*, pp. 4–8. Oxford Forestry Institute, Oxford.

Garwood, N.C. (1996). Functional morphology of tropical tree seedlings. In Swaine, M.D. (ed.) *Ecology of Tropical Forest Tree Seedlings*, pp. 59–183. UNESCO/Parthenon, Paris/Carnforth.

Grubb, P.J., Turner, I.M. and Burslem, D.F.R.P. (1994). Mineral nutrient status of coastal hill dipterocarp forest and adinandra belukar in Singapore: analysis of soil, leaves and litter. *Journal of Tropical Ecology*, **10**, 559–77.

Grubb, P.J. (in press). Rain forest dynamics: the need for new paradigms. In Choy, S.C., Edwards, D.S. and Booth, W.E. (eds.), *Tropical Rain Forest Research: Current Issues*. Kluwer, The Hague.

Hall, J.B. (1996). Seedling ecology and tropical forestry. In Swaine, M.D. (ed.) *Ecology of Tropical Forest Tree Seedlings*, pp. 139–59. UNESCO/Parthenon, Paris/Carnforth.

Hallé, F., Oldeman, R.A.A. and Tomlinson, P.B. (1978). *Tropical Trees and Forests. An Architectural Analysis*. Springer, Berlin.

Hladik, A. and Mitja, D. (1996). Seedlings, saplings and tree temperaments: potential for agroforestry in the African rain forest. In Swaine, M.D. (ed.) *Ecology of Tropical Forest Tree Seedlings*, pp. 173–91. UNESCO/Parthenon, Paris/Carnforth.

Kitajima, K. (1996). Cotyledon functional morphology, patterns of seed reserve utilization and regeneration niches of tropical tree seedlings. In Swaine, M.D. (ed.) *Ecology of Tropical Forest Tree Seedlings*, pp. 193–210. UNESCO/Parthenon, Paris/Carnforth.

Kyereh, B. (1994). *Seed Phenology and Germination of Ghanaian Forest Trees*. Ph.D. Thesis, University of Aberdeen.

Lieberman, D. (1996). Demography of tropical tree seedlings: a review. In Swaine, M.D. (ed.) *Ecology of Tropical Forest Tree Seedlings*, pp. 131–8. UNESCO/Parthenon, Paris/Carnforth.

Lieberman, M., Lieberman, D. and Peralta, R. (1989). Forests are not just Swiss cheese: canopy stereogeometry of non-gaps in tropical forests. *Ecology*, **70**, 550–2.

Li, M., Lieberman, M. and Lieberman, D. (1996). Seedling demography in undisturbed tropical wet forest in Costa Rica. In Swaine, M.D. (ed.) *Ecology of Tropical Forest Tree Seedlings*, pp. 285–314. UNESCO/Parthenon, Paris/Carnforth.

Press, M.C., Brown, N.D., Barker, M.G. and Zipperlen, S.W. (1996). Photosynthetic responses to light in tropical rain forest tree seedlings. In Swaine, M.D. (ed.) *Ecology of Tropical Forest Tree Seedlings*, pp. 41–58. UNESCO/Parthenon, Paris/Carnforth.

Richards, P.W. (1952). *The Tropical Rain Forest*. Cambridge University Press, Cambridge.

Still, M.J. (1996). Rates of mortality and growth in three groups of dipterocarp seedlings in Sabah, Malaysia. In Swaine, M.D. (ed.) *Ecology of Tropical Forest Tree Seedlings*, pp. 315–32. UNESCO/Parthenon, Paris/Carnforth.

Swaine, M.D. (1989). Population dynamics of tree species in tropical forests. In Holm-Nielsen, L.B., Nielsen, I.C. and Balslev, H. (eds.), *Tropical Forests. Botanical Dynamics, Speciation and Diversity*, pp. 101–10. Academic Press, London.

Swaine, M.D. (1990). Population dynamics of moist tropical forest at Kade, Ghana. In Maitre, H.F. and Puig, H. (eds.), *Actes de l'Atelier sur l'Aménagement de l'Ecosystème Forestier Tropical Humide*, pp. 40–61. UNESCO/MAB, Paris.

Swaine, M.D. (1994). Long-term studies of tropical forest dynamics. In Leigh, R.A. and Johnston, A.E. (eds.), *Long-term Experiments in Agricultural and Ecological Sciences*, pp. 305–19. CAB International, Oxford.

Whitmore, T.C. (1996). A review of some aspects of tropical rain forest seedling ecology with suggestions for further enquiry. In Swaine, M.D. (ed.) *Ecology of Tropical Forest Tree Seedlings*, pp. 3–39. UNESCO/Parthenon, Paris/Carnforth.

Section 1

Reviews

CHAPTER 1

A REVIEW OF SOME ASPECTS OF TROPICAL RAIN FOREST SEEDLING ECOLOGY WITH SUGGESTIONS FOR FURTHER ENQUIRY

T.C. Whitmore

INTRODUCTION

The torrent of articles on forest regeneration, so-called 'gap-phase dynamics', continues unabated. The attempt to discover patterns to reduce the complexity of nature as a basis from which to make generalizations has led to the wide recognition of guilds or classes of ecologically similar tree species. The attempt to define these by Swaine and Whitmore (1988) and the subsequent debate (e.g. Platt and Strong, 1989) has contributed to this flood, see p. 8 below.

Studies on aspects of gap-phase dynamics have been made and are ongoing in forests in many parts of the world (Platt and Strong, 1989) with strong concentrations in Japan (e.g. Yamamoto, 1992a,b) and North America (e.g. Canham and Marks, 1985). Part of the interest has, naturally, focused on tree seedling ecology. The present review is confined to tree seedling studies made in tropical rain forests. Many of the workers actively studying rain forest tree seedlings presented their findings at a UNESCO Workshop held in Aberdeen, Scotland, in September, 1992 (Swaine, 1995). Here those findings are set in the context of other recent work. This article does not attempt to cover all aspects comprehensively. In particular, seedling demography and functional morphology are covered elsewhere, by Lieberman (1996) and Garwood (1996). From this review various gaps in knowledge or understanding can be identified. It is suggested that future effort might profitably be directed towards them.

The focus is very strongly on tropical rain forests. Tropical dry forests have attracted less recent attention (but see Hytteborn and Skarpe, 1992) and it has been suggested that in dry forests gap-phase dynamics may be less important (Swaine et al., 1990). Most of the world's forests have many similar dynamic features but space, time and the author's competence preclude more than a few references to work outside the humid tropics. Seed ecology is also excluded, and was outside the remit of the UNESCO Workshop. The focus here is on seedlings from germination through establishment and survival to release and growth to sapling size which, following a common foresters' convention, is taken as 2.7 m (9 feet) tall (Whitmore, 1984a).

THE SETTING

Forest canopies are dynamic, in a continual state of flux. The simple model of this is the forest growth cycle with gap, building and mature phases (Watt, 1947; Whitmore, 1975). Seedling growth takes place in this setting. Swaine and Whitmore (1988) defined pioneer species as those that required full light for both germination and establishment and climax (non-pioneer, late successional) species as those that could germinate and establish below a forest canopy. Gap size is important. Seedlings of climax species are released from a forest-floor seedling bank in small gaps to form the next growth cycle but are replaced in big gaps by pioneer species, germinated from seed after gap creation. Within the climax guild of species there are many different degrees of seedling shade tolerance. Very shade-tolerant species form the next growth cycle where gaps are tiny, and as gap size increases progressively less shade-tolerant (more light-demanding) climax species form the next growth cycle until in the biggest gaps pioneer species do so instead.

Much recent work has been to test particular forest ecosystems and species against these paradigms. Various refinements are now realized to be necessary.

Forest structure

'Forests are not just Swiss Cheese' (Lieberman et al., 1989): the division of forests into gaps and closed canopy is not sharp. In fact, in physical terms, the boundary commonly is sharp, but in terms of microenvironment there is a continuum across the physical edge of a gap. This was pointed out by Popma et al. (1988). Ashton (1990) found no sudden air temperature change at gap edges and Brown (1993) has demonstrated, for ten artificially created gaps in a Sabah rain forest ranging in size from $1,500\,m^2$ downwards, a steady gradient away from the gap centre of maximum air temperature, relative humidity, photosynthetically active radiation (PAR) and light quality as measured by the ratio of the red:far red wavelengths (R:FR, 660:730 nm). Increasing gap size increases the extreme values of microclimatic parameters and the size of the 'penumbral' influence of the gap. Brown found the influence of his largest gap extended 5–10 m beyond its physical edge. Raich (1989) found elevated ground-level PAR for at least 20 m into the forests from a gap edge at Pantai Aceh, Penang.

Canopy gap definition

Gap size is commonly measured as the area between the edges of the crowns of peripheral trees projected vertically down to ground level, a definition codified by Brokaw (1982). In practice the vertical projection is not always easy to make precisely. Moreover, at ground level gaps in tall canopies are exposed to less sky than those in short canopies and the 'Brokaw' definition cannot allow for this. It can be allowed for by ranking gaps in size according to the ratio of canopy height to gap diameter but both parts of this ratio are difficult to measure in tropical rain forests which commonly have a very uneven canopy top and often have emergent trees. Physical measures of gap size cannot allow for tiny canopy holes and these become increasingly important sources of radiation as gaps get smaller (Mitchell and Whitmore, 1993). They are the main source below closed canopies.

The realization that microclimate does not change sharply at the physical gap edge but that the physical gap has a 'penumbral' influence beyond its periphery has important implications for seedling ecological studies and these now need to be explored. But for some ecological purposes it is still useful and necessary to be able to rank gaps in size. Whitmore et al. (1993) argued that because plants respond to microclimate the most useful measure of gap size is that which most clearly relates to microclimate. They demonstrated that either percentage canopy openness or proportion of radiation transmitted (i.e. total, indirect, or direct site factors *sensu* Anderson (1964)) were better measures on this criterion than physical gap size. These measures are easily obtained from canopy (hemispherical) photographs, provided appropriate protocols are followed (Rich, 1989, 1990) and precautions taken (Mitchell and Whitmore, 1993).

Gap microenvironments

We cannot regard a gap as a homogeneous hole any more than we can regard it as sharply bounded. There are differences from place to place and from time to time within a gap.

The light climate

At and near the equator and over an extended period of time the physical gap centre receives the most incident radiation and the other microclimate parameters dependent on radiation also have their extreme values in the centre where radiation is maximal. Direct solar radiation and indirect sky radiation are the two major components. Their relative proportion depends on hours of sunshine. The third component, transmitted and reflected radiation, has usually been ignored. Below closed canopies it was shown to be 25 and 43 per cent of the total in Nigeria and Singapore respectively (Evans, 1956; Whitmore and Wong, 1959), but it is a negligible fraction of the radiation received in a gap.

During the course of a year the sun's track describes a belt that runs from east to west. On the equator this belt is balanced about the zenith. Polewards it moves progressively northwards or southwards and becomes more strongly curved. Thus the point receiving maximum radiation shifts from the gap centre towards the north or south side and penetration into the forest around the

5

gap increases. Canham et al. (1990) gave a clear description. All microclimatic parameters determined by solar radiation will have a similar pattern. The difference between north and south sides of a gap becomes considerable at temperate latitudes.

Tropical rain forest lumber companies have long known that forest roads aligned north to south dry out more quickly than roads that run east to west (P.F. Burgess, personal communication). This is another consequence of solar track geometry: the sun can reach to ground of a north–south road every day, but an east–west road can only be sunlit for a fraction of the year which decreases with increasing canopy height and with latitude.

Sidelight. Oberbauer et al. (1988) and Clark and Clark (1992) in studies at the Costa Rican La Selva forest have demonstrated the importance for seedling growth of sidelight (i.e. solar radiation received by a forest floor plant from the side instead of from overhead) for which they developed a simple subjective scale. Physical measures of gap size cannot allow for sidelight but those based on hemispherical photographs can. Future studies aimed to relate seedling performance closely to different degrees of canopy closure need to use canopy measures that make allowance for sidelight.

Variability in small and big gaps. Brown (1993) has demonstrated from his study on ten artificially created gaps in a Sabah rain forest that there is much greater variability between small gaps than big ones in solar radiation received, and hence also in the values of all the parameters dependent on it. Direct sunlight is a major component, about half, of the total radiation on the canopy. Big gaps are exposed to most of the sun's annual belt so receive sunlight almost whenever it occurs. Small gaps are exposed to much less of the belt and the amount of sunlight that enters is much more dependent on the vagaries of whether when the sun shines it is opposite the gap or not. The afternoons in Sabah are more cloudy and receive less sunshine than the mornings, so a small gap centred west of the zenith will receive less sunlight than a same-sized gap to its east. The possible consequences for seedling occurrence and performance of these aspects of the forest light climate clearly must be allowed for in the design and interpretation of ecological research.

Soils and roots

Below ground aspects of canopy gaps are still little investigated and poorly understood. It is not the case, as sometimes assumed, that gaps inevitably have reduced or no root competition. In the case where a gap is created by windthrow roots will have been wrenched out and root competition will indeed be locally reduced. But many gaps are formed by other means without soil disturbance, such as tree snap, and in these root competition will continue much as before.

6

Gaps and closed forest compared. Gap near-to-surface soil temperature is linked to incident radiation. Kennedy (1991) in Sabah reported elevated temperatures, at 5 cm depth, increasing with gap size and greatest at gap centre. Gap soils have been found to be wetter than below closed forest at Barro Colorado Island (as also in all temperate forests investigated, Becker et al., 1988) and at La Selva (Vitousek and Denslow, 1986; Denslow et al., 1991). But gap soils were drier at Pantai Aceh, Penang (Turner et al., 1992a), at Sinharaja, Sri Lanka (Ashton, 1992), and in north-east Costa Rica, where Parker (1985 in Bruijnzeel, 1992) found greater dryness in the top 70 cm which increased both with gap size and through the dry season.

Three of the five studies made of plant mineral nutrients in gap soil report little difference from closed forest. At San Carlos, Venezuela, Uhl et al. (1988) found no difference after gap creation from closed forest nutrient levels except for a short pulse of nitrate nitrogen loss by leaching. Vitousek (1985) in a general review had predicted that just such a nutrient pulse is to be expected as the disturbed ecosystem reorganizes. In a tropical seasonal forest at Maraca Island, north Brazil, very little nitrogen mineralization was found after the creation of artificial gaps up to 2,500 m^2 (Marrs et al., 1991). In north-east Costa Rica however Parker (1985 in Bruijnzeel, 1992) found that a distinct rise in the concentrations of certain solutes in soil moisture occurred 4 months after creation of artificial gaps of 500 m^2 and 2,500 m^2. Nitrate, calcium and magnesium all showed a pulse of elevated concentrations and this reached a peak at 6–8 months after gap creation and lasted about 1 year. Potassium, phosphate and ammonium showed no rise, possibly, as Bruijnzeel suggests, due to uptake by vigorous pioneer vegetation. At La Selva, two studies report contrary findings. Vitousek and Denslow (1986) found gaps to have no increase in the pool size of nitrogen or its mineralization and only an insignificant increase in extractable phosphorus. They believed that phosphorus mineralized from litterfall was quickly adsorbed on to clay or taken up by plants and that any increase in nitrogen that might have occurred could not be detected against high original levels. Overall, they considered that nutrient availability in gaps was being buffered by the surrounding forest. But Sanford et al. (1991), also at La Selva, found soil nitrogen, but not phosphorus, availability enhanced in gaps for approximately the first 8 weeks.

Within-gap variability. The French term *chablis* for a forest canopy gap reflects the considerable internal heterogeneity that exists. There are crown, bole and root zones. Where a tree has been upturned the forest floor is disturbed, hollows and root mounds (root plates) will have been created and root competition locally eliminated. Root mounds disrupt the litter layer and expose bare mineral soil. The hummock and hollow microtopography treefalls create introduces heterogeneity in soil moisture, temperature and roots that have scarcely been investigated. Putz (1983) explored some of the consequences of this heterogeneity for seedlings.

7

At La Selva, Sanford (1989) found fewer fine roots in both crown and root-throw zones, whilst in the bole zone the amount was similar to closed forest. In another study, at San Carlos, he found no differences within gaps but that whole gaps did differ from each other, with more fine roots in the smaller ones (Sanford, 1990). In a third study, also at La Selva, Sanford et al. (1991) discovered fine root biomass after treefall to be significantly greater for 1 year than in adjacent forest. Denslow et al. (1991) found a 30 per cent change in fine roots within small areas isolated by trenching at La Selva, but this was less than the 50 per cent of the natural fluctuation. Sanford's (1990) opinion was that the gap zones that develop above ground do not produce a congruent zonation below ground.

Clark (1990) has pointed out that the leaf cutter ant *Atta* and termites can create patches of nutrient-enriched soil. These may occur either below forest or in a gap. Enhanced seedling growth in response to such 'hot spots' has not apparently been reported. B. Finegan, however, (personal communication) has observed that *Atta* nests are devoid of vegetation and seem to remain so for some time after abandonment.

ECOLOGICAL CLASSES OF TREE SPECIES

Attempts to group tropical rain forest tree species into ecological guilds or classes continue unabated. Recent manifestations are Alexandre (1989), Martinez-Ramos and Alvarez-Buylla (1986), Clark and Clark (1992), Hawthorne (1993), Oldeman and Dijk (1991) and Thompson et al. (1988). The division into pioneer and climax (non-pioneer) guilds of Swaine and Whitmore (1988) has provided a starting point. This paradigm was restated by Whitmore (1989a) in a Special Feature in *Ecology* (Platt and Strong, 1989) and scrutinized in fifteen short articles. Pioneers are defined on their requirement for full light for both germination and establishment. Regrettably Whitmore (1989a) failed to mention establishment and this led Alvarez-Buylla and Martinez-Ramos (1992) to reject the classification, which has otherwise proved robust. The germination of pioneers below closed canopies (presumably in response to the full light of ephemeral sunflecks) followed soon by death at tiny size (i.e. failure to establish) has been reported by these authors as well as by Kennedy and Swaine (1992, several species) and by Vazquez-Yanes and Smith (1982, *Cecropia obtusifolia*). The ecophysiological basis of this early death is discussed later (p. 16).

The two guilds can be recognized in most classifications. Within the climax guild species of a wide range of seedling shade tolerance exist. This was, in fact, pointed out by Swaine and Whitmore, part of whose thesis was that this variation is continuous. Many of the recent publications attempt to identify ecologically meaningful groups within the continuum. It can now be seen that the Swaine and Whitmore dichotomy is a necessary but not a sufficient description of the variety of tree autecology found in nature. It gives overemphasis to just two features, germination and establishment. Apart from these two features the most light-demanding climax species are very similar to most pioneers (e.g. with fast growth and pale, low-density timber). Closer scrutiny is warranted and this would be particularly useful in the neotropics given the wide geographical range and high economic importance there of the most light-demanding climax species (Finegan, 1992). One point to scrutinize is whether pioneers *sensu* Swaine and Whitmore (1988) always have tiny diaspores whilst those fast-growing, light-demanding species seen in secondary forest which have big seeds (e.g. *Artocarpus, Campnosperma, Endospermum*) are, in fact, climax species *sensu* Swaine and Whitmore (1988). On p. 18 and Table 1.1 below an ecophysiological difference between members of the two guilds is exhibited.

A guild of species recognized by both Hawthorne (1993) in Ghana and by Oldeman and Dijk (1991) requires full light for germination, establishment and early growth but then continues growth below canopy shade. Hawthorne (1993, p. 10) called this guild 'cryptic pioneers', all are small trees.

Further exploration of species guilds and their loci for successful regeneration is needed for montane forests. Kramer (1926, 1933), working in lower montane rain forest on Gunung Gedeh in west Java, found that in gaps of area $1,000 \, m^2$ climax species seedlings were released from the seedling bank but at $2,000 \, m^2$ and $3,000 \, m^2$ pioneers formed the regenerating forest. This switch size is much larger than occurs in lowland rain forest, and presumably reflects the cool, cloudy montane climate. Healey (1990), working in a Jamaican upper montane rain forest at $1,600 \, m$ elevation, found that twenty-two of his twenty-nine species regenerated from seed in both gaps and below closed forest. There were only two true pioneer species. In south-east Asia the well-known pioneer trees of the lowlands (notably *Macaranga* spp., *Mallotus* spp.) do not occur in montane forests. In the Talamanca mountain range of Costa Rica oak forests grow between 1,800 and $3,200 \, m$ altitude and these also have no pioneer tree species (Blaser and Camacho, 1991), although on landslips and riverbanks *Alnus jorullensis* is present (B. Finegan personal communication). Is it the case that in cool, cloudy upper montane rain forest the distinctive hot, dry microclimatic niche exploited by pioneers in the lowlands does not exist, and so therefore this species guild is absent or at best poorly represented?

A corollary of the definition of pioneers is that they cannot regenerate *in situ* below their own canopy. Big areas of forest consisting of pioneer species are being created by excessively heavy timber extraction (e.g. in Sabah) and also resulted from the 1983 Great Fire of Borneo which destroyed or severely damaged several million hectares of lowland rain forest. A problem still not investigated and which has important practical implications is the nature of succession in these extensive forests of pioneers. They did not exist in the past, because before mankind achieved his present numbers and potency pioneers were confined to landslips and fresh riverine alluvial banks that only formed patches of a few hectares. In the temperate zone pioneer species can in some circumstances perpetuate themselves *in situ*, i.e. can locally behave as climax species. One example is *Betula* near the tree line in Scotland, another is *Nothofagus* on Chilean mountains above the elevational limits of the species which replace it in climax forests at lower altitudes (Veblen et al., 1981). A tropical example of probably the same phenomenon, the *Cavanillesia platanifolia* forests of Darién Province Panama, was discussed by Hartshorn (1980). This is a shade-intolerant species capable of very fast growth. In the Darién forests, which Hartshorn believes should be regarded as secondary, it forms 60 per cent of the timber volume. These forests are believed to have developed on pasturelands abandoned after the Spanish conquest four centuries ago. The implication is that, in the absence of more shade-tolerant species, *Cavanillesia* replaces itself *in situ*.

Shade tolerance defined

The term 'shade-tolerant' is widely employed as a useful phrase to describe the ecology of many climax species. Closer study of its manifestation and mechanisms leads to the realization that the term has three intertwined meanings (Whitmore, 1990, p. 115). Greater precision is needed to distinguish between these as ecological research probes ever deeper.

Firstly, shade tolerance can mean the minimum PAR level needed for seedling survival. If this kind of tolerance is in operation we will expect to find different species occupying different parts of the forest floor.

Secondly, shade tolerance can refer to the length of time for which seedlings can survive at low PAR levels. In this case populations of strongly shade-tolerant species will die away more slowly than those of less shade-tolerant species. Differential survival of twelve species in the Solomon Islands was shown by Whitmore (1974). Other examples are given in p. 13 below.

Thirdly, shade tolerance can refer to the amount of PAR required for release from the seedling bank, namely to secure rapid height growth (see p. 14 below). This is the meaning tropical foresters give the term and on which silviculture by canopy manipulation is based.

These different meanings are not independent, nor are they absolute measures. In fact, shade tolerance is a useful and easily understood concept, but is difficult to define precisely. One major development of the past decade has been the exploration of seedling ecophysiology in its many facets. This has led to some understanding of the mechanisms behind shade tolerance, as will be described below on p. 18 et seq.

SEEDLING ESTABLISHMENT, SURVIVAL AND GROWTH

The simple matter of the availability of seedlings of any given species to grow up to fill a gap is of basic importance. This necessitates a sufficiently close seed source. Kennedy, working in artificially created gaps in Sabah many kilometres from the closest stand of old secondary forest, found almost none of the well-known local pioneers (notably *Macaranga* spp., *Mallotus* spp., *Trema* spp.) (Kennedy and Swaine, 1992). At La Selva, in four recent tree-fall gaps, pioneers were only 2–33 per cent of seed rain, and came from 750 m or more distance (Denslow and Gomez Diaz, 1990). The considerable number of studies of seed banks and seed rain that have found pioneers predominant (reviewed by Whitmore, 1983) were all made at sites close to forest edges so were close to a source of pioneer seed.

At La Selva Denslow et al. (1991) found tree seedlings sparse and of patchy occurrence on the forest floor due to competition with a ground layer of big-leaved palms and cyclanths. They drew attention to the general importance of such competition in neotropical rain forests.

Major differences occur between species in frequency and density of seedling recruitment and in longevity. This, and the implications for the composition of regenerating forest, are reviewed by Lieberman (1996).

We have little evidence whether vegetative reproduction from root or stem coppice shoots (sprouts) is important in natural tropical rain forests. After human disturbance coppicing of many species can occur (Riswan, 1982 for Kalimantan, Stocker, 1981 for Queensland). Putz and Brokaw (1989) reported that at Barro Colorado Island about half the trees that suffered natural complete stem breakage sprouted, biased to stems under 22 cm diameter. Sagers (1996) reported vegetative reproduction on Barro Colorado Island from fallen leaves. Regrowth from sprouts is important in some temperate tree species, for example in Japanese evergreen broad-leaved forests (Yamamoto, 1992a) and basal sprouting is common in tropical dry forests (e.g. Swaine et al., 1990).

Seedling establishment

The establishment phase gives the biggest 'demographic squeeze' to the seedling population. Alvarez-Buylla and Martinez-Ramos (1992) showed this very clearly for *Cecropia obtusifolia* in the Los Tuxtlas rain forest in Mexico where the greatest loss was between seed germination and seedlings of 3 mm stem diameter. Flores (1992) found 50 per cent mortality in the first year in two species studied in a Venezuelan cloud forest. Studies on the comparative ecology of four *Shorea* species in the Sinharaja rain forest in Sri Lanka led Ashton (1990) and Ashton and Berlyn (1991) to conclude that the establishment stage was important in determining the distinct site specializations these species exhibit. The three brobdingnagian studies of the demography of

11

all plants of 1 cm or greater diameter on 50-ha plots at Barro Colorado Island (Hubbell and Foster, 1983), Pasoh, and Lambir Hills, Malaysia (Kochummen et al., 1990; Manokaran and LaFrankie, 1990; K. Ogino et al. personal communication) miss out the establishment phase which may, in fact, be crucial in the interpretation of forest composition. The conclusion for the Barro Colorado Island plot that 79 per cent of the species are indifferent to gaps (Welden et al., 1991) would not necessarily be true if the establishment phase had been studied, nor if they had used a more refined method of estimating microclimate than canopy height at points on a 5 m × 5 m grid.

Conditions for establishment

Establishment can fail if seedlings occur on the wrong microsites. Differences in abundance with elevation and in species composition of dipterocarps in Malayan hill forests, and also between soils derived from shale and from granite, were found to be explicable in terms of differences in microsite for establishment (Burgess in Whitmore, 1984a).

In the lowland dipterocarp forest at Danum, Sabah, mass fruiting in 1990 was followed by very poor seedling establishment, probably because of unusually low rainfall during the period of fruit fall (N.D. Brown, T.C. Whitmore personal observation).

Leaf litter was found to be heterogeneous and highly variable at 1–20 m scale on Barro Colorado Island (Molofsky and Augspurger, 1992). Experiments on six species of different seed sizes and ecological guilds revealed that they all responded differently to 0, 6 and 12 cm thickness of litter. It was concluded that leaf litter variability can potentially increase seedling diversity due to this heterogeneity in establishment.

Within-gap zonal preference

Another example of the importance of suitable microsites for successful seedling establishment is the demonstration of differences between different zones of a gap. Orians (1982) postulated such differences and they were first demonstrated at La Selva by Brandani et al. (1988) where root, bole and crown zones were found more similar in seedling species composition than different zones of the same gap. Preference for root mounds has been shown by Riera (1985) for *Cecropia obtusa*. In the Los Tuxtlas forest Nuñez-Farfán and Dirzo (1988) discovered a marked contrast in the seedling species assemblage between root and crown zones and believed it due to both differential germination and establishment. The root zone had more individuals and species, seventy-two species compared to only thirty-three. Two pioneers, *Cecropia obtusifolia* and *Heliocarpus appendiculatus*, studied in detail, performed better in crown and root zones respectively; differential herbivory and ability to survive traumatic injury were important. By contrast, at San Carlos in south Venezuela, where virtually all seedlings came from the seedling bank and there were very few pioneers, Uhl et al. (1988) found that neither the internal microhabitats, the size, or the age of gaps produced measurable effects on plant density, establishment, or mortality, though growth rate increased with gap size. It was found at Danum, Sabah, that pot-grown dipterocarp seedlings performed similarly at the edge of a large gap as in the centre of a smaller one (Brown and Whitmore, 1992). Rooted cuttings of seven *Miconia* and *Piper* species at La Selva showed relative height growth rates decreasing from gap centre to gap edge to forest understorey (Denslow et al., 1990). There has not yet, however, been much exploration of the biotic effect of the 'penumbra' around the physical gap, except for the study at Los Tuxtlas of Popma et al. (1988) who found different species predominating in gap centres and this bordering zone. There is clearly scope for further work.

Thus, we now have evidence from several studies that the physical differences between parts of a gap lead to biotic differences.

Seedling survival

Tiny seedlings suffer the heaviest mortality (Lieberman, 1996; Alvarez-Buylla and Martinez-Ramos, 1992). Progressively lower mortality at increasing sizes has been shown in Penang by Turner (1990a), for dipterocarps at Danum (Brown and Whitmore, 1992) and at Kade, Ghana (Swaine, 1990). Mortality of newly established seedlings was less in larger gaps and in the absence of competition from advance regeneration at Danum (Kennedy and Swaine, 1992). Still (1996) found mortality rates of dipterocarp seedlings at Danum much higher in species regarded as light-demanders compared to shade-tolerant species. At Pasoh, Malaya, seedling populations of the shade-tolerant dipterocarp *Shorea maxwelliana* showed much lower mortality over 2 years than the light-demander *S. leprosula*, 16 and 27 per cent yr^{-1} respectively (Becker, 1983), and had less leaf damage by insects and fewer insect species feeding on them (Becker, 1981). The amount of mature leaf area missing was 5 and 13 per cent respectively. This points to differential susceptibility to herbivory as a mechanism for shade tolerance, though in this case Becker (1983) discovered that artificial defoliation of 25 per cent did not in fact significantly alter mortality rates. Another study, on three *Shorea* species at Penang, by Turner (1990b), emphasized that survival and growth depend on multiple factors.

In Ghana, over 19 years, differences were found between strongly shade-tolerant and less shade-tolerant climax species (Swaine, 1990). Seedlings of the strongly shade-tolerant species guild were more numerous and had less mortality. This could mean that the forest has unstable species composition, although during this period there were no systematic trends in change of composition of the big trees ≥30 cm diameter, despite 25 per cent mortality. This study reveals something of the complexity of the relationships between seedling ecology and canopy species composition; even 19 years is a tiny fraction of the life of a tree. Investigations over several decades and many hectares are needed (cf. Whitmore, 1989b) to expose more of the dynamics and to elucidate whether a forest is in equilibrium or not. The 50-ha plot studies referred to above will, in due course, make a valuable contribution.

The 'escape hypothesis'

The hypothesis that tree seedlings survive best at distance from the parent tree and that this mechanism helps maintain rain forest species richness, due to Janzen (1970) and Connell (1971), stimulated several studies, reviewed by Howe and Smallwood (1982) and Clark and Clark (1984) who found a few cases where it applied. Analysis of recruitment between 1982 and 1985 for eighty species of trees and shrubs on the mapped 50-ha plot on Barro Colorado Island found a few species (including the commonest tree *Trichilia tuberculata*) showed significant reduction in recruitment probability close to an adult, more showed a significant increase, and many showed no significant spatial pattern (Condit et al., 1992). 'Janzen–Connell spacing', as it is sometimes called, has now been shown to be too simple in determining seedling spatial distribution (Lieberman, 1996). Other processes are often more important. For example on Barro Colorado Island seedlings of *Tachigalia versicolor* and *Faramea occidentalis* perform best in gaps and proximity to mother tree is less important (Kitajima and Augspurger, 1989; Schupp, 1988). Amongst nine other species at Barro Colorado Island Augspurger (1984) showed a change with time and differences between species in the distance from the parent tree at which survival was best.

Seedling release

It is a matter of common observation that tree seedlings in the below-canopy seedling bank (sometimes referred to as advance regeneration), grow only very slowly in height but then quickly commence rapid height growth after a canopy gap develops above them. This is what foresters refer to as seedling release, and much of silviculture consists of canopy manipulation to create gaps of sizes which favour particular species. Analysis of this common observation reveals great complexity.

Height growth rate of a seedling commonly increases with increasing gap size, shown for example at Danum by dipterocarps (Brown and Whitmore, 1992) and colonizing species (Kennedy and Swaine, 1992) and at San Carlos (Uhl et al., 1988). But this simple generalization is not always true. In Queensland, seeds of six species of pioneer, intermediate and strongly shade-tolerant guilds were planted in small, medium and big gaps. Their height growth did not closely correlate with gap size in the way that would be predicted and, moreover, the rank order changed over the 7 years of the observations (Thompson et al., 1988). More study is needed of the growth of released seedlings during several years after their release. Change in height-rank through time, as found in Queensland, could contribute to the foresters' perception of gap-size requirement for successful regeneration.

Closer study is needed to see if seedling release is an all or nothing response. Is there a threshold at which rapid height growth is triggered or not?

Multiple release

In temperate forests seedlings very commonly grow to tree size after a series of releases, pulses of rapid growth followed by stasis, in successive gaps forming at the same place over many years (see e.g. Runkle and Yetter, 1987) and this can be followed by study of the annual growth rings in the wood. Tropical rain forest trees do not have growth rings, and multiple release has scarcely been documented. It is probably equally as common as in other forests. For example polycyclic silvicultural systems, developed for dipterocarp and other rain forests (see Whitmore, 1990), depend on the release of poles by felling-caused canopy gaps to produce the next timber harvest and these poles will very probably have been through several cycles of release and stasis.

Significance of gap size

Maximum growth of seedlings of different species in gaps of different size is the third meaning that can be given to shade tolerance (p. 10) and, as pointed out above, is the concept that underpins much of silviculture. Denslow (1980, 1984) drew the logical conclusion that this specialization should lead to the greatest abundance in any region of species specialized to the gap size commonest there. This hypothesis was refuted by Whitmore (1984b), who pointed out that throughout the humid tropics pioneer species are few in number, with no marked difference between very stable regions (e.g. Malaya) whose forests suffer very little catastrophic disturbance and regions (such as Panama (Garwood et al., 1979) or Papua New Guinea) where earthquakes, landslips, volcanic activity and windstorms cause frequent heavy damage to the forests.

The absence of specialization on a particular gap size has been demonstrated by D.U.U. Okali and M. Dike (personal communication) at Omo forest, Nigeria, by Barton (1984) who found no differences at La Selva between the abundance in small and large gaps of five climax species, and at Danum, Sabah, for seedlings coming in after gap creation by Kennedy and Swaine (1992) who believed spatial heterogeneity in the soil seed bank to be of overriding importance. Raich and Christensen (1989) found at Pantai Aceh,

Penang, that species composition of seedlings in gaps was more closely similar to that of adjacent gaps than to size, surface microtopography or other factors. D.U.U. Okali and M. Dike (personal communication) also found gap species composition was most similar to the closest gaps.

Nevertheless, the hypothesis that different species succeed in different gap sizes persists, either explicitly or implicitly, as a tenet underpinning much work on seedling ecology. It certainly appears to explain the observations of foresters that the greater the canopy disturbance (e.g. by logging or by artificial manipulation such as poison girdling) the more successful the most light-demanding species become in the subsequent regeneration. Closer investigation of what lies behind this silvicultural observation is warranted, with particular attention to the possible importance of multiple release and of species changing height rank as they grow up from seedling to sapling and pole.

It has been observed several times that although germination may occur seedlings of pioneer species do not succeed in the smallest gaps, for example at Omo (D.U.U. Okali and M. Dike, personal communication). This has now been related to the amount of PAR needed by pioneers. Fernandez and Fetcher (1991) measured PAR below the canopy in Puerto Rico in forests damaged by Hurricane Hugo and found good growth of the pioneers *Cecropia, Didymopanax*, etc., at $7.7–10.8\,\mathrm{mol\,m^{-2}\,day^{-1}}$. Torquebiau (1988) had found pioneers failed in a $320\,\mathrm{m^2}$ gap receiving $6.6–7.8\,\mathrm{mol\,m^{-2}\,day^{-1}}$ PAR and Fernandez and Fetcher concluded that pioneers need at least $8\,\mathrm{mol\,m^{-2}\,day^{-1}}$ to succeed. At the Mabura Hill forest, Guyana, Boot (1996) also found that pioneers had very low relative growth rate (RGR) and failed in dense shade and in the smallest gaps, in this case at below 6–7 per cent full-sky PAR. In the centre of large gaps his pioneers had high RGR. The climax species he studied had a low RGR in shade and only a marginally larger one in gaps. The prime cause of death of pioneers at low PAR is very likely their negative carbon balance, i.e. they are below their compensation point and respired carbon exceeds carbon fixed by photosynthesis.

As a generalization, most pioneers have tiny seeds (Whitmore, 1990, Table 7.4), and so can only form very tiny seedlings from them. With adequate PAR these have high RGR and soon catch up in size with bigger seedlings grown from larger seeds, but in the smallest gaps, or below the canopy in dense shade, PAR is insufficient, the seedlings remain tiny and are suppressed by competition or succumb to disease or injury. Osunkoya et al. (1993), in experiments on seedlings of six tree species in the Queensland rain forests, found height at 4 and 16 months from planting out correlated with seed weight in dark forest understorey sites but not in gaps.

Contrary to these various findings Turnbull (1991) found in glasshouse experiments on six Queensland rain forest species that the two pioneers tested (*Homalanthus populifolius, Solanum aviculare*) tolerated radiation down to 5 per cent full PAR. He believed these and the two 'mid-successional' species tested (*Duboisia myoporoides, Euodia micrococca*) are absent below forest canopies, not because of inadequate PAR, but by requirements for germination. Brokaw (1987) claimed at Barro Colorado Island that three pioneer species were specialized to different gap sizes but Kennedy and Swaine (1992) have pointed out that the abundance he observed in different sized gaps is, in fact, directly correlated with, and they suggest a consequence of, total numbers of each species in this forest.

Brown and Whitmore (1992), working at Danum, Sabah, investigated the behaviour of seedlings of three common and several uncommon dipterocarp species when released from the seedling bank by the creation of artificial gaps 10–1,500 m^2 in size. Over the first 40 months there was no specialization on gap size, the most successful seedlings were those tallest at time of gap creation. There were considerable differences in mortality in the closed canopy control plot, with *Hopea nervosa* surviving much the best, thus confirming the foresters' view that this is a shade-tolerant species, but exhibiting the second expression of shade tolerance discussed above (p. 10) not the third definition, release and success at smallest gap size, which had been expected. It remains to be seen as the study continues whether species of known different shade tolerance change rank, in the way discovered in Queensland over 7 years by Thompson et al. (1988), see above.

ECOPHYSIOLOGY

Photosynthesis and growth

The investigation of the physiological differences between light-demanding and shade-tolerant tree species has developed fast in recent years, mainly using seedlings and is reviewed by Press et al. (1996). The research has produced much data to substantiate the generalizations in the early review by Bazzaz and Pickett (1980), although at present the picture is still not always clear.

The light response of photosynthesis has received much attention. For example, results of observations on the gas exchange characteristics of single leaves of nine species representing four ecological guilds at the Gambari forest, Nigeria, are shown in Table 1.1, with means recalculated from Riddoch et al. (1991a). These are typical findings (cf. Oberbauer and Strain, 1984). Pioneers have higher dark respiration, a result also found, for example, for two out of four pioneer species studied at La Selva by Fetcher et al. (1987), and for the two most light-demanding of five species of Moraceae studied at Los Tuxtlas by Strauss-Debenedetti and Bazzaz (1991). Likewise, Field (1988) found the pioneer *Piper auritum* had only a limited ability to reduce dark respiration in shade. The pioneers in Table 1.1 also, and characteristically, have higher

Table 1.1 Photosynthetic parameters of seedlings of nine Nigerian species (based on Riddoch et al., 1991a, Table 2)

Species group	a Dark respiration	b Apparent quantum efficiency	c Mesophyll conductance	d Light compensation point (a/b)
Weedy shrubs of gaps (two spp.)	1.75	0.037	0.028	47
Pioneer trees (three spp.)*	1.10	0.034	0.028	32
Light-demanding climax trees (two spp.)†	0.35	0.018	0.010	19
Shade-tolerant climax trees (two spp.)	0.5	0.028	0.008	18

a: μmol CO_2 m^{-2} s^{-1}; b: mol CO_2 $photon^{-1}$; c: mol CO_2 m^{-2} s^{-1}; d: μmol CO_2 m^{-2} s^{-1}
For full species list see original. Species regrouped by M.D. Swaine personal communication
* *Ceiba, Milicia (= Chlorophora), Ricinodendron;* † *Pterygota, Sterculia*

mesophyll conductances, apparent quantum efficiencies and light compensation points.

Ramos and Grace (1990), working in growth cabinets, did not find such clear differences in the variables shown in Table 1.1 between *Brosimum alicastrum*, a shade-tolerant climax species, and three pioneers (*sensu* Swaine and Whitmore, 1988) *Cedrela odorata, Cordia alliodora* and *Swietenia macrophylla*. (I revise these authors interpretation of their results because *Swietenia* is a pioneer, not a climax/late successional species.) In 'sun' conditions there were no consistent differences between the guilds. In 'shade' conditions *Brosimum* did show one-third or lower rates of dark respiration and light compensation points. The species differed more in the allocation of biomass to different parts and allocation was considered more important in determining performance.

The close similarity in Table 1.1 of the weedy shrubs to the pioneer trees and the contrast of both these to the light-demanding climax species supports their distinction as separate guilds (Swaine and Whitmore, 1988).

Rates of light-saturated photosynthesis decrease with increasing shade tolerance (e.g. Oberbauer and Strain, 1984; Kwesiga and Grace, 1985; Fetcher et al., 1987; Mori et al., 1990; Press et al., 1996 for the sequence *Macaranga depressa*, ten dipterocarps, *Begonia* sp.)

At Danum, Sabah and within Dipterocarpaceae, which are all climax species, Barker (unpublished results, see also Press et al., 1996, Figure 2.1) found ten species of *Dipterocarpus, Dryobalanops, Hopea, Parashorea* and *Shorea* which he investigated had rates of light-saturated photosynthesis that ranged from 3.3 to 5.8 μmol m^{-2} s^{-1}. There was a significant relationship between these rates and the PAR required to saturate photosynthesis (300–470 μmol m^{-2} s^{-1}) but species known to foresters to have different degrees of shade tolerance (ranging from very shade-tolerant *Hopea sangal* to the strongly light-demanding *Shorea parvifolia*) did not segregate out. Barker worked on potted seedlings measured in a forest clearing. Mori et al. (1990), from studies on dipterocarp seedlings in a growth cabinet, found a similar difference between species. In their case the maximum net photosynthesis of two shade tolerants (*Dryobalanops sumatrensis* (aromatica), *Neobalanocarpus heimii*) was only 60 per cent that of two more light-demanding species (*Shorea assamica, S. parvifolia*: 3.8 and 6.5 μmol $CO_2\,m^{-2}\,s^{-1}$, respectively, no standard deviation stated).

Zainuddin (1989) and Mori et al. (1990) both found that the extremely shade-tolerant dipterocarp *Neobalanocarpus heimii* had its maximum rate of photosynthesis at intermediate levels of PAR, dropping at high levels. Mori et al. (1990) found this very shade-tolerant species was the only one of those tested to show such a drop. It also had a very low light compensation point compared to the others (*N. heimii* 5, *Dryobalonops sumatrensis, S. parvifolia* 12 and *S. assamica* 25 μmol $m^{-2}\,s^{-1}$). (All these values except the last are very low compared to the Nigerian climax tree species reported in Table 1.1 above.)

Most of the research on rates of photosynthesis has been with seedlings. Much higher rates were obtained by Koyama (1978, 1981) who made measurements on leaves detached from twigs 12 hours after the twigs were removed from the crowns of full grown trees.

Amongst the ten dipterocarps studied in Sabah there was a two-fold range in stomatal conductance, in some cases between species with very similar maximum rates of photosynthesis (Press et al., 1996, Figure 2.2). This discovery is of interest, because it suggests that within these rain-forest Dipterocarpaceae the very well-known differences in seedling growth rate and shade tolerance which could not be related to maximum rates of photosynthesis (see above) may arise from differences in water-use efficiency. *Dryobalanops lanceolata* had stomata open for the shortest period, hence showed lowest water loss. Two foresters' observations can be explained on the basis of this finding. Firstly, nursery-raised *Dryobalanops* seedlings are well known to show high survival on planting out so are much favoured by foresters for enrichment planting, secondly *D. sumatrensis* seedlings suffer leaf browning if the canopy above them is removed (J. Wyatt-Smith personal communication). It is also relevant to recall that, in his very detailed study of the autecology of *Shorea curtisii* in Peninsular Malaysia, Burgess (1975) found that the superior ability of the seedlings of this species to withstand periodic drought was the most important single factor in controlling its distribution.

Dipterocarpaceae still present many challenges to the ecophysiologist. For example, *Shorea leprosula* and *S. parvifolia*, both very widespread and fast-growing species, are well known to foresters to survive and to grow exceptionally well on open road sides and log dumps (J. Wyatt-Smith personal communication) The ecophysiological basis for this remains to be ascertained.

Another interesting difference between light-demanding and shade-tolerant species discovered by Mori et al. (1990) is an increasing sensitivity of photosynthesis to leaf temperature with increasing shade tolerance. The most shade-tolerant species studied, *Neobalanocarpus heimii*, showed the strongest reduction away from maximum (to 35 per cent) and *Acacia auriculiformis*, a pioneer, was relatively insensitive (10 per cent drop).

Several studies have found that shade-tolerant species are less able than light-demanders to adjust to changed conditions. This was the case with the growth of seven *Miconia* and *Piper* species at La Selva (Denslow et al., 1990). At Los Tuxtlas, amongst five Moraceous species grown in a range of light regimes, early successional *Cecropia obtusifolia* and *Ficus insipida* had the highest physiological plasticity and acclimation potential, though the latter could not always be deduced from the former (Strauss-Debenedetti and Bazzaz, 1991). Experiments in shade houses with four Sri Lankan *Shorea* species showed greatest plasticity of physiological response in the most light-demanding species (Ashton and Berlyn, 1991). The single light-demander amongst four Nigerian species studied in growth chambers by Kwesiga et al. (1986) was the most adaptable. However, contrary results have also been obtained. Field (1988) found that both *Piper auritum* (a pioneer) and *P. hispidum* (which occurs in both the open and in shade) had a similar capacity to acclimate their leaf photosynthesis rate to past light environments. Turnbull (1991) discovered in Queensland the greatest capacity to acclimate occurred in *Acmena ingens*, one of two 'late-successional' species studied, and was greater than in two 'mid-successional' and two 'pioneer' species (his terminology). Fetcher et al. (1987), working with potted plants of ten species at La Selva, found the capacity to adjust photosynthesis rate to be unrelated to ecological ranking.

In glasshouse experiments with the Nigerian pioneer *Nauclea diderrichii* and the climax species *Entandrophragma angolense* Riddoch et al. (1991b) found both had a considerable capacity to acclimate to a changed radiation regime, with the leaves of the pioneer showing a greater anatomical difference when grown at increased radiation and also with photosynthesis continuing to increase to higher radiation levels.

Popma and Bongers (1991) conducted an experiment at Los Tuxtlas, Mexico, with seedlings of three 'canopy species', *Cordia megalantha*, *Lonchocarpus guatemalensis* and *Omphalea oleifera* (these species all have a seedling bank so they are climax species *sensu* Swaine and Whitmore (1988)). All three species showed similar growth rates in mesh-clad shade-houses set up in three different forest light climates. Seedlings were then transferred between the three environments, to simulate gap dynamics. All three species showed both morphological/architectural and growth rate adjustment. They all performed well in shade and were able to acclimate rapidly to a brighter light climate, with greater plasticity in physiological than morphological traits.

20

Adjustment to a darker light climate was slower. Some differences in response were found between the three species. This experiment could be misleading, however, because, as will be discussed below (p. 23), light climate inside shade houses is unnatural.

Differences found in growth rate between different species of *Miconia* and *Piper* (Denslow et al., 1990) did not relate to differences in photosynthesis. These authors point out the many physiological processes that contribute to growth and the difficulties in making measurements. The absence of clear patterns in the results summarized above presumably reflects this complexity.

There are great differences between sun and shade leaves. For example, Pearcy (1987) showed for three Australian rain forest tree species that canopy-top leaves had a higher rate of light-saturated photosynthesis, of dark respiration, and greater stomatal conductances than understorey leaves. Oberbauer and Strain (1985) found *Pentaclethra macroloba* seedlings dropped their sun-formed leaves when switched from full or 25 per cent sun to 1 per cent sun. By contrast Kamaluddin and Grace (1992a,b) have shown by growth cabinet experiments that, for a Bangladeshi provenance of *Bischofia javanica*, the fully expanded shade leaves grown under simulated forest shade light ($40 \, \mu mol \, m^{-2} \, s^{-1}$) have a considerable ability to acclimate when the seedlings are transferred to simulated full light (1,000–1,200 $\mu mol \, m^{-2} \, s^{-1}$) and vice versa. As Kamaluddin and Grace point out this capacity to acclimate in *Bischofia* could be ecologically advantageous.

Measurements made on single leaves are difficult to extrapolate to performance of the whole plant. Some of the problems are overcome by classic growth analysis (Evans, 1972; Hunt, 1978) which integrates whole plant performance over a period of time. Early studies summarized by Whitmore and Gong (1983), extended by an investigation of the unit leaf rate (ULR) and relative growth rate of seven species grown in the open at La Selva (Oberbauer and Donnelly, 1986), have shown that the unit leaf rate of pioneer trees is not significantly different from the herb sunflower (*Helianthus annuus*) grown as a reference. In the La Selva study ULR decreased in climax species with increasing shade tolerance, to only 30–40 per cent in the most tolerant species. These results were only partly substantiated by Popma and Bongers (1988), working with seedlings of ten species at Los Tuxtlas, but their most open site received only 39–53 per cent of total daily PAR. Popma and Bongers also showed that species of different degrees of shade tolerance had different morphogenetic responses to their three different radiation climates and that these interacted with unit leaf rate to give the range of observed relative growth rates. Although the extreme light-demanding and shade-tolerant species responded in the manner to be expected, intermediate species did not. However, these findings might be misleading because of the unnatural microclimate created within textile-covered shade houses (see p. 23). In this case the plants were grown in light filtered through mosquito netting screens. It thus lacked the high intensity short bursts of radiation that come from full sunflecks.

Response to sunflecks

The importance of sunflecks to understorey plants has recently been comprehensively reviewed (Chazdon, 1988; Pearcy, 1988, 1990). There are several key findings. Current evidence suggests that, taking whole plants not single leaves, growth of understorey forest plants varies approximately linearly with radiation up to about 20 per cent of full sunlight. (Kwesiga et al., 1986, found photosynthetic rate linearly related to radiation up to $50 \, \mu mol \, m^{-2} \, s^{-1}$). Sunfleck light is thus of great significance because in many forests only about 2 per cent of PAR incident on the forest canopy reaches the floor and about 50–70 per cent of this is sunfleck light, though with high variability in both space and time. The few sunflecks of longer than 10 minutes duration and with photon flux density $1,500$–$2,000 \, \mu mol \, m^{-2} \, s^{-1}$ may contribute two-thirds of the daily photon flux. It is common for 30–60 per cent of total carbon gain by forest floor plants to be due to sunflecks. It would be of interest to investigate whether differences in the amount of sunfleck light between microsites (mapped for example by Evans et al., 1960) can be correlated with patchy distribution of undergrowth plants.

Pearcy (1990) also recorded that it is common for leaves exposed to a sunfleck to show an induction period before carbon dioxide uptake rises. Later sunflecks may result in greater carbon gain than the first. Post-illumination carbon fixation can significantly enhance the carbon gained in short 5–20 second sunflecks. It has also been found that excessive sunlight can damage leaves. This was observed for small dipterocarp seedlings in newly created gaps in Sabah (Brown and Whitmore, 1992), is common in the dipterocarp *Dryobalanops sumatrensis* (J. Wyatt-Smith personal communication) and is also shown by the contrast between seedlings of the pioneer *Trema tomentosa* and the dipterocarp *Shorea macroptera* when transferred out of shade (Turner and Newton, 1990).

Diffuse undergrowth light is depleted in red wavelengths and has a low ratio of red to far red (R:FR). Sunfleck light has a high R:FR ratio, as does the radiation climate of canopy gaps in contrast to the floor of closed forest (see e.g. Brown, 1993). The R:FR ratio is known to influence morphogenesis, but there have as yet been few investigations of this for rain forest plants. The maximum rate of photosynthesis and quantum efficiency of shade-grown leaves was greater in low R:FR than high R:FR light in a growth-chamber experiment with seedlings of *Khaya senegalensis* and *Terminalia ivorensis* both light-demanders from Nigeria (Kwesiga et al., 1986). (These authors wrongly state that *Khaya senegalensis* is shade-tolerant. In fact, it is a savannah tree and not therefore expected to be shade-tolerant; the three forest species of

Khaya are all light-demanding climax species: M.D. Swaine, personal communication.) The increases were accompanied by greater mesophyll conductance. The experiment shows both these species adapting similarly to the radiation climate found on the floor of closed canopy forest, though because *K. senegalensis* is a savannah species it probably does not naturally encounter low R:FR conditions so the significance of the experiment is hard to interpret. In another growth-chamber experiment with seedlings of the same species Kwesiga and Grace (1985) showed that *T. ivorensis* was considerably affected when grown in low R:FR radiation conditions, simulating the ratio of forest shade conditions: leaves were larger and thinner (higher specific leaf area (SLA), bigger leaf area ratio) and relative growth rate (RGR) was increased. There was little effect on *K. senegalensis*, which in fact had an increased SLA and somewhat higher RGR in the high R:FR treatment, but again this experiment simulates conditions the species is unlikely to encounter. There is no published evidence yet of etiolation of light-demanding tropical tree seedling species at low R:FR, although it might be expected.

For experiments on PAR and seedling growth it is common to reduce radiation by the use of shade-houses clad with fine mesh material, such as mosquito netting, that acts as a neutral filter by cutting out a known proportion of incident radiation. The ecological significance of such experiments is equivocal, however, for plants never in nature experience such a radiation climate. Their total daily PAR in the forest is made up of three components: sunflecks, and background shade light which comes partly from the sky and partly relatively impoverished in red wavelengths from leaves (hence with reduced R:FR ratio). The light quality in a shade house can be changed to simulate the background shade light by the use of coloured film (e.g. Brown, 1990; Lee, 1985). But there is no way in such mesh-clad houses to simulate the short bursts of very high intensity sunflecks, which may in nature be the main source of radiation for photosynthesis (see above). An improvement is to construct the shelters from slats so that a certain predetermined fraction of the light penetrates. This more closely simulates natural conditions and was the approach of Nicholson (1960) and Ashton (1990). But the addition to this artificial sunfleck light of the filtered background shade light with its altered R:FR ratio has not been achieved. Because of these problems it seems preferable, in fact, to conduct experiments within the forest using its canopy as the light filter and to analyse the experimental conditions using hemispherical photography (Rich, 1990; Mitchell and Whitmore, 1993; Whitmore et al., 1993).

Seedling architecture

Several investigators have found differences between species or within a species between different environments in biomass allocation between different parts of the seedling crown and between shoot and root and made suggestions on functional significance.

Differences in the relative allocation to roots and shoots with the amount of PAR received were shown for seedlings of several dipterocarp species by Mori (1980) and Sasaki and Mori (1981) (reported in Whitmore, 1984a, p.79). Differences in allocation were also found for seedlings of three Asian rain forest species (*Bombax valetonii, Duabanga grandifolia, Shorea assamica*) tested in growth chambers, as the day:night temperature regime was altered (Mori et al., 1990). Seedlings of four Queensland rain forest species all showed an increase in shoot:root ratios with decreasing radiation in a low nutrient treatment and the 'early successional' species amongst them (*Toona australis*) also showed an increased ratio in a high nutrient treatment (Thompson et al., 1992). Turner (1991), however, found no difference in seedlings of two pioneers in root:shoot ratio with either light climate or the addition of fertilizers. A study of ten tree species at Los Tuxtlas revealed complex morphological responses that resulted in different relative growth rates between the different light conditions inside mesh-clad shade houses erected in the forest understorey, small gaps ($50\,m^2$) and big gaps ($500\,m^2$) (Popma and Bongers, 1988; Bongers et al., 1988). In the big-gap treatment they obtained the common response of a larger root:shoot ratio. These experiments have however to be interpreted with caution as explained above.

Amongst six shade-tolerant primary forest species at Barro Colorado Island King (1990) found that at 2.5 m height undergrowth tree species had thicker trunks and heavier, wider, leafier crowns than saplings of taller growing species. He considered these life forms to optimise respectively light interception plus persistence versus opportunities for efficient height growth. In another study at La Selva (King, 1991), saplings of shade-tolerant species in heavy shade were found to shift biomass to leaves, whereas light-demanding species put two-thirds of biomass into axes in all light regimes. King suggested this differential plasticity may be an important contribution to shade tolerance.

Comparison of three ecologically contrasting *Piper* species at Los Tuxtlas by formal growth analysis showed that *P. hispidum*, which grows well in a wide range of conditions, is morphologically plastic whereas *P. auritum* and *P. aequale,* which are pioneer and shade-tolerant species respectively, are morphologically less flexible (Sanchez-Coronado et al., 1990). Field (1988) found *P. hispidum* had a deep crown with internal shading compared to the shallow umbrella-shaped crown of *P. auritum* which has non-overlapping leaves.

Gunatilleke et al. (1996) found differences between seedlings of eight Sri Lankan rain forest *Shorea* species when grown in shade houses. Lower altitude and valley species differed from higher altitude and ridge species in having fewer leaves of higher specific leaf area.

The trade-offs between height growth for future exploitation of better lit conditions higher in the canopy ('optimists') and lateral growth to maximize light interception at present near the forest floor ('pessimists') (Kohyama, 1987) were used to account for interspecific differences between saplings 60–300 cm tall of nine shade-tolerant species at Ulu Gadut, Sumatra (Kohyama and Hotta, 1990). A growth model showed that the optimal allocation, which maximizes height growth in the understorey light environment, is within the range observed amongst shade-tolerant tree species (Kohyama, 1991).

The trade-offs involved to optimize performance could perhaps be investigated further by examining a single species in different parts of its range. In India the small pioneer tree *Trema* sp. changes its branching pattern with elevation (P.S. Ramakrishnan personal communication). The wide ranging pioneer *Macaranga tanarius* changes its crown form and leaf size and texture between equatorial Asia and southern Japan and Hong Kong (personal observation).

Three older analyses of rain forest tree seedling architecture need to be reinterpreted against the insights provided by these recent studies.

Drude (1890) (in Richards, 1952) recognized a guild of *Schopfbäumchen*, namely unbranched undergrowth treelets with a terminal tuft of leaves. These perhaps represent, in fact, the extreme strategy, optimists in the sense of Kohyama, the seedlings or saplings that invest their all in height growth (see Kohyama, 1987).

Corner (1949) drew a distinction between pachycaul and leptocaul treelets, with thick and thin axes respectively, as part of the phylogenetic speculations of his Durian Theory. We have yet to discover the functional significance of these contrasting constructions, or of his claim (demonstrated for *Ficus*, Corner, 1975, 1977) that the originating and primitive species of series of related species within a genus is a 'pachycaul starter'.

The scheme of classification of crown architecture of Hallé and Oldeman (1970) recognized twenty-three models. Later a few more were added. These models are based on the interplay of three main morphogenetic factors, namely apical versus lateral growth, radial versus bilateral symmetry, and intermittent and rhythmic versus continuous growth. The models have not been found to correlate well either with taxonomy or ecology. Perhaps in functional terms there is a convergence, different models reaching the same ecophysiological trade-off by different morphogenetic processes. Fuller analysis by experiment is needed.

Response to mineral nutrients

Stewart et al. (1990) examined leaf nitrate reductase activity in a range of Australian plant communities from rain forest through wet sclerophyll forest to rain forest/xeric forest mixtures and savannah. In all communities they discovered a continuously declining gradient of this enzyme from pioneer to mature forest species. Nitrate reductase reduces nitrate to nitrite which, following subsequent reduction to ammonia, enters amino acid biosynthesis. They pointed out that disturbance of forest soil leads to rapid production of nitrate ions and that this will favour pioneer species because of their high nitrate reductase activity. Stewart et al. (1988) suggested that climax species become less competitive following disturbance because, in contrast to pioneers, their roots take up ammonium ions or organic nitrogen that are translocated to the leaves and metabolized.

The relatively few studies on the influence of fertilizers on the growth of rain forest tree seedlings, compared to the considerable work done on the effects of radiation, need to be interpreted against the findings and propositions of Stewart and his colleagues and extended by further studies to verify them. In most experiments fertilizers have been found to have little or no effect and no clear distinction between the two forms of nitrogen has yet emerged. Thus, Denslow et al. (1990) found no significant effect of fertilization (N as NH_4Cl) on relative height growth at La Selva of seven *Miconia* and *Piper* species, either as the main factor or in interaction with light. By contrast, however, when the same species were grown with a restricted rooting volume in pots (under 20 per cent shade cloth) a response was found to fertilizer addition (N in this case as NH_4NO_3) (Denslow et al., 1987) and growth plasticity was not consistently greater in light-demanding than shade-tolerant species. In four independent experiments application of fertilizers has had no effect on the growth of dipterocarp seedlings (Turner et al., 1992b; Burslem, 1996) though there is evidence that under conditions of very low nutrient availability ectomycorrhizal infection may be of importance for seedling growth. In two of these experiments only nitrate nitrogen was added, in the others ammonium nitrogen was added also. In a Jamaican montane forest the lack of seedling response to fertilizers led Healey (1990) to abandon his experiment and conflate observations on seedling growth with another experiment on the influence of radiation.

Fredeen et al. (1991), working with six *Piper* species at Los Tuxtlas grown under a wide range of light climates, found that gap species were 'inherently more competent to assimilate nitrate than shade species' which supports the generalization of Stewart et al. (1988, 1990).

Turner (1991), in Penang, grew seedlings of the two pioneers *Trema tomentosa* and *Melastoma malabathricum* in pots at about 60 per cent and 10–15 per cent full light. Only *Trema* showed significantly better growth with the addition of NPK fertilizer. Turner pointed out that the secondary forests where *Trema* grows occupy relatively good soils and that *Melastoma* forms shrublands on degraded sites. Neither species showed any nutrient/shade interaction. Burslem (1996) in Singapore, also working with *M. malabathricum*, did find a fertilizer effect. His pot-grown seedlings were strongly limited by phosphorus, when this was added all other macronutrients and a mixture of micronutrients became limiting to growth. As *Melastoma* habitually occupies degraded sites, the ecological significance of this discovery is not clear.

Burslem (1996) found that potted, forest-grown seedlings of only one of four climax species tested showed a response to nutrients, added to a level considerably greater than they would encounter in the forest.

The evidence gathered so far is that there is not always a pulse of nutrients on the creation of a canopy gap (p. 7) and it is now clearly established that most rain forest soils are very low in plant mineral nutrients. Thus many rain forest species may never experience high nutrient concentrations. Seedling failure to respond to experimental nutrient addition is perhaps not therefore surprising, and if a response can be induced its ecological significance may be hard to interpret, especially where nutrients are increased to unnaturally high levels.

There is not yet much experimental evidence of nutrient/shade interactions in rain forests, namely that more fertile soils can compensate for conditions of very low radiation, but Riddoch et al. (1991b) did find, in glasshouse experiments with two Nigerian tree species (*Entandrophragma angolense, Nauclea diderrichii*, climax and pioneer respectively) a positive response of photosynthesis to added mineral nutrients, including a significant interaction between nitrogen and light. They considered that 'nutrient supply may be crucial in achieving the full range of acclimation to productive habitats'. The very plastic species *Flindersia brayleyana* showed a shade/nutrient interaction in a pot experiment in Queensland. At low soil nutrient concentrations this species was unable to respond to high light regimes (Thompson et al., 1988). This was confirmed in a later growth cabinet experiment which also showed for seedlings of three other Queensland rain forest tree species an interaction between the light climate (three levels of radiation) and the amount of mineral nutrients (two treatments) (Thompson et al., 1992). In this experiment *Toona australis*, an 'early successional' species, showed a much greater response of whole plant biomass than two *Argyrodendron* spp. which are shade tolerants, and *Flindersia* was intermediate.

Water availability

As with nutrients, few studies have explicitly addressed the possible importance of periodic water shortage for rain forest tree seedling ecology. Even in perhumid climates with no regular or marked dry season, there are periods when evapotranspiration exceeds rainfall (Whitmore, 1984a). There are also rare droughts that have dramatic effects, for example, that of 1982–83 (Whitmore, 1990; Figure 7.19) which killed many trees over thousands of hectares of primary rain forest in east Kalimantan.

Two recent studies have both been made in rain forests where there is annually a marked dry season. At Sinharaja, Sri Lanka, Ashton (1990) conducted experiments in slat-constructed shade houses and in the forest on four *Shorea* species and found different responses amongst species to radiation and soil moisture in interaction from which he was able to explain the differential abundance of these species between ridge, slope and valley sites. At Barro Colorado Island, Fisher et al. (1991) found the common big tree species *Virola surinamensis* germinates without dormancy in both gap and forest floor sites. Its early death in shade can be prevented by irrigation.

There have also been a few studies in perhumid rain forests that experience no regular dry season. At La Selva Denslow et al. (1991) found understorey soil drier than gap soil, but that trenching to prevent root competition for soil moisture had no effect on seedling survival during a two-year period that included two of the mild annual dry seasons this forest experiences. Brown (1990) at Danum, Sabah, found that tiny seedlings of the dipterocarp *Parashorea malaanonan* suffered heavy drought-induced mortality in the first 6 months after he created artificial canopy gaps. Larger seedlings of this and other dipterocarps survived much better. The question of potential combined effects of light and water availability was addressed by Burslem (1996) in experiments on four species in Singapore. He found that all four species studied (*Antidesma cuspidatum, Calophyllum tetrapterum, Garcinia scortechinii, Hopea griffithii*) showed phenotypic responses to his low-watering regime but that only the *Hopea* showed a significant interaction on growth between the two factors.

Further study of nutrient/shade/water availability interactions might, as Burslem (1996) suggests, throw up subtle examples of niche differentiation amongst, for example, the species of *Calophyllum* or *Shorea* that co-occur in many Malesian lowland rain forests. On present superficial evidence these appear to have identical seedling ecology.

CONCLUSIONS

There are now a great number of individual research studies and previous reviews on aspects of tropical rain forest seedling ecology, and not all have been covered in this review. But the selection included is believed to be representative of the present state of knowledge and a few general conclusions emerge that might be useful in guiding future endeavour.

The current state of knowledge of tree seedling community ecology is well summarized in a recent review by Yamamoto (1992b). As he says, there is some evidence of gap-size partitioning at the level of the pioneer and climax species guilds but beyond that there is growing evidence that species have broadly overlapping distributions along a gap-size gradient. This is not surprising given the now well-documented spatial heterogeneity of microclimate within and between gaps (p. 6). Solar radiation is probably the most important microclimatic parameter, given that both PAR and many other microclimatic variables are related to it. The enhanced solar radiation within a gap extends beyond its physical boundary, is heterogeneous within the gap, and variability is to be expected between small gaps of the same size. Given such heterogeneity in this important parameter it is difficult to see how climax species can specialize on any particular physical size of gap (remembering also the problems in the definition thereof, p. 4). The particular definition of shade tolerance that specifies a certain gap size for seedling release (p. 10, p. 15) cannot hold. For clear understanding future discussions need to distinguish between the two other meanings of the term, namely the level of PAR at which seedling survival is possible, and the length of survival (or rate of decay) of a population at a given PAR level. Field (1988) reported that up to fifty *Piper* species can co-exist in a single Central American rain forest and that these are mostly sorted along light gradients, with soil moisture and nutrients sometimes playing a role.

Further studies are needed to elucidate what mechanisms do, in fact, operate to support the view, which is common although often only implicit, that different climax species are successfully released in gaps of different size. Changes in rank order of height as seedlings grow into saplings and poles may hold the solution and more long-term studies are needed. For a few pioneer species an ecophysiological basis for failure in tiny gaps has been discovered (p. 16), but this guild also merits further investigation.

It seems that the most probable trigger for seedling release in a gap is the change in solar radiation. This increases up to about one hundred-fold in a canopy gap compared to the closed canopy forest floor and is the controlling factor for many other microclimatic variables (as described above) so these also change. Whereas radiation is increased in all gaps, it seems, from the evidence gathered from tropical rain forests so far, that soil moisture, plant mineral nutrients (cf. Vitousek and Denslow, 1986) and potentially competing roots change less, not in all gaps, and sometimes patchily within gaps. It remains to be investigated under what circumstances radiation and other environmental factors, and their interactions with each other and and with attributes of particular species (such as seed size), are important. It might be expected that in such interactions lie the subtle aspects of niche distinction that might operate between, for example, ecologically closely similar and taxonomically closely related sympatric species of for example *Calophyllum, Shorea* etc., that co-occur in many Malesian rain forests. The general appearance of lowland tropical rain forest is of many seedlings with apparently identical ecology, and one challenge for the future continues to be to see whether niche-differentiation occurs or not.

Amongst ecophysiological studies there has been considerable investigation of gas exchange and hence the characterization of differences between species in photosynthesis and respiration. A general picture is emerging of consistent differences from pioneers at one extreme to species of increasing shade tolerance. Indications are emerging that water-use efficiency can be important, for example, between species of Dipterocarpaceae (Press et al., 1996).

A few studies have investigated nitrogen-use efficiency (e.g. Field, 1988). Putative differences between species in the form in which nitrogen is absorbed (p. 25) need pursuing. These are all likely to be fruitful avenues for exploration and to reveal more about the ways in which species have evolved to co-exist in hyper-rich tropical rain forests, especially on the perpetually intriguing question of whether all species do indeed have distinct physical niches, a question which has been, and continues to be, the driving force behind much scientific enquiry.

However, to probe for and unravel environmental mechanisms that help account for the extreme species richness of tropical rain forests is fraught with difficulty. On the one hand facets of the physical environment vary continuously and on the other different species have optima but no sharp cut-off, as well as responses that overlap species to species. Moreover, plants respond to the whole physical environment not discrete factors. Could it be that to attempt fully to characterize the rain forest tree/environment nexus is, in fact, to pursue a chimera? Perhaps we should accept that the ultimate achievement will be simply to discern the outlines and major patterns.

ACKNOWLEDGEMENTS

This paper was largely written while the writer was a visiting professor at Ehime University, Japan. Thanks are due to Monbusho, the British Council and Professor K. Ogino for making this visit possible. Many colleagues have provided data or helped by discussion. Critical comments were made on a draft by N.D. Brown, B. Finegan, M.C. Press and M.D. Swaine. These are all gratefully thanked, as are M.D. Swaine and UNESCO for the invitation to participate in the Aberdeen workshop and to contribute this review.

REFERENCES

Alexandre, D.Y. (1989). *Dynamiques de la Régénération Naturelle en Forêt Dense de Côte d'Ivoire*. Editions ORSTOM, Paris.

Alvarez-Buylla, E.R. and Martinez-Ramos, M. (1992). Demography and allometry of *Cecropia obtusifolia*, a neotropical pioneer tree – an evaluation of the climax–pioneer paradigm for tropical rain forests. *Journal of Ecology*, **80**, 275–490.

Anderson, M.C. (1964). Light relations of terrestrial plant communities and their measurement. *Biological Reviews*, **39**, 425–86.

Ashton, P.M.S. (1990). *Seedling response of* Shorea *species across moisture and light regimes in a Sri Lankan rain forest*. Ph.D. dissertation, Yale University.

Ashton, P.M.S. (1992). Some measurements of the microclimate within a Sri Lankan tropical rain forest. *Agriculture and Forest Meteorology*, **59**, 217–35.

Ashton, P.M.S. and Berlyn, G.P. (1991). Leaf adaptations of some *Shorea* species in sun and shade. *New Phytologist*, **121**, 587–96.

Augspurger, C.K. (1984). Seedling survival of tropical tree species: interactions of dispersal distance, light-gaps and pathogens. *Ecology*, **65**, 1705–12.

Barton, A.M. (1984). Neotropical pioneer and shade-tolerant tree species: do they partition treefall gaps? *Tropical Ecology*, **25**, 196–202.

Bazzaz, F.A. and Pickett, S.T.A. (1980). Physiological ecology of tropical succession: a comparative review. *Annual Review of Ecology and Systematics*, **11**, 287–310.

Becker, P. (1981). Potential physical and chemical defences of *Shorea* seedlings. Leaves against insects. *Malaysian Forester*, **44**, 346–57.

Becker, P. (1983). Effects of insect herbivory and artificial defoliation on survival of *Shorea* seedlings. In Sutton, S.L., Whitmore, T.C. and Chadwick, A.C. (eds.) *Tropical Rain Forest Ecology and Management*, pp. 241–52. Blackwell, Oxford.

Becker, P., Rabenold, P.E., Idol, J.R. and Smith, A.P. (1988). Water potential gradients for gaps and slopes in a Panamanian tropical moist forest's dry season. *Journal of Ecology*, **4**, 173–84.

Blaser, J. and Camacho, M. (1991). *Estructura, Composición y Aspectos Silviculturales de un Bosque de Robles (*Quercus *spp.) del Piso Montano en Costa Rica.* CATIE, Turrialba.

Bongers, F., Popma, J. and Iriarte-Vivar, S. (1988). Response of *Cordia megalantha* seedlings to gap environments in tropical rain forest. *Functional Ecology*, **2**, 379–90.

Boot, R.G.A. (1996). The significance of seedling size and growth rate of tropical rain forest tree seedlings for regeneration in canopy openings. In Swaine, M.D. (ed.) *Ecology of Tropical Forest Tree Seedlings*, pp. 267–83. UNESCO/Parthenon, Paris/Carnforth.

Brandani, A., Hartshorn, G.S. and Orians, G.H. (1988). Internal heterogeneity of gaps and species richness in Costa Rican tropical wet forest. *Journal of Tropical Ecology*, **4**, 99–119.

Brokaw, N.V.L. (1982). The definition of treefall gaps and its effect on measures of forest dynamics. *Biotropica*, **11**, 158–60.

Brokaw, N.V.L. (1987). Gap-phase regeneration of three pioneer tree species in a tropical forest. *Journal of Ecology*, **75**, 9–19.

Brown, N.D. (1990). *Dipterocarp regeneration in tropical rain forest gaps of different sizes*. D. Phil. thesis, University of Oxford.

Brown, N.D. (1993). The implications of climate and gap microclimate for seedling growth conditions in a Bornean lowland rain forest. *Journal of Tropical Ecology*, **9**, 153–68.

Brown, N.D. and Whitmore, T.C. (1992). Do dipterocarp seedlings really partition tropical rain forest gaps? *Philosophical Transactions Royal Society* series B, **335**, 369–78.

Bruijnzeel, L.A. (1992). Managing tropical watersheds for production: where contradictory theory and practice co-exist. In Miller, F.R. and Adam, K.L. (eds.) *Wise Management of Tropical Forests*, pp. 37–76. Oxford Forestry Institute, Oxford.

Burgess, P.F. (1975). Silviculture in the hill forests of the Malay Peninsula. *Malaysian Forest Department Research Pamphlet*, **66**.

Burslem, D. (1996). Differential responses to nutrients, shade and drought among tree seedlings of lowland tropical rain forest in Singapore. In Swaine, M.D. (ed.),

Ecology of Tropical Forest Tree Seedlings, pp. 211–43. UNESCO/Parthenon, Paris/Carnforth.

Canham, C.D., Denslow, J.S., Platt, W.J., Runkle, J.R., Spies, T.A. and White, P.S. (1990). Light regimes beneath closed canopies and tree-fall gaps in temperate and tropical forests. *Canadian Journal of Forest Research*, **20**, 620–31.

Canham, C.D. and Marks, P.L. (1985). The response of woody plants to disturbance: patterns of establishment and growth. In Pickett, S.T.A. and White, P.S. (eds.), *The Ecology of Natural Disturbance and Patch Dynamics*. Academic Press, New York.

Chazdon, R.L. (1988). Sunflecks and their importance to forest understorey plants. *Advances in Ecological Research*, **18**, 1–63.

Clark, D.A. and Clark, D.B. (1984). Spacing dynamics of a tropical rain forest tree: evaluation of the Janzen-Connell model. *American Naturalist*, **124**, 769–88.

Clark, D.A. and Clark, D.B. (1992). Life history diversity of canopy and emergent trees in a neotropical rain forest. *Ecological Monographs*, **62**, 315–44.

Clark, D.B. (1990). The role of disturbance in the regeneration of neotropical moist forests. In Bawa, K.S. and Hadley, M. (eds.), *Reproductive Ecology of Tropical Forest Plants*, pp. 291–315. UNESCO/Parthenon, Paris/Carnforth.

Condit, R., Hubbell, S.P. and Foster, R.B. (1992). Recruitment near conspecific adults and the maintenance of tree and shrub diversity in a neotropical forest. *American Naturalist*, **140**, 261–86.

Connell, J.H. (1971). On the role of natural enemies in preventing competitive exclusion in some marine animals and in rain forest trees. In Den Boer, P.J. and Gradwell, G. (eds.), *Dynamics of Populations*. PUDOC, Wageningen.

Corner, E.J.H. (1949). The durian theory or the origin of the modern tree. *Annals of Botany*, **52**, 367–414.

Corner, E.J.H. (1975). The climbing species of *Ficus*: derivation and evolution. *Philosophical Transactions Royal Society*, B, **273**, 359–86.

Corner, E.J.H. (1977). *Ficus* in the Solomon Islands and its bearing on the post-Jurassic history of Melanesia. *Philosophical Transactions Royal Society* B, **253**, 23–159.

Denslow, J.S. (1980). Gap partitioning among tropical rain forest trees. *Biotropica*, **12** (Suppl.), 47–55.

Denslow, J.S. (1984). Influence of disturbance on species diversity: reply to T.C. Whitmore. *Biotropica*, **16**, 240.

Denslow, J.S. and Gomez Diaz, A.E. (1990). Seed rain to tree fall gaps in a neotropical rain forest. *Canadian Journal of Forest Research*, **20**, 642–8.

Denslow, J.S., Newell, E. and Ellison, A.M. (1991). The effect of understorey palms and cyclanths on the growth and survival of *Inga* seedlings. *Biotropica*, **23**, 225–34.

Denslow, J.S., Shultz, J.C., Vitousek, P.M. and Strain, B.R. (1990). Growth responses of tropical shrubs to treefall gaps. *Ecology*, **71**, 165–79.

Denslow, J.S., Vitousek, P.M. and Schultz, J.C. (1987). Bioassays of nutrient limitation in a tropical rain forest soil. *Oecologia* (Berlin), **74**, 370–6.

Evans, G.C. (1956). An area survey method of investigating the distribution of light intensity in woodlands, with particular reference to sunflecks. *Journal of Ecology*, **44**, 391–428.

Evans, G.C. (1972). *The Quantitative Analysis of Plant Growth*. Blackwell, Oxford.

Evans, G.C., Whitmore, T.C. and Wong, Y.K. (1960). The distribution of light reaching the ground vegetation in a tropical rain forest. *Journal of Ecology*, **48**, 193–204.

Fernandez, D.S. and Fetcher, N. (1991). Changes in light availability following Hurricane Hugo in a subtropical montane forest in Puerto Rico. *Biotropica*, **23**, 393–9.

Fetcher, N., Oberbauer, S.F., Roja, G. and Strain, B.R. (1987). Efectos del régimen de luzsobre la fotosintesis y el crecimiento en plántulas de árboles de un bosque lluviose tropical de Costa Rica. *Revista Biologia Tropical,* supplemento 1, **35**, 97–110.

Field, C.B. (1988). On the role of photosynthetic responses in constraining habitat distribution of rain forest plants. *Australian Journal of Plant Physiology*, **15**, 343–58.

Finegan, B. (1992). The management potential of neotropical secondary lowland rain forest. *Forest Ecology and Management*, **47**, 295–321.

Fisher, B.L., Howe, H.F. and Wright, S.J. (1991). Survival and growth of *Virola surinamensis* seedlings: water augmentation in gap and understorey. *Oecologia*, **86**, 292–7.

Flores, S. (1992). Growth and seasonality of seedlings and juveniles of primary species of a cloud forest in northern Venezuela. *Journal of Tropical Ecology*, **8**, 299–305.

Fredeen, A.L., Griffin, K. and Field, C.B. (1991). Effects of light quantity and quality and soil nitrogen status on nitrate reductase activity in rain forest species of the genus *Piper*. *Oecologia*, **86**, 441–6.

Garwood, N.C. (1996). Functional morphology of tropical tree seedlings. In Swaine, M.D. (ed.), *Ecology of Tropical Forest Tree Seedlings*, pp. 59–138. UNESCO/Parthenon, Paris/Carnforth.

Garwood, N.C., Janos, D.P. and Brokaw, N. (1979). Earthquake-caused landslides: a major disturbance to tropical forests. *Science*, **205**, 997–9.

Gunatilleke, C.V.S., Perera, G.A.D., Ashton, P.S., Ashton, P.M.S. and Gunatilleke, I.A.U.N. (1996). Seedling growth of *Shorea* section Doona (Dipterocarpaceae) in soils from different forest sites of south west Sri Lanka. In Swaine, M.D. (ed.), *Ecology of Tropical Forest Tree Seedlings*, pp. 245–65. UNESCO/Parthenon, Paris/Carnforth.

Hallé, F. and Oldeman, R.A.A. (1970). Essai sur l'architecture et la dynamique de croissance des arbres tropicaux. *Collect. Monogr. Bot. Biol. Veget.*, **6**, Masson, Paris. [translated into English by B.C. Stone, University of Malaya Press, Kuala Lumpur (1975)].

Hartshorn, G.S. (1980). Neotropical forest dynamics. *Biotropica*, **12** (Supplement), 23–30.

Hawthorne, W. (1993). *Forest Regeneration after Logging in Bia South Game Production Reserve, Ghana*. Natural Resources Institute, Chatham.

Healey, J.R. (1990). *Regeneration in a Jamaican Montane Tropical Rain Forest*. Ph.D. dissertation, Cambridge University.

Howe, H.F. and Smallwood, J. (1982). Ecology of seed dispersal. *Annual Review of Ecology and Systematics*, **13**, 201–28.

Hubbell, S.P. and Foster, R.B. (1983). Diversity of canopy trees in a neotropical forest and implications for conservation. In Sutton, S.L., Whitmore, T.C. and Chadwick, A.C. (eds.), *Tropical Rain Forest Ecology and Management*, pp. 25–41. Blackwell, Oxford.

Hunt, R. (1978). *Plant Growth Analysis*. Arnold, London.

Hytteborn, H. and Skarpe, C. (eds.) (1992). Vegetation dynamics and regeneration in seasonal tropical climates. *Journal of Vegetation Science*, **3**, 291–417.

Janzen, D.H. (1970). Herbivores and the number of tree species in tropical forests. *American Naturalist*, **104**, 501–28.

Kamaluddin, M. and Grace, J. (1992a). Photoinhibition and light acclimation in seedlings of *Bischofia javanica*, a tropical forest tree from Asia. *Annals of Botany*, **69**, 47–52.

Kamaluddin, M. and Grace, J. (1992b). Acclimation in seedlings of a tropical tree, *Bischofia javanica*, following a stepwise reduction in light. *Annals of Botany*, **69**, 557–62.

Kennedy, D.N. (1991). *The Role of Colonising Species in the Regeneration of Dipterocarp Rain Forest*. Ph.D. thesis, University of Aberdeen .

Kennedy, D.N. and Swaine, M.D. (1992). Germination and growth of colonizing species in artificial gaps of different sizes in dipterocarp rain forest. *Philosophical Transactions Royal Society of London* series B, **335**, 357–68.

King, D.A. (1990). Allometry of saplings and understorey trees of a Panamanian forest. *Functional Ecology*, **4**, 27–32.

King, D.A. (1991). Correlations between biomass allocation, relative growth rate and light environment in tropical forest saplings. *Functional Ecology*, **5**, 485–92.

Kitajima, K. and Augspurger, C.K. (1989). Seed and seedling ecology of a monocarpic tropical tree, *Tachigalia versicolor*. *Ecology*, **70**, 1102–14.

Kochummen, K.M., LaFrankie, J.V. Jr. and Manokaran, N. (1990). Floristic composition of Pasoh forest reserve, a lowland rain forest in Peninsular Malaysia. *Journal of Tropical Forest Science*, **3**, 1–13.

Kohyama, T. (1987). Significance of architecture and allometry in saplings. *Functional Ecology*, **1**, 399–404.

Kohyama, T. (1991). A functional model describing sapling growth under a tropical forest canopy. *Functional Ecology*, **5**, 83–90.

Kohyama, T. and Hotta, M. (1990). Significance of allometry in tropical saplings. *Functional Ecology*, **4**, 515–21.

Koyama, H. (1978). Photosynthesis studies in Pasoh forest. *Malayan Nature Journal*, **30**, 253–8.

Koyama, H. (1981). Photosynthetic rates in lowland rain forest trees of Peninsular Malaysia. *Japanese Journal of Ecology*, **31**, 361–9.

Kramer, F. (1926). Onderzoek naar de natuurlijke verjonging in den uitkap in Preanger gebergte-bosch. Mededeeling van het Boschbouwproefstation [Buitenzorg] 14.

Kramer, F. (1933). De natuurlijke verjonging in het Goenoeng Gedeh complex. *Tectona*, **26**, 156–85.

Kwesiga, F. and Grace, J. (1985). The role of the red:far red ratio in the response of tropical tree seedlings to shade. *Annals of Botany*, **57**, 283–90.

Kwesiga, F., Grace, J. and Sandford, A.P. (1986). Some photosynthetic characteristics of tropical timber trees as affected by the light regime during growth. *Annals of Botany*, **58**, 23–32.

Lee, D.W. (1985). Duplicating foliage shade for research on plant development. *Horticultural Science*, **20**, 116–18.

Lieberman, D. (1996). Demography of tropical tree seedlings: a review. In Swaine, M.D. (ed.), *Ecology of Tropical Forest Tree Seedlings*, pp. 131–8. UNESCO/ Parthenon, Paris/Carnforth.

Lieberman, M., Lieberman, D. and Peralta, R. (1989). Forests are not just swiss cheese: canopy stereogeometry of non-gaps in tropical forests. *Ecology*, **70**, 550–2.

Manokaran, N. and LaFrankie, J.V. Jr. (1990). Stand structure of Pasoh forest reserve, a lowland rain forest in Peninsular Malaysia. *Journal of Tropical Forest Science*, **3**, 14–24.

Marrs, R.H., Thompson, J., Scott, D. and Proctor, J. (1991). Nitrogen mineralisation and nitrification in terra firme forest and savanna soils on Ilha de Maráca Roraima, Brazil. *Journal of Tropical Ecology*, **7**, 123–37.

Martinez-Ramos, M. and Alvarez-Buylla, E. (1986). Seed dispersal, gap dynamics and tree recruitment: the case of *Cecropia obtusifolia* at Los Tuxtlas, Mexico. In Estrada, A. and Fleming, T.H. (eds.), *Frugivores and Seed Dispersal*. Junk, Dordrecht.

Mitchell, P.L. and Whitmore, T.C. (1993). Use of hemispherical photographs in forest ecology: calculation of absolute amount of radiation beneath the canopy. *Oxford Forestry Institute Occasional Papers*, **44**.

Molofsky, J. and Augspurger, C.K. (1992). The effect of leaf litter on early seedling establishment in a tropical forest. *Ecology*, **73**, 68–77.

Mori, T., Nakashizuka, T., Sumizono, T. and Yap, S.K. (1990). Growth and photosynthetic responses to temperature in several Malaysian tree species. *Journal of Tropical Forest Science*, **3**, 44–57.

Nicholson, D.I. (1960). Light requirements of seedlings of five species of Dipterocarpaceae. *Malayan Forester*, **23**, 344–56.

Nuñez-Farfán, J. and Dirzo, R. (1988). Within gap spatial heterogeneity and seedling performance in a Mexican tropical forest. *Oikos*, **51**, 274–84.

Oberbauer, S.F., Clark, D.B., Clark, D.A. and Quesada, M. (1988). Crown light environments of saplings of two species of rain forest emergent trees. *Oecologia*, **75**, 207–12.

Oberbauer, S.F. and Donnelly, M.A. (1986). Growth analysis and successional status of Costa Rican rain forest trees. *New Phytologist*, **104**, 517–21.

Oberbauer, S.F. and Strain, B.R. (1984). Photosynthesis and successional status of Costa Rican rain forest trees. *Photosynthesis Research*, **5**, 227–32.

Oberbauer, S.F. and Strain, B.R. (1985). Effects of light regime on the growth and physiology of *Pentaclethra macroloba* (Mimosaceae) in Costa Rica. *Journal of Tropical Ecology*, **1**, 303–20.

Oldeman, R.A.A. and Dijk, J. van (1991). Diagnosis of the temperament of tropical forest trees. In Gomez-Pompa, A., Whitmore, T.C. and Hadley, M. (eds.) (1990). *Rain Forest Regeneration and Management*, pp. 21–65. UNESCO/Parthenon, Paris/Carnforth.

Orians, G.H. (1982). The influence of tree falls in tropical forests on tree species richness. *Tropical Ecology*, **23**, 255–79.

Osunkoya, O.O., Ash, J.E., Graham, A.W. and Hopkins, M.S. (1993). Growth of tree seedlings in tropical rain forests of north Queensland, Australia. *Journal of Tropical Ecology*, **9**, 1–18.

Pearcy, R.W. (1987). Photosynthetic gas exchange responses of Australian tropical forest trees in canopy, gap and understorey microenvironments. *Functional Ecology*, **1**, 169–78.

Pearcy, R.W. (1988). Photosynthetic utilisation of light flecks by understorey plants. *Australian Journal of Plant Physiology*, **15**, 223–38.

Pearcy, R.W. (1990). Sunflecks and photosynthesis in plant canopies. *Annual Review of Plant Physiology and Plant Molecular Biology*, **41**, 421–543.

Platt, W.J. and Strong, D.R. (eds.) (1989). Special feature: treefall gaps and forest dynamics. *Ecology*, **70**, 535–76.

Popma, J. and Bongers, F. (1988). The effect of canopy gaps on growth and morphology of seedlings of rain forest species. *Oecologia*, **75**, 625–32.

Popma, J. and Bongers, F. (1991). Acclimation of three Mexican tropical rain forest tree species to a change in light availability. *Journal of Tropical Ecology*, **7**, 85–97.

Popma, J., Bongers, F., Martinez-Ramos, M. and Veneklaas, E. (1988). Pioneer species distribution in treefall gaps in neotropical rain forest: a gap definition and its consequences. *Journal of Tropical Ecology*, **4**, 77–88.

Press, M.C., Brown, N.D., Barker, M.G. and Zipperlen, S.W. (1996). Photosynthetic responses to light in tropical rain forest tree seedlings. In Swaine, M.D. (ed.) *Ecology of Tropical Forest Tree Seedlings*, pp. 41–58. UNESCO/Parthenon, Paris/ Carnforth.

Putz, F.E. (1983). Treefall pits and mounds, buried seeds and the importance of soil disturbance to pioneer trees on Barro Colorado Island, Panama. *Ecology*, **64**, 1069–74.

Putz, F.E. and Brokaw, N.V.L. (1989). Sprouting of broken trees in Barro Colorado Island, Panama. *Ecology*, **70**, 508–12.

Raich, J.W. (1989). Seasonal and spatial variation in the light environment in a tropical dipterocarp forest and gaps. *Biotropica*, **21**, 299–302.

Raich, J.W. and Christensen, N.L. (1989). Malaysian dipterocarp forest: tree seedling and sapling species composition and small-scale disturbance patterns. *National Geographic Research*, **5**, 348–63.

Ramos, J. and Grace, J. (1990). The effects of shade on the gas exchange of seedlings of four tropical trees from Mexico. *Functional Ecology*, **4**, 667–77.

Rich, P.M. (1989). A manual for analysis of hemispherical canopy photography. *Los Alamos National Laboratory Technical Report* LA-11733-M.

Rich, P.M. (1990). Characterizing plant canopies with hemispherical photographs. *Remote Sensing Reviews*, **5**, 13–29.

Richards, P.W. (1952). *The Tropical Rain Forest*. Cambridge University Press, Cambridge.

Riddoch, I., Grace, J., Fashehun, F.E., Riddoch, B. and Lapido, D.O. (1991a). Photosynthesis and successional status of seedlings in a tropical semideciduous rain forest in Nigeria. *Journal of Ecology*, **79**, 491–504.

Riddoch, I., Lehto, T. and Grace, J. (1991b). Photosynthesis of tropical tree seedlings in relation to light and nutrient supply. *New Phytologist*, **119**, 137–47.

Riera, B. (1985). Importance des buttes de racinement dans la régéneration forestière en Guyane Française. *Revue Ecologie* (Terre Vie), **40**, 321–9.

Riswan, S. (1982). *Ecological studies on primary, secondary and experimentally cleared mixed dipterocarp forest and kerangas forest in east Kalimantan, Indonesia.* Ph.D. thesis, University of Aberdeen.

Runkle, J.R. and Yetter, T.C. (1987). Treefalls revisited: gap dynamics in the southern Appalachians. *Ecology*, **68**, 417–24.

Sagers, C.L. (1996). Persistence in a tropical understorey: clonal growth in *Psychotria horizontalis*. In Swaine, M.D. (ed.), *Ecology of Tropical Forest Tree Seedlings*, pp. 163–72. UNESCO/Parthenon, Paris/Carnforth.

Sanchez-Coronado, M.E., Rincon, E. and Vazquez-Yanes, C. (1990). Growth responses of three contrasting *Piper* species growing under different light conditions. *Canadian Journal of Botany*, **68**, 1182–6.

Sanford, R.L. Jr. (1989). Fine root biomass under a tropical forest light gap opening in Costa Rica. *Journal of Tropical Ecology*, **5**, 521–6.

Sanford, R.L. Jr. (1990). Fine root biomass under light gap openings in an Amazon rain forest. *Oecologia*, **83**, 541–5.

Sanford, R.L. Jr., Vitousek, P.M. and Bratt, A.L. (1991). Dynamics of litter decomposition, soil nutrient availability and fine roots following treefall. *Association Tropical Biology 1991 Annual Meeting Abstracts.*

Schupp, E.W. (1988). Seed and early seedling predation in the forest understorey and in treefall gaps. *Oikos*, **51**, 71–8.

Stewart, G.R., Hegarty, E.E. and Specht, R.L. (1988). Inorganic nitrogen assimilation in plants of Australian rain forest communities. *Physiologia Plantarum*, **74**, 26–33.

Stewart, G.R., Gracia, C.A., Hegarty, E.E. and Specht, R.L. (1990). Leaf nitrate reductase activity and chlorophyll content in sunleaves of subtropical Australian closed-forest (rain forest) and open-forest communities. *Oecologia*, **82**, 544–51.

Still, M. (1996). Rates of mortality and growth in three groups of dipterocarp seedlings in Sabah, Malaysia. In Swaine, M.D. (ed.), *Ecology of Tropical Forest Tree Seedlings*, pp. 315–32. UNESCO/Parthenon, Paris/Carnforth.

Stocker, G.C. (1981). Regeneration of a north Queensland rain forest following felling and burning. *Biotropica*, **13**, 86–92.

Strauss-Debenedetti, S. and Bazzaz, F.A. (1991). Plasticity and acclimation to light in tropical Moraceae of different successional positions. *Oecologia*, **87**, 377–87.

Swaine, M.D. (1990). Population dynamics of moist tropical forest at Kade, Ghana. In Maitre, H.F. and Puig, H. (eds.), *Atelier sur l'aménagement et la conservation de l'écosystème forestier tropical humide*, pp. 40–61. UNESCO-MAB /IUFRO/FAO, Paris

Swaine, M.D. (ed.) (1996). *Ecology of Tropical Forest Tree Seedlings*, pp. xxi–xxviii. UNESCO/Parthenon, Paris/Carnforth.

Swaine, M.D., Lieberman, D. and Hall, J.B. (1990). Structure and dynamics of a tropical dry forest in Ghana. *Vegetatio*, **88**, 31–51.

Swaine, M.D. and Whitmore, T.C. (1988). On the definition of ecological species groups in tropical rain forests. *Vegetatio*, **75**, 81–6.

Thompson, W.A., Kriedemann, P.E. and Craig, I.E. (1992). Photosynthetic response to light and nutrients in sun-tolerant and shade-tolerant rain forest trees I. Growth, leaf anatomy and nutrient content. *Australian Journal of Plant Physiology*, **19**, 1–18.

Thompson, W.A., Stocker, G.C. and Kriedemann, P.E. (1988). Growth and photosynthetic response to light and nutrients of *Flindersia brayleyana* F. Muell., a rain forest tree with broad tolerance to sun and shade. *Australian Journal of Plant Physiology*, **15**, 299–315.

Torquebiau, E.F. (1988). Photosynthetically active radiation environment, patch dynamics and architecture in a tropical rain forest in Sumatra. *Australian Journal of Plant Physiology*, **15**, 327–42.

Turnbull, M.H. (1991). The effect of light quantity and quality during development on the photosynthetic characteristics of six Australian rain forest species. *Oecologia*, **87**, 110–7.

Turner, I.M. (1990a). Tree seedling growth and survival in a Malaysian rain forest. *Biotropica*, **22**, 146–54.

Turner, I.M. (1990b). The seedling survivorship and growth of three *Shorea* species in a Malaysian tropical rain forest. *Journal of Tropical Ecology*, **6**, 469–78.

Turner, I.M. (1991). Effects of shade and fertiliser addition on the seedlings of two tropical woody pioneer species. *Tropical Ecology*, **32**, 24–9.

Turner, I.M., Brown, N.C. and Newton, A.C. (1992b). The effect of fertiliser application on dipterocarp seedling growth and mycorrhizal infection. *Forest Ecology and Management*, **57**, 329–37.

Turner, I.M. and Newton, A.C. (1990). The initial responses of some tropical rain forest tree seedlings to a large gap environment. *Journal of Applied Ecology*, **27**, 605–8.

Turner, I.M., Raich, J.W., Gong, W.-K., Ong, J.E. and Whitmore, T.C. (1992a). The dynamics of Pantai Acheh Forest Reserve: a synthesis of recent research. *Malayan Nature Journal*, **45**, 166–74.

Uhl, C., Clark, K., Dezzeo, N. and Maquirino, P. (1988). Vegetation dynamics in Amazonian treefall gaps. *Ecology*, **69**, 751–63.

Vazquez-Yanes, C. and Smith, H. (1982). Phytochrome control of seed germination in the tropical rain forest pioneer trees *Cecropia obtusifolia* and *Piper auritum* and its ecological significance. *New Phytologist*, **92**, 477–85.

Veblen, T.T., Donoso, C.Z., Schlegel, F.M. and Escobar, B.R. (1981). Forest dynamics in south-central Chile. *Journal of Biogeography*, **8**, 211–47.

Vitousek, P.M. (1985). Community turnover and ecosytem nutrient dynamics. In Pickett, S.T.A. and White, P.S. (eds.), *The Ecology of Natural Disturbance and Patch Dynamics*. Academic Press, Orlando.

Vitousek, P.M. and Denslow, J.S. (1986). Nitrogen and phosphorus availability in treefall gaps of a lowland tropical rain forest. *Journal of Ecology*, **74**, 1167–78.

Watt, A.S. (1947). Pattern and process in the plant community. *Journal of Ecology*, **35**, 1–22.

Welden, C.W., Hewett, S.W., Hubbell, S.P. and Foster, R.B. (1991). Sapling survival, growth and recruitment: relationship to canopy height in a neotropical forest. *Ecology*, **72**, 35–50.

Whitmore, T.C. (1974). Change with time and the role of cyclones in tropical rain forest on Kolombangara, Solomon Islands. *Commonwealth Forestry Institute Paper*, **46**.

Whitmore, T.C. (1975). *Tropical Rain Forests of the Far East*. Clarendon, Oxford.

Whitmore, T.C. (1983). Secondary succession from seeds in tropical rain forests. *Forestry Abstracts*, **44**, 767–79.

Whitmore, T.C. (1984a). *Tropical Rain Forests of the Far East*. 2nd edn. Clarendon, Oxford. [translated into Malay 1991].

Whitmore, T.C. (1984b). Gap size and species richness in tropical rain forests. *Biotropica*, **16**, 139.

Whitmore, T.C. (1989a). Canopy gaps and the two major groups of forest tree species. *Ecology*, **70**, 536–8.

Whitmore, T.C. (1989b). Changes over 21 years in the Kolombangara rain forests. *Journal of Ecology*, **77**, 469–83.

Whitmore, T.C. (1990). *An Introduction to Tropical Rain Forests*. Clarendon, Oxford. [translated into German 1992].

Whitmore, T.C., Brown, N.D., Swaine, M.D., Kennedy, D., Goodwin-Bailey, C.I. and Gong, W.-K. (1993). Use of hemispherical photographs in forest ecology: measurement of gap size and radiation totals in a Bornean tropical rain forest. *Journal of Tropical Ecology*, **9**, 131–51.

Whitmore, T.C. and Gong, W.-K. (1983). Growth analysis of the seedlings of balsa (*Ochroma lagopus*). *New Phytologist*, **95**, 305–11.

Whitmore, T.C. and Wong, Y.-K. (1959). Patterns of sunlight and shade in tropical rain forest. *Malayan Forester*, **21**, 50–62.

Yamamoto, S. (1992a). Gap characteristics and gap regeneration in primary evergreen broad-leaved forests of western Japan. *Botanical Magazine Tokyo*, **105**, 29–45.

Yamamoto, S. (1992b). The gap theory in forest dynamics. *Botanical Magazine Tokyo*, **105**, 375–83.

Zainuddin, S.R. (1989). *Studies of germination and seedling growth of* Neobalanocarpus heimii *(King) Ashton*. M.Sc. thesis, Universiti Pertanian Malaysia.

Revised manuscript received October 1993

CHAPTER 2

PHOTOSYNTHETIC RESPONSES TO LIGHT IN TROPICAL RAIN FOREST TREE SEEDLINGS

Malcolm C. Press, Nick D. Brown, Martin G. Barker and Simon W. Zipperlen

INTRODUCTION

Tropical rain forests cover approximately 7 per cent of the world's land surface area, and yet are thought to contain more than half of all known terrestrial species. Although unifying theories explaining high biodiversity remain elusive, for plants at least a relatively constant and 'favourable' macro-physical environment for growth distinguishes tropical rain forests from many other less diverse habitats. However, the microenvironment in tropical rain forests varies markedly in both space and time. Theories, such as gap regeneration dynamics, where seedlings of different species are favoured by different amounts of canopy disturbance, have been proposed as a mechanism which accounts for species diversity, assuming species-specific requirements for resources. However, attempts to explain species diversity in terms of only a few factors of overriding importance have proved to be flawed (Brown, 1990; Brown and Whitmore, 1992). It is certainly possible to identify ecological groups of species within rain forests with different requirements, for example pioneer and climax trees (Swaine and Whitmore, 1988), but this dichotomy really reflects a disjunction in an ecological continuum.

In temperate habitats, attempts to understand the physiological basis of plant growth and distribution have relied heavily on measurements of photosynthesis, despite the fact that instantaneous rates of carbon fixation by leaves are by no means the only determinant of growth (see e.g. Körner, 1991). However, photosynthetic (and respiratory) responses to the environment may yield important information not only about the ability of rain forest tree seedlings to survive and grow under a given suite of environmental conditions, but also about their acclimation potential to a long-term change in the environment (such as gap creation) and their capacity to utilize temporally heterogeneous environments in the short-term (such as sunflecks).

In this chapter we examine the influence of light on carbon dioxide fixation and, less extensively, water-use efficiency and interactions with nitrogen supply, in ecologically and taxonomically diverse tropical rain forest species, principally at the seedling stage. The extent to which physiological perform-

41

ance at the leaf level can be extrapolated to explain species ecology is also discussed.

PHOTOSYNTHETICALLY ACTIVE RADIATION

Steady state responses

Photosynthetic photon flux density (PPFD) is highly variable in both space and time within forests. The small quantity of diffuse radiation that is transmitted through the leafy canopy has a low red:far red light quotient (ca. 0.1–0.7). However, patches of high irradiance with a higher red:far red quotient (ca. 0.4–1.3) occur where direct sunlight penetrates through canopy holes or gaps (see e.g. Chazdon and Fletcher, 1984; Lee, 1987). The red:far red quotient affects the action of phytochrome and probably other, less well-known, photoresponsive molecules directing plant development. Phytochrome-mediated responses can vary widely, even between closely related species (Smith, 1975), although Kwesiga and Grace (1986) found that seedlings of a West African tropical rain forest pioneer tree grown in red-deficient light had larger and thinner leaves and, in a brief review, showed these responses to be fairly universal. Photosynthetic studies which have been conducted under neutral shade conditions, may not therefore relate directly to performance in the forest shade environment (Sasaki and Mori, 1981; Nicholson, 1960; Brown, 1990). Similarly the use of green filters to simulate low red:far red quotients may also provide an unrealistic light environment in the absence of red-rich flecked radiation.

The photosynthetic, morphological and anatomical responses to light of temperate 'sun' (heliophytic) and 'shade' (sciaphytic) species, ecotypes and leaves have been well characterized (see e.g. Givnish, 1988; McKiernan and Baker, 1992), and some of these are listed in Table 2.1. Tropical species are believed to show similar patterns of response (Langenheim et al., 1984). For example, Riddoch et al. (1991a) examined photosynthetic responses to light of pioneer and climax species from a secondary forest in Nigeria, in an attempt to relate successional status to the shape of photosynthetic light response curves. Pioneer species had higher light saturated rates of photosynthesis when expressed on a leaf area basis, resulting from both higher mesophyll and stomatal conductances. The pioneer species also had higher light compensation points, attributable to higher rates of dark respiration, rather than lower apparent quantum efficiencies (but see Whitmore, 1996; Table 1). Fredeen and Field (1991) positively correlated leaf respiration with mean daily PPFD for six species of *Piper*, each characteristic of microsites with very different light availabilities. Low rates of leaf respiration are a common response to growth under low irradiance, and may be critical in enabling plant survival in shaded environments. However, measurements made on leaves do not take account of the respiration rate of other plant tissues and

Table 2.1 Some characteristic features of leaves grown in 'high light', compared to those of the same species grown in 'low light' environments. The responses of 'sun'- and 'shade'-acclimated leaves from the same species do not necessarily parallel those of 'sun' and 'shade' species (see Attridge, 1990; Coombes et al., 1987; Daubenmire, 1959; Givnish, 1988; Levitt, 1980; Riddoch et al., 1991b).

'High light' grown leaf characteristics, in comparison to 'low light' grown plants of the same species	*Functional significance*
Thicker lamina, resulting from a well-developed palisade layer and a relatively poorly-developed mesophyll layer.	Increased shielding of cells within the leaf blade from high irradiance.
Thicker shiny cuticle.	Increased reflectance of irradiance incident on the leaf surface and lower evaporative loss.
Increased anthocyanin concentration in the epidermis.	Greater reflectance of longer wavelengths, reducing heat load.
Lower chlorophyll content per unit volume (because of fewer, smaller, chloroplasts per unit volume, with a lower chlorophyll concentration).	Greater transmission of light through the leaf. Avoids harvesting excess light energy per unit cell volume that could drive potentially damaging reactions. Lower photosynthetic rate when calculated on a leaf weight basis. Carotenoid pigments more apparent giving the leaf a greenish-yellow appearance.
Greater chlorophyll and ribulose-1,5-bisphosphate carboxylase-oxygenase (Rubisco) content per unit area as a consequence of a thicker lamina.	Higher photosynthetic rate when calculated on a leaf area basis. Higher Rubisco content per unit area results in a higher mesophyll conductance to carbon dioxide on a leaf area basis.
Chloroplasts often absent from epidermis.	Avoids photodamage
Smaller cells.	Smaller leaf area. More densely packed hairs if pubescent. Stomata smaller and more densely packed, allowing better control of water loss. Smaller internal air spaces resulting in greater internal : external surface area ratio and a higher potential mesophyll conductance.
Chloroplasts have smaller grana and less granal stacking.	Lower photosystem II : photosystem I quotient to avoid excessive photolysis of water and electron transport.
Lower chlorophyll : cytochrome f quotient.	Indicative of lower light harvesting capacity per photosystem.
Higher chlorophyll a: chlorophyll b quotient.	Lower light harvesting capacity.
Greater rate of light-saturated photosynthesis with saturation occurring at higher photon flux densities.	Greater efficiency in high light.
Higher rates of dark respiration.	Higher light compensation point
No difference in quantum efficiency in many cases.	

therefore may not accurately reflect the carbon economy of the whole plant (see Givnish, 1988).

Having established the photosynthetic characteristics of a species grown under a given light climate, it is instructive to consider responses to growth under different light climates. This approach may yield important information on the physiological amplitude of the species at the photosynthetic level. In a controlled environment study, Riddoch et al. (1991b) examined responses to high (600–800 μmol m^{-2} s^{-1}) and low (25–35 μmol m^{-2} s^{-1}) PPFD at realistic red:far red quotients (1.5–1.8 and 0.2–0.3, respectively), in two West African species: the light demanding pioneer *Nauclea diderrichii*, and the relatively shade-tolerant climax species *Entandrophragma angolense*. *Nauclea diderrichii* showed marked responses to the growth light environment, with photosynthesis becoming light saturated at 200 and 1,000 μmol m^{-2} s^{-1} in low and high light grown plants, respectively. Light-saturated rates of photosynthesis in the high light grown plants were more than double those in the low light grown plants, when expressed on a leaf area basis. Thus, this pioneer species demonstrated considerable plasticity in its response to the light environment during growth. *Entandrophragma angolense* responded in a similar, though less marked manner, with the species showing less plasticity. Changes in photosynthetic characteristics can be interpreted with respect to changes in the anatomy of leaves formed under different light climates. The leaves of *N. diderrichii* formed under the high light treatment had two layers of large, clearly defined, tightly packed palisade mesophyll cells, in contrast to the low light grown plants which had one layer of much shorter cells (Riddoch et al., 1991b). As with the physiological differences between the species, the shade-tolerant *E. angolense* showed a much lower level of adaptation at the anatomical level.

Fewer studies have focused on differences in physiology and anatomy between closely related taxa. In a study on the gas exchange characteristics of ten species of dipterocarp we found that light-saturated rates of photosynthesis ranged from 3.3 to 5.8 μmol m^{-2} s^{-1}, and there was a significant relationship between these rates and the PPFD required in order to saturate photosynthesis, which ranged from 300 to 470 μmol m^{-2} s^{-1} (unpublished data) (Figure 2.1). However, the relationship between the photosynthetic measurements and the ecology of the seedlings is not strong, as can be seen, for example, by the similar photosynthetic characteristics of the more light-demanding species *Shorea parvifolia* and the much more shade-tolerant species *S. faguetiana* and *Hopea sangal*. In absolute terms, the range of photosynthetic rates observed for the dipterocarps is small, as illustrated by the rates measured for a shade-tolerant *Begonia* species, and the light-demanding pioneer *Macaranga depressa* (Figure 2.1).

Strauss-Debenedetti and Bazzaz (1991) examined photosynthetic light response curves of five co-occurring Mexican species of Moraceae, which differ

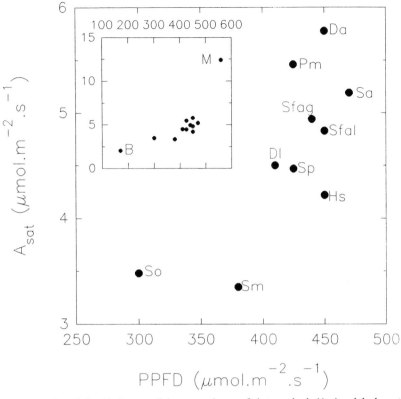

Figure 2.1 The relationship between light saturated rates of photosynthesis (A$_{sat}$) and the lowest PPFD at which this is achieved for ten species of dipterocarp seedlings (main graph). The inset is plotted using larger scales, and includes a shade-demanding *Begonia* species (B) and the light-demanding pioneer *Macaranga depressa* (M), for comparison.
Key to dipterocarp species: Sp = *Shorea parvifolia*; Sfal = *S. fallax*; Sfag = *S. faguetiana*; Sa = *S. argentifolia*; Sm = *S. mecistopteryx*; So = *S. ovalis*; Pm = *Parashorea malaanonan*; Dl = *Dryobalanops lanceolata*; Hs = *Hopea sangal*; Da = *Dipterocarpus applanatus*

in successional stage and location within the forest canopy, in plants grown under different light regimes. Within each species, there were several fold-differences in light-saturated rates of photosynthesis across light regimes, consistent with a high physiological plasticity. Distinct differences in species ability to respond to increasing light regimes correlated with known habitat diversity and successional status. Consistent with other tropical species (see e.g. Fetcher et al., 1983; Oberbauer et al., 1993) the early successional species *Ficus insipida* and the pioneer *Cecropia obtusifolia* had the highest light-saturated rates of photosynthesis when grown under the highest light regime. Both species also showed the highest degree of photosynthetic plasticity. *C. obtusifolia* showed a sixfold difference in light-saturated rates of photosynthesis between the two most extreme light environments. A twofold difference in photosynthesis was observed in *F. insipida* between low- and high-light grown plants, which is more typical of other early successional tropical species and also temperate species (Wallace and Dunn, 1980; Bazzaz and Carlson, 1982). In contrast the late successional species, *Poulsenia armata* and *Pseudolmedia oxyphyllaria*, were characterized by comparatively limited photosynthetic plasticity.

Such differences also exist within genera, as demonstrated by the study of Koyama (1981) on Malaysian *Shorea* species, and more recently that of Ashton and Berlyn (1992) on four Sri Lankan late successional shade-tolerant endemic *Shorea* species. Foliar adaptations to sun and shade were examined by growing the plants in four different light environments. Although detailed light response curves were not constructed, maximum rates of photosynthesis were observed in different light climates: *S. worthingtonii* peaked at $350 \, \mu mol \, m^{-2} s^{-1}$, *S. disticha* and *S. trapezifolia* both peaked at approximately $800 \, \mu mol \, m^{-2} s^{-1}$, and *S. megistophylla* peaked at $1,600 \, \mu mol \, m^{-2} s^{-1}$. Similar differences in leaf anatomy to those reported by Riddoch et al. (1991b) were observed, and the greatest difference in leaf thickness between high- and low-light grown leaves approximately followed the photosynthetic responses of each species.

These studies demonstrate that the light environment can have profound influences on the anatomy and photosynthetic activity of the leaves of tropical rain forest species. The degree of plasticity is high in the most light-demanding species, and more limited in late successional, shade-tolerant species. The extent to which these differences translate into growth, and their possible role in controlling niche differentiation in potentially competing species will be considered later.

Dynamic responses: short term

Responses to changes in light climate may be considered over both the short- (up to minutes), and longer-term (days upwards). Both are important ecologically. The former are encountered as sunflecks, and the latter as a consequence of gap creation as part of the natural forest regeneration cycle, and on a larger scale still as a result of commercial timber extraction.

In the understorey seedlings are subjected to low-light for a large proportion of the day, and PPFD will commonly be below $50 \, \mu mol \, m^{-2} s^{-1}$, less than 5 per cent of the flux incident on the top of the canopy. However, they will be subjected to bursts of higher irradiance in the form of sunflecks. Sunfleck frequency, duration and magnitude will decrease with increasing canopy height. In a densely shaded tropical rain forest understorey the majority of sunflecks will be extremely brief; for example, in a Hawaiian rain forest more than 60 per cent of the sunflecks were shorter than 30 s in duration (Chazdon and Pearcy, 1991). Sunflecks tend to be clustered temporally, and are normally in the range of $50–500 \, \mu mol \, m^{-2} s^{-1}$ PPFD in tropical rain forests (Chazdon and

Pearcy, 1991). Flecked radiation may account for up to 75 per cent of the total daily PPFD on the tropical rain forest floor (Chazdon, 1988). However, some of this radiation may be in excess of that required for photosynthetic light saturation.

All plants undergo photosynthetic induction when first irradiated, resulting from increases in both stomatal conductance and changes in cell metabolism, although the latter predominate initially (see e.g. Kirschbaum and Pearcy, 1988; Pearcy and Seemann, 1990; Pearcy, 1990). Induction of photosynthesis does not require constant irradiation, and for the Australian understorey herb *Alocasia macrorrhiza* the rate of induction during a sequence of 60-s light flecks, 120 s apart, was not substantially different from that observed during constant irradiation (Chazdon and Pearcy, 1986a). Thus each fleck becomes increasingly more efficient in driving carbon dioxide fixation than the previous one. After leaves which are fully induced are returned to low irradiance, the potential for carbon dioxide fixation follows a negative exponential function, with a half life of approximately 25 minutes for *A. macrorrhiza* (Chazdon and Pearcy, 1986a). A slow rate of induction loss will ensure the efficient utilization of radiation received subsequently as non-continuous bursts of high light. In addition the build up of 'assimilatory charge', defined by Laisk et al. (1987) as the sum of all energetically-rich compounds that support continued carbon dioxide fixation, during high-light irradiation, can result in a few seconds of post-irradiation carbon dioxide fixation (Sharkey et al., 1986). For *A. macrorrhiza* this has been shown to make the utilization of radiation received as discrete sunflecks more efficient (by as much as 60 per cent) than that of the same quantity of continuous radiation (Chazdon and Pearcy, 1986b). However, as the duration of each sunfleck is increased, the efficiency of utilization is reduced because of the appearance of a post-irradiation loss of fixed carbon resulting from the metabolism of residual photorespiratory metabolites (Artus et al., 1986; Vines et al., 1983). Despite much interest in the biochemistry of sunfleck utilization (see e.g. Pearcy, 1990; Seemann et al., 1988; Sharkey et al., 1986), it is disappointing that relatively few studies have focused on the most shade-tolerant understorey rain forest species. An exception is a study of the sunfleck utilization efficiency of *Claoxylon sandwicense*, a shade-tolerant tree from Hawaii (Pearcy and Calkin, 1983). The relative growth rate of *C. sandwicense* was found to be directly related to the potential daily total sunfleck duration. Sixty per cent of the plant's total daily carbon gain was attained during sunflecks. Rapid photosynthetic induction to light-saturation meant that the diurnal pattern of photosynthesis closely matched that of the rapidly fluctuating PPFD.

Potential species-specific differences in sunfleck utilization efficiency are of great ecological interest. There is certainly some evidence which correlates sunfleck responses with shade tolerance. *A. macrorrhiza* shows a greater rate of initial induction and a slower rate of induction loss, attains a greater proportion of its light-saturated rate of photosynthesis in a sunfleck sequence, and has a higher apparent quantum efficiency, than the shade-intolerant *Toona australis*. *A. macrorrhiza* also shows greater post-irradiation photosynthetic activity (Chazdon and Pearcy, 1986a; see also Woodward, 1990). Two *Piper* species, *P. auritum*, a pioneer tree, and *P. aequale*, a shade-tolerant shrub, also conform to this general pattern of response (Tinoco-Ojanguren and Pearcy, 1992). Seedlings with an ability to utilize sunflecks may exhibit enhanced growth and survival in the forest understorey, and thereby have a longer-term selective advantage, as large seedlings are known to have lower mortality and faster growth when gaps form over them (Brown and Whitmore, 1992; Turner, 1990). However, relatively few species have been studied in detail. Evidence from a study on West African species suggests that difference in responses to flecked light among ecological groups may not always be large (Riddoch et al., 1991a), although some confusion regarding the ecology of the species studied (Whitmore, 1996) means that these findings must be treated with some caution.

Although flecked radiation can contribute to more than half of the carbon fixed by plants in the understorey, high radiation sunflecks can induce photoinhibitory damage, as described for the understorey herb *Elatostema repens* when subjected to flecks of $700\,\mu mol\,m^{-2}\,s^{-1}$ PPFD (Le Gouallec et al., 1990). This study was conducted under laboratory conditions where leaf temperature and water supply were not perturbed during periods of irradiation. Since sunflecks in the forest will be associated with higher leaf temperatures and leaf-air vapour pressure deficits, sunfleck-induced photoinhibitory damage may also occur within the range of PPFDs normally encountered and may not be an infrequent event.

Dynamic responses: long term

Responses to changes in the light environment have attracted much interest in tropical rain forest ecology, and play a central role in gap regeneration dynamics. Despite this there have been relatively few attempts to characterize the growth and photosynthetic characteristics of potentially competing species in the forest. Our understanding of species responses to changes – usually increases – in PPFD are based more on studies covering a broad range of ecological types. Again, these are largely predictable on the basis of our understanding of such responses in temperate species.

Strauss-Debenedetti and Bazzaz (1991) transferred individuals of the early successional *Ficus insipida* and *Cecropia obtusifolia* grown at low light to higher light environments, and both species produced leaves which photosynthesized at rates as high or higher than those of plants grown continually in high light, indicating a high photosynthetic acclimation potential. In contrast, late successional species were characterized by a more restricted acclimation potential: two late successional canopy emergents, *Poulsenia armata* and *Pseudolmedia oxyphyllaria*, did not significantly increase their photosynthetic rates when transferred to high light, despite demonstrating a limited range of photosynthetic plasticity in longer-term growth studies under different light environments (see above).

Thus extrapolating the plasticity of responses between time scales is not always straightforward. Similarly the magnitude of an acclimation response can be unexpected. For example, Popma and Bongers (1991) found that for three species of shade-tolerant tree seedlings (*Cordia megalantha*, *Lonchocarpus guatemalensis* and *Omphalea oleifera*) plants transferred from low light to high light conditions had higher relative growth rates than plants grown continuously under high light. Less surprisingly, plants transferred from high light to low light conditions had lower relative growth rates than plants grown continuously under low light.

Many shade-tolerant species show 'damage' responses following exposure to high light, even if they have been grown in a moderately high light environment. For example, leaves of the shade-tolerant species *Entandrophragma angolense* grown at high PPFD became light-saturated at a PPFD of $300 \, \mu mol \, m^{-2} \, s^{-1}$, and at higher PPFDs lower rates of photosynthesis were observed, resulting from photoinhibition (Riddoch et al., 1991b). It is important to establish whether these responses occur in leaves which exist at the time of transfer or in newly formed tissue. *Bischofia javanica* germinates and establishes in the shade, although it has a moderately wide ecological range. Shade leaves of this species suffered photoinhibitory damage immediately after transfer from the low light under which they were formed ($40 \, \mu mol \, m^{-2} \, s^{-1}$) to a high light ($1,200 \, \mu mol \, m^{-2} \, s^{-1}$) environment (see Kamaluddin and Grace, 1992a,b). Chlorophyll bleaching also occurred, although this was not immediate and so was not the cause of the initial photoinhibition. Chlorophyll concentrations declined to 50 per cent of their initial value over a period of 14 days. Chlorophyll concentrations then increased over a subsequent 28-day period, together with some recovery from photoinhibition. Photosynthetic rates declined initially, but recovered, and 40 days after transfer the final rate was 75 per cent higher than before exposure, but still more than 30 per cent less than that measured in high light grown leaves. Anatomical changes in leaves, consistent with those described above also occurred over the 40-day experimental period. Elongation of the palisade cells caused leaf thickness to increase by almost 45 per cent so that the weight per unit area (specific leaf weight) approached that of high light grown leaves. Thus in this species acclimation capacity is demonstrated in fully expanded shade leaves. However, it is also important to consider whole plant adaptations to transfer, such as the formation of epicormic shoots, leaf movements, and the formation of new sun leaves, all of which were also observed in *B. javanica* (see also Popma and Bongers, 1991). In contrast, for *A. macrorrhiza* (Sims and Pearcy, 1992) only leaves which were still expanding showed anatomical and physiological responses to transfer from low- to high-light, and the extent to which leaves adapted depended on their developmental stage.

PHOTOSYNTHESIS–NITROGEN RELATIONS

More than half the nitrogen in plant leaves is used for the construction of photosynthetic machinery, and hence the acquisition of carbon is intimately linked with plant nitrogen relations. There is a well-recognized relationship between the light-saturated rate of photosynthesis and the nitrogen concentration in plant leaves within a species (Field and Mooney, 1986; Chazdon and Field, 1987).

For a given tissue nitrogen concentration, light saturated rates of photosynthesis can vary by more than an order of magnitude between species, for example from approximately 3 to $30\,\mu mol\,m^{-2}\,s^{-1}$ for plants containing $100\,mmol\,m^{-2}$ nitrogen (Evans, 1989), and the term photosynthetic nitrogen-use efficiency (PNUE) is used to express rates of photosynthesis on a tissue nitrogen basis. In six *Piper* species from contrasting light environments Chazdon and Field (1987) positively related PNUE to both light availability and light-saturated rates of photosynthesis. For example, PNUEs of 36 and $127\,\mu mol\,CO_2\,mol^{-1}\,N\,s^{-1}$ were measured for leaves of *P. aequale* and *P. auritum*, respectively, with the species having light-saturated rates of photosynthesis of 2.6 and $9.5\,\mu mol\,m^{-2}\,s^{-1}$, and daily PPFDs of 0.36 and $13.54\,mol\,m^{-2}\,day^{-1}$, respectively. For five species from the Moraceae, a strong relationship was found between light-saturated rates of photosynthesis and leaf nitrogen concentration within each species, although little correlation was observed between species, again demonstrating large differences in PNUE (Strauss-Debenedetti and Bazzaz, 1991). Similarly for ten species of dipterocarp, we found no correlation between light-saturated rates of photosynthesis and total foliar nitrogen concentration (unpublished data).

These differences in PNUE may result from differences in nitrogen allocation between photosynthetic and non-photosynthetic components of leaf tissue. Species with lower PNUEs may invest more leaf nitrogen in compounds required for leaf longevity and herbivore defence (Field and Mooney, 1986). Nitrogen which is allocated to photosynthetic apparatus may be sub-divided between soluble proteins (dominated by ribulose-1,5-bisphosphate carboxylase-oxygenase (Rubisco)) and thylakoid membranes (proportional to chlorophyll concentration), which functionally divides nitrogen between the dark (carbon dioxide fixation) and light (light capture) reactions of photosynthesis, respectively (Evans, 1989). The extent to which nitrogen is allocated to each of these pools differs between light-demanding and shade-tolerant species. *A. macrorrhiza* has approximately 15 per cent of its leaf nitrogen invested in Rubisco, compared to up to 30 per cent in light-demanding species. In addition, the proportion of Rubisco-N in *A. macrorrhiza* does not respond to irradiance during growth, in contrast to the positive relationship seen in light-demanding species. Conversely, shade-tolerant species, such as *A. macrorrhiza*, can partition far more nitrogen into thylakoids than light-demanding species, particularly at higher nitrogen supplies. At low irradiance thylakoid-N can account for 71 per cent of total leaf nitrogen in *A. macrorrhiza*, which decreases to 29 per cent as growth irradiance is increased.

WATER USE

Most rain forest species will be subjected to periods when water supply is restricted (see e.g. Brown, 1993). Although adaptations to drought have been examined in species from tropical forests with a distinct dry season (Mulkey et al., 1991; Wright et al., 1992) less is known about species performance in forests which lack a distinct dry season. Even in such areas, protracted periods (weeks) with low rainfall can occur occasionally. For example, three periods of 30 days with rainfall less than 100 mm were recorded at Danum Valley Field Centre, Sabah, between March, 1987 and March, 1991 (Brown, 1990). In addition, lower relative humidities and higher temperatures following gap creation may also predispose plants to water stress. Tropical species may employ a number of metabolic and behavioural acclimation responses to water deprivation, similar to those observed in temperate species, for example osmotic adjustment and turgor maintenance, which are frequently correlated with the ability to maintain high leaf conductances and hence higher carbon dioxide fixation rates (Mulkey et al., 1991).

Water deficit is a major cause of seedling death in gaps (Brown and Whitmore, 1992; Turner, 1990), and species-specific differences in the water cost of carbon dioxide fixation may play an important role in determining survival following gap creation. There is some evidence to suggest that this may indeed be the case, from our study of ten species of dipterocarp (unpublished data). Although no significant relationship was found between stomatal conductance and light-saturated rates of photosynthesis (Figure 2.2), some species did show similar rates of photosynthesis at very different stomatal conductances. For example, similar rates of photosynthesis were measured in *Shorea argentifolia* and *Dipterocarpus applanataus*, despite a twofold increase in the rate of stomatal conductance respectively between the two. Thus rates of mesophyll conductance in the former must exceed those of the latter.

Diurnal patterns of stomatal opening also differed between the species (unpublished data), with *D. lanceolata* showing much more conservative potential water loss. The gas exchange characteristics of *D. lanceolata* are consistent with its ecology (see Whitmore, 1996) and water-use efficiency (μmol CO_2 fixed/mol H_2O transpired) may play an important role in determining which dipterocarps survive following gap creation.

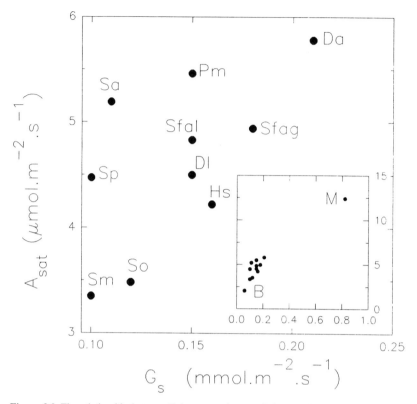

Figure 2.2 The relationship between light saturated rates of photosynthesis (A_{sat}) and stomatal conductance (G_s) in ten species of dipterocarp seedlings, and a shade-demanding *Begonia* species and the light-demanding pioneer *Macaranga depressa*, for comparison (as in Figure 2.1). See Figure 2.1 for key to species

PHOTOSYNTHETIC RESPONSES AND ECOLOGY

Leaf photosynthetic characteristics can be related to the ecology of some tropical rain forest species. However, it is important to consider the extent to which observed responses are adequate to account for the observed differences in distribution.

Riddoch et al. (1991b) suggest that the differences between both the leaf anatomy and photosynthetic characteristics of the two species they studied, one a pioneer and the other a climax species, were much smaller than might be predicted from their ecological behaviour. This study was conducted in controlled environment chambers and it is important to understand how interactions with other factors, such as nutrient, water supply and temperature might influence their response to light in the forest.

Despite the importance of nitrogen for the construction of photosynthetic machinery, positive growth responses to nitrogen addition have not always been observed for tropical rain forest species, suggesting that perhaps other elements, such as phosphorus might be more limiting. Despite this, nitrogen may play a more subtle role in determining species plasticity and acclimation potential. For example, shade clones of the temperate climber *Solanum dulcamara* grown in the shade with a low nitrate supply (0.6 mM) had similar photosynthetic properties to leaves with a high nitrate supply (12 mM) (Ferrar and Osmond, 1986). Transfer of both sets of plants to high light resulted in photoinhibition, although recovery from photoinhibition and subsequent acclimation of photosynthesis to the high light regime occurred only in plants supplied with high nitrate (Ferrar and Osmond, 1986). More recently Nuñes et al. (1993) demonstrated the importance of nitrogen fertilizer to the survival of *Coffea arabica* following transfer from a low light to a high light environment. The degree of both photodamage, and photoinhibition and potential for subsequent recovery, may be important determinants of plasticity and acclimation. The extent to which nitrogen may influence these processes in rain forest species, and its interaction with other variables (e.g. light and temperature (see Seemann et al., 1987)) is largely unknown.

Although photosynthetic measurements have been correlated with growth parameters, they are not the only determinant of dry matter gain. In a study of gas exchange characteristics of shade-tolerant and light-demanding Mexican trees, Ramos and Grace (1990) conclude that the species differed from each other much more in their growth than in their rates of photosynthesis. Biomass partitioning, and factors which control assimilate distribution may therefore be more diagnostic of the ecological status of a species than its rate of carbon dioxide fixation per unit area of leaf. Differential plasticity in wood and leaf allocation may be an important factor in determining the shade tolerance and plasticity of species. There is evidence to support this view from a study of biomass allocation and growth in nine Costa Rican tree species (King, 1991). Shade-tolerant seedlings shift most of their above-ground growth to leaf replacement when heavily shaded, while light-demanding species allocate about 65 per cent of above-ground dry matter to stem and branches under all conditions. The importance of allometry and plant architecture is further illustrated by of the response of five tropical species to elevated concentrations of carbon dioxide. Carbon dioxide did not affect photosynthesis or plant growth, but did influence canopy architecture (Reekie and Bazzaz, 1989).

Further evidence to support the view that foliar gas exchange characteristics cannot always be related to seedling ecology is provided from studies in Australia. Turnbull (1991) demonstrated that the degree of photosynthetic acclimation to light in six rain forest species representing different successional stages was not clearly related to the successional status of the species. Thompson et al. (1992) found that photosynthetic responses to light and nutrient treatments did not correlate with the degree of shade tolerance accorded to each species by rain forest ecologists.

One difficulty which might result from attempting to correlate light regimes with leaf anatomy and physiology, is that of temporal variability in light supply. Chabot et al. (1979) and Nobel and Hartstock (1981) suggest that integrated PPFD is a more important determinant than peak PPFDs. However, this is unlikely to be true in the understorey where the temporal pattern of light distribution (sunflecks) may have far greater consequences for leaf carbon gain than the total integrated PPFD (Chazdon and Pearcy, 1986b).

More importantly, species adaptation to environment cannot be considered in terms of the response of only one or a small number of variables. Factors other than instantaneous rates of photosynthesis are important determinants of carbon gain, and photosynthetic characteristics should form only part of the range of attributes used to define the ecological niche of rain forest species, and their ability to acclimate to changes in environment. It is also important to consider the role of extreme events in determining plant survival. The capability of adapting and responding to such events at the physiological level is likely to provide a competitive advantage. This may be of particular relevance in highly disturbed logged forest, which may be exposed to high irradiance, lower relative humidity and low soil moisture availability.

In conclusion, a search for physiological bases of niche differentiation should extend beyond measurements of photosynthesis, and thus there may be no universal indicator of shade tolerance or acclimation potential within tropical rain forest species. Photosynthetic characteristics and ecology can certainly be correlated in many species, although differences in physiology may not be large enough to account for differences in ecology, and may not necessarily provide a universally acceptable method for assessing species plasticity and acclimation to different light environments.

REFERENCES

Artus, N.N., Somerville, S.C. and Somerville, C.R. (1986). The biochemistry and cell biology of respiration. *Critical Reviews of Plant Science*, **4**, 121–47.

Ashton, P.M.S. and Berlyn, G.P. (1992). Leaf adaptations of some *Shorea* species to sun and shade. *New Phytologist*, **121**, 587–96.

Attridge, T.H. (1990). *Light and Plant Responses*. Edward Arnold, London.

Bazzaz, F.A. and Carlson, R.W. (1982). Photosynthetic acclimation to variability in the light environment of early and late successional plants. *Oecologia*, **54**, 313–16.

Brown, N.D. (1990). *Dipterocarp regeneration in tropical rain forest gaps of different sizes*. D.Phil. Thesis, University of Oxford.

Brown, N.D. (1993). The implications of climate and gap microclimate for seedling growth conditions in a Bornean lowland rain forest. *Journal of Tropical Ecology*, **9**, 153–68.

Brown, N.D. and Whitmore T.C. (1992). Do dipterocarps seedlings really partition tropical rain forest gaps? *Philosophical Transactions of the Royal Society*, B, **335**, 369–78.

Chabot, B.F., Jurik, T.W. and Chabot, J.F. (1979). Influence of instantaneous and integrated light flux density on leaf anatomy and photosynthesis. *American Journal of Botany*, **86**, 940–5.

Chazdon, R.L. (1988). Sunflecks and their importance to forest understorey plants. *Advances in Ecological Research*, **18**, 1–63.

Chazdon, R.L. and Field, C.B. (1987). Determinants of photosynthetic capacity in six rain forest *Piper* species. *Oecologia*, **73**, 222–30.

Chazdon, R.L. and Fetcher, N. (1984). Light environments of tropical forests. In Medina, E., Mooney, H.A. and Vázquez-Yánes, C. (eds.), *Physiological Ecology of Plants of the Wet Tropics*, pp 27–36. Dr W. Junk, The Hague, The Netherlands.

Chazdon, R.L. and Pearcy, R.W. (1986a). Photosynthetic responses to light variation in rainforest species I. Induction under constant and fluctuating light conditions. *Oecologia*, **69**, 517–23.

Chazdon, R.L. and Pearcy, R.W. (1986b). Photosynthetic responses to light variation in rainforest species II. Carbon gain and photosynthetic efficiency during light-flecks. *Oecologia*, **69**, 524–31.

Chazdon, R.L. and Pearcy, R.W. (1991). The importance of sunflecks for forest understory plants. *BioScience*, **41**, 760–5.

Coombes, J., Hall, D.O., Long, S.P. and Scurlock, J.M.O. (1987). *Techniques in Bioproductivity and Photosynthesis*, (2nd edition). UNEP/Pergamon Press, Oxford.

Daubenmire, R.F. (1959). *Plants and Environment* (2nd edition). John Wiley & Sons Inc., New York.

Evans, J.R. (1989). Photosynthesis and nitrogen relationships in leaves of C_3 plants. *Oecologia*, **78**, 9–19.

Ferrar, P.J. and Osmond, C.B. (1986). Nitrogen supply as a factor influencing photoinhibition and photosynthetic acclimation after transfer of shade-grown *Solanum dulcamara* to bright light. *Planta*, **168**, 563–70.

Fetcher, N., Strain, B.R. and Oberbauer, S.F. (1983). Effects of light regime on the growth, leaf morphology and water relations of seedlings of two species of tropical trees. *Oecologia*, **58**, 314–19.

Field, C. and Mooney, H.A. (1986). The photosynthesis-nitrogen relationship in wild plants. In Givnish, T.J. (ed.) *On the Economy of Form and Function*, pp 25–55. Cambridge University Press, Cambridge.

Fredeen, A.L. and Field, C.B. (1991). Leaf respiration in *Piper* species native to a Mexican rainforest. *Physiologia Plantarum*, **82**, 85–9.

Givnish, T.J. (1988). Adaptation to sun and shade, a whole-plant perspective. *Australian Journal of Plant Physiology*, **15**, 63–92.

Kamaluddin, M. and Grace, J. (1992a). Acclimation in seedlings of a tropical forest tree from Asia, *Bischofia javanica*. *Annals of Botany*, **69**, 47–52.

Kamaluddin, M. and Grace, J. (1992b). Acclimation in seedlings of a tropical tree, *Bischofia javanica*, following a stepwise reduction in light. *Annals of Botany*, **69**, 557–62.

King, D.A. (1991). Correlations between biomass allocation, relative growth rate and light environment in tropical forest saplings. *Functional Ecology*, **5**, 485–92.

Kirschbaum, M.U.F. and Pearcy, R.W. (1988). Gas exchange analysis of the relative importance of stomatal and biochemical factors in photosynthetic induction in *Alocasia macrorrhiza. Plant Physiology*, **86**, 782–5.

Körner, C. (1991). Some often overlooked plant characteristics as determinants of plant growth: a reconsideration. *Functional Ecology*, **5**, 162–3.

Koyama, H. (1981). Photosynthetic rates in lowland rain forest trees of Peninsular Malaysia. *Japanese Journal of Ecology*, **31**, 361–9.

Kwesiga, F. and Grace, J. (1986). The role of the red/far-red ratio in the response of tropical tree seedlings to shade. *Annals of Botany*, **57**, 283–90.

Laisk, A., Kiirats, O., Eichemann, H. and Oja, V. (1987). Gas exchange studies of carboxylation kinetics in intact leaves. In Biggins, J. (ed.) *Progress in Photosynthesis Research*, vol. 4, pp. 245–52. Martinus Nijhoff, Dordrecht.

Langenheim, J.H., Osmond, C.B., Brooks, A. and Ferrar, P.J. (1984). Photosynthetic responses to light in seedlings of selected Amazonian and Australian rain forest tree species. *Oecologia*, **63**, 215–44.

Le Gouallec, J.L., Cornic, G. and Blanc, P. (1990). Relations between sunfleck sequences and photoinhibition of photosynthesis in a tropical rain forest understory herb. *American Journal of Botany*, **77**, 999–1006.

Lee, D.W. (1987). The spectral distribution of radiation in neotropical rainforests. *Biotropica*, **19**, 1–66.

Levitt, J. (1980). Responses of plants to environmental stresses, Vol. II: water, radiation, salt and other stresses, 2nd ed. In Kozlowski, T.T. (ed.) *Physiological Ecology*. (2nd edn.), pp. 283–303. Academic Press, New York.

McKiernan, M. and Baker, N.R. (1992). A method for the rapid monitoring of photosynthetic shade adaptation in leaves. *Functional Ecology*, **6**, 405–10.

Mulkey, S.M., Wright, S.J. and Smith, A.P. (1991). Drought acclimation of an understory shrub *(Psychotria limonensis;* Rubiaceae) in a seasonally dry tropical forest in Panama. *American Journal of Botany*, **78**, 579–87.

Nicholson, D.I. (1960). Light requirements of five species of Dipterocarpaceae. *Malaysian Forester*, **23**, 344–56.

Nobel, P.S. and Hartsock, T.L. (1981). Development of leaf thickness for *Plectranthus parvifolius.* Influence of photosynthetically active radiation. *Physiologia Plantarum*, **51**, 163–6.

Nuñes, M. A., Ramalho, J.D.C. and Dias, M.A. (1993). Effect of nitrogen supply on the photosynthetic performance of leaves from coffee plants exposed to bright light. *Journal of Experimental Botany*, **44**, 893–9.

Oberbauer, S.F., Clark, D.B., Clark, D.A., Rich, P.M. and Vega, G. (1993). Light environment, gas exchange and annual growth of saplings of three species of rain forest trees in Costa Rica. *Journal of Tropical Ecology*, **9**, 511–23.

Pearcy, R.W. (1990). Sunflecks and photosynthesis in plant canopies. *Annual Review of Plant Physiology and Plant Molecular Biology*, **41**, 421–53.

Pearcy, R.W. and Calkin, H.C. (1983). Carbon dioxide exchange of C_3 and C_4 tree species in the understory of a Hawaiian forest. *Oecologia*, **58**, 26–32.

Pearcy, R.W. and Seemann, J.R. (1990). Photosynthetic induction state of leaves in a soybean canopy in relation to light regulation of ribulose-1,5 bisphosphate carboxylase and stomatal conductance. *Plant Physiology*, **94**, 628–33.

Popma, J. and Bongers, F. (1991). Acclimation of seedlings of three Mexican tropical rain forest tree species to a change in light availability. *Journal of Tropical Ecology*, **7**, 85–97.

Ramos, J. and Grace, J. (1990). The effect of shade on the gas exchange of seedlings of four tropical trees from Mexico. *Functional Ecology*, **4**, 667–77.

Reekie, E.G. and Bazzaz, F.A. (1989). Competition and patterns of resource use among seedlings of five tropical trees grown at ambient and elevated CO_2. *Oecologia*, **79**, 212–22.

Riddoch, I., Grace, J., Fasehun, F.E., Riddoch, B. and Ladipo, D.O. (1991a). Photosynthesis and successional status of seedlings in a tropical semi-deciduous rain forest in Nigeria. *Journal of Ecology*, **79**, 491–503.

Riddoch, I., Lehto, T. and Grace, J. (1991b). Photosynthesis of tropical tree seedlings in relation to light and nutrient supply. *New Phytologist*, **119**, 137–47.

Sasaki, S. and Mori, T. (1981). Growth responses of dipterocarp seedlings to light. *Malaysian Forester*, **44**, 319–43.

Seemann, J.R., Sharkey, T.D., Wang, J.L. and Osmond, C.B. (1987). Environmental effects on photosynthetic nitrogen use efficiency, nitrogen partitioning and metabolite pools in leaves of sun and shade plants. *Plant Physiology*, **84**, 796–802.

Seemann, J.R., Kirschbaum, M.U.F., Sharkey, T.D. and Pearcy, R.W. (1988). Regulation of ribulose-1,5-bisphosphate carboxylase activity in *Alocasia macrorrhiza* in response to step changes in irradiance. *Plant Physiology*, **88**, 148–52.

Sharkey, T.D., Seemann, J.R. and Pearcy, R.W. (1986). Contribution of metabolites of photosynthesis to postillumination CO_2 assimilation in response to lightflecks. *Plant Physiology*, **82**, 1063–8.

Smith, H. (1975). *Phytochrome and Photomorphogenesis*. McGraw-Hill, London.

Sims, D.A. and Pearcy, R.W. (1992). Responses of leaf anatomy and photosynthetic capacity in *Alocasia macrorrhiza* (Araceae) to a transfer from low to high light. *American Journal of Botany*, **79**, 449–55.

Strauss-Debenedetti, S. and Bazzaz, F.A. (1991). Plasticity and acclimation to light in tropical Moraceae of different successional positions. *Oecologia*, **87**, 377–87.

Swaine, M.D. and Whitmore, T.C. (1988). On the definition of ecological species groups in tropical rain forests. *Vegetatio*, **75**, 81–6.

Tinoco-Ojanguren, C. and Pearcy, R.W. (1992). Dynamic stomatal behaviour and its role in carbon gain during lightflecks of a gap phase and an understory *Piper* species acclimated to high and low light. *Oecologia*, **92**, 222–8.

Thompson, W.A., Huang, L-K. and Kriedemann, P.E. (1992). Photosynthetic responses to light and nutrients in sun-tolerant and shade-tolerant rainforest trees. II. Leaf gas exchange and component processes of photosynthesis. *Australian Journal of Plant Physiology*, **19**, 19–42.

Turnbull, M.H. (1991). The effect of light quantity and quality during development of the photosynthetic characteristics of six Australian rainforest tree species. *Oecologia*, **87**, 110–17.

Turner, I.M. (1990). The seedling survivorship and growth of three *Shorea* species in a Malaysian tropical rain forest. *Journal of Tropical Ecology*, **6**, 469–78.

Vines, H.M., Tu, Z-P., Armitage, A.M., Chen, S-S. and Black, C.C. Jr (1983). Environmental responses of the post-lower illumination CO_2 burst as related to leaf photorespiration. *Plant Physiology*, **73**, 25–30.

Wallace, L.L. and Dunn, E.L. (1980). Comparative photosynthesis of three gap phase successional tree species. *Oecologia*, **45**, 331–40.

Whitmore, T.C. (1996). A review of some aspects of tropical rain forest seedling ecology with suggestions for further enquiry. In Swaine, M.D. (ed.) *Ecology of Tropical Forest Tree Seedlings*, pp. 3–39. UNESCO/Parthenon, Paris/Carnforth.

Woodward, F.I. (1990). From ecosystems to genes, the importance of shade tolerance. *Trends in Ecology and Evolution*, **5**, 111–15.

Wright, S.J., Machado, J.L., Mulkey, S.S. and Smith, A.P. (1992). Drought acclimation among tropical forest shrubs (*Psychotria*, Rubiaceae). *Oecologia*, **89**, 457–63.

Revised manuscript received November 1993

CHAPTER 3

FUNCTIONAL MORPHOLOGY OF TROPICAL TREE SEEDLINGS

Nancy C. Garwood

INTRODUCTION

Tropical forest trees display an extraordinary diversity of seedling morphologies, as a walk through the forest or a quick glance through the manuals noted below will show. Height after initial expansion ranges from a few millimetres to more than one metre. The arrangement, relative sizes and contrasting shapes of leaves and cotyledons vary enormously among taxa, as do other structures such as scale leaves and pubescence. The diversity among tropical tree seedlings is generally conceded to be greater than that of their temperate counterparts.

Research on tropical seedling morphology has followed three intertwining paths, descriptive, systematic and ecological. Early descriptions appeared in silvicultural manuals (e.g. Troup, 1921) and monographs of tropical taxa (e.g. Wright, 1904). Quite a few identification manuals and shorter reports have been published for Africa (Voorhoeve, 1965; de la Mensbruge, 1966), Asia (Burger Hzn., 1972; Ng, 1975, 1976, 1991–1992; de Vogel, 1980; Webb and Curran, 1992), and America (Duke, 1965; del Amo, 1979; Barrera Torres, 1985–1986; Ricardi et al., 1987). The demand for identification manuals is increasing, primarily for management and conservation purposes, and priority work in this area continues (e.g. N.C. Garwood, in preparation).

The distribution of seedling traits across families is still rather poorly known, although the importance of seedling traits in systematics was recognized quite early (see reviews by Duke, 1969; de Vogel, 1980). The inclusion of seedling traits in systematic analyses of tropical families and subfamilies is relatively recent (e.g. Léonard, 1957; Sousa and Peña de Sousa, 1981; Ladiges and Humphries, 1983; Ladiges et al., 1983). That there are relatively few such studies perhaps indicates the difficulty of finding sufficient seedling material from widely distributed species in particular tropical taxa.

Surprisingly, investigations into the ecological significance of the morphological diversity within tropical tree seedlings have been slow to develop. Some of the earliest studies were of special morphological and behavioural adaptations to avoid fire damage in woody species of tropical savannahs (Rizzini, 1965; Jackson, 1974). Large-scale community analyses of seedling traits in tropical forests of Asia (Ng, 1978), America (Garwood, 1979, 1983) and Africa (Miquel, 1987; Hladik and Miquel, 1990) followed. There has been an upsurge of interest in tropical tree seedlings over the past twenty years, as evidenced by this Workshop. Of the numerous published papers on seedling growth and survival in the forest and greenhouse (see Whitmore, 1996; Lieberman., 1996), only a handful describe the initial morphology, size, or developmental stage of the seedlings studied (e.g. Augspurger, 1984a). Therefore, it is difficult at this stage to assess directly the role that morphology plays in seedling establishment of tropical tree species.

My goal in this review is to stimulate ecological interest in the functional morphology of tropical tree seedlings. We assume that much of the morphological diversity among seedlings will reflect adaptations to specific abiotic or biotic factors, because survival through the seedling stage of the life cycle is critical for reproductive success of a species. Although there has been much discussion of the ecological significance of particular traits, few hypotheses have been rigorously tested until very recently. First, I wish to emphasize the need for further experimental work on a wide range of morphological traits. Second, I hope to generate a greater appreciation of seedling functional morphology among tropical ecologists, so that more information on seedling morphology is routinely included and considered in related studies of seedling ecology.

Throughout the review, I use 'seedling' to mean any early developmental stage that contains at least some still functioning structures produced from the initial seed reserves, and 'initial morphology' to indicate the form of the seedling at the time the first entirely photosynthetic organs have fully expanded. Developmental stages are discussed in more detail later. This use of 'seedling' is more liberal than that of some ecologists, who would restrict it to stages with the seed reserves still attached (e.g. Fenner, 1987), but more restricted than that used by most foresters, who include individuals to 2.7 m (9 feet) tall (Whitmore, 1996).

In the first half of the review, I discuss the development of the seedling classification most often used in tropical ecology to categorize initial seedling morphology, summarize the distribution of seedling types in different floras and forest types, then reassess the association between seedling types and other ecologically relevant traits to determine whether these morphological seedling groups are ecologically informative. This section updates earlier reviews and analyses by Ng (1978), Miquel (1987), and Hladik and Miquel (1990).

In the second half of the review, I try to refocus attention on the functional aspects of functional morphology, rather than morphological aspects used in seedling classifications. Seedlings must carry out a wide range of functions, from photosynthesis to water uptake and defence from herbivores. The morphological parts performing each function vary among species, but also change through development within each species. Kitajima (1992a,b, 1996) has extensively studied the dual functions of cotyledons, photosynthesis and storage, but there has been little experimental work on other functions. I review her work in this section, emphasizing unanswered questions about cotyledon functions; please refer to her chapter (Kitajima, 1996) for a more thorough discussion. I try to direct attention to other seedling functions which need further study. Emphasis in this review is on the initial morphology of tropical tree seedlings, as this stage has been less studied than later stages and many unique morphological structures are present in this but not later stages. References are primarily from the tropical literature.

SEEDLING CLASSIFICATION

To discuss functional morphology of tropical tree seedlings, it would be useful if we could reduce the great morphological variety to a limited number of groups of contrasting morphology, ascertain whether the groups are homogeneous, then test whether differences among groups are ecologically relevant. De Vogel (1980) reviewed the history of seedling classification systems, used primarily for systematic studies. He also proposed a new system of sixteen seedling types, some with several subtypes, but this has not been embraced by tropical ecologists. In this section, I briefly discuss the development of five seedling types (Figure 3.1) currently used in tropical ecology, which are based on three cotyledon characters of presumed ecological significance: position, texture and exposure.

Dichotomies in cotyledon position and texture were well-established by the last century (De Vogel, 1980). Cotyledons raised above ground are epigeal; those below ground are hypogeal. Hypogeal is usually used loosely to include cotyledons which rest on the soil surface, which are sometimes called geal. Leaf-like (foliaceous) cotyledons are usually thin, green and presumably primarily photosynthetic; whereas, fleshy cotyledons are usually thick, non-green and presumably primarily food-storing. Use of epigeal and hypogeal in the older literature often implies a photosynthetic or food-storing function, because epigeal cotyledons were almost always foliaceous in temperate species studied, and hypogeal cotyledons fleshy. Duke (1965) suggested that cotyledon exposure should be emphasized instead of cotyledon position. Cotyledons that emerge from the seed coat and become totally exposed are phanerocotylar; those that do not emerge but remain hidden within the seed coat are cryptocotylar. Ng (1978) recognized that cotyledon position and exposure were independent traits and used these to divide seedlings into four types: epigeal (phanero-epigeal), hypogeal (crypto-hypogeal), semi-hypogeal (phanero-hypogeal), and durian (crypto-epigeal). I prefer the longer descriptive terms of Duke and Polhill (1981), given in parenthesis, because epigeal and hypogeal are confusing restricted uses of older terms. Ng (1978) restricts use of epigeal

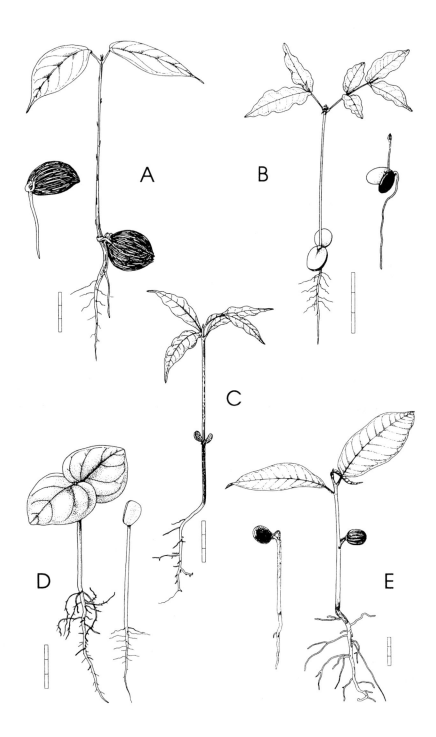

to cases where the hypocotyl is developed, usually lifting the cotyledons off the ground, excluding cases where the lifting is performed by long cotyledon petioles. In his recent seedling manual, Ng (1991–1992) illustrates some of the variation which can be found within the epigeal, hypogeal, semi-hypogeal and durian types.

Garwood (1979, 1983) separated phanero-epigeal seedlings into two groups using the old dichotomy of cotyledon texture, noting that foliaceous cotyledons tended to be persistent, while those that were fleshy were not. Garwood (1979, 1983) also combined crypto-hypogeal and phanero-hypogeal seedlings because both had fleshy, hypogeal, and usually persistent cotyledons. Two rare groups recognized in Garwood (1979), Ng's durian type and Duke's (1969) tardily emergent phanero-epigeal type, were combined with other types in Garwood (1983) under editorial pressure for statistical reasons.

Finally, Miquel (1987) combined the schemes of Ng (1978) and Garwood (1983) to produce five seedling types, similar to Ng's originals except that the phanero-epigeal type has been divided into those with foliaceous versus fleshy cotyledons (Figure 3.1; see also Figure 7.2 in Hladik and Mitja, 1996, for a schematic diagram of types). Because exposure and thickness vary continuously, divisions between types are somewhat arbitrary (Duke, 1965; Ng, 1978). For convenience, seedlings with storage reserves in the hypocotyl or root, which often have reduced or no cotyledons, are classified as fleshy crypto-hypogeal. Haustorial cotyledons, which break down and absorb endosperm reserves then transfer them to the growing seedling, are classified in two ways. If the cotyledons eventually emerge and become photosynthetic, they are considered foliaceous; if the cotyledons are specialized haustorial organs and never emerge from the seed, they are classified as 'fleshy cryptocotylar' because of the presence of reserves in the endosperm.

Throughout the following discussion, I refer to the five seedling types by short unambiguous codes: PEF, PER, PHR, CHR, and CER. These are produced by combining abbreviations (identical in English, French and Spanish) for the dichotomous traits of exposure, position, and texture (in that order): phanerocotylar (P) or cryptocotylar (C); epigeal (E) or hypogeal (H); and

---

Figure 3.1 Seedling types proposed by Miquel (1987) and Hladik and Miquel (1990). See Hladik and Mitja (1995) (Figure 7.2) for a diagrammatic representation of these types. The initial morphology of each type is illustrated, with some examples of the expanding seedling. A, Cryptocotylar-hypogeal-reserve (CHR): *Quararibea pterocalyx* Hemsl. (Bombacaceae), a small tree; B, Phanerocotylar-hypogeal-reserve (PHR): *Pithecellobium rufescens* (Benth.) Pitt. (Leguminosae – Mimosoideae), a small tree; C, Phanerocotylar-epigeal-reserve (PER): *Pouteria unilocularis* (Donn. Sm.) Baehni (Sapotaceae), a canopy tree; D, Phanerocotylar-epigeal-foliaceous (PEF): *Tocoyena pitteri* (Standl.) Standl. (Rubiaceae), a medium-sized tree; E, Cryptocotylar-epigeal-reserve (CER): *Virola surinamensis* (Rol.) Warb. (Myristicaceae), a canopy tree. See text for descriptions of these types. Examples of tree seedlings in this and later figures are from the Barro Colorado Island, Panama, Seedling Flora Project (Garwood, in preparation); nomenclature follows Croat (1978); illustrations are by Margaret Tebbs. Scale bars: 1-cm units

foliaceous (F) or reserve storage or absorption (R). Thus, phanero-epigeal-foliaceous is shortened to PEF. Although eight combinations are possible, CEF, CHF and PHF seedling types have not been described or reported, as it is generally assumed that photosynthesis will not occur within the seed or at ground level.

Do these five seedling types, based on simple morphological characters of the cotyledons, represent five distinct ecological strategies? If so, are they the most appropriate groupings to address all aspects of seedling establishment and early growth? If not, how should seedlings be grouped together to best reflect their functional morphology?

DISTRIBUTION OF SEEDLING TYPES BETWEEN FLORISTIC REGIONS AND FOREST TYPES

We need to know whether the proportion of seedling types in different tropical forests varies with floristic province or along environmental gradients. If there are no differences between Neotropical and Paleotropical floras, for example, it will be reasonable to generalize results from one region to the other. If there are large differences along environmental gradients, we can more quickly identify which environmental factors are important in understanding the functional morphology of tropical tree seedlings.

The abundance of each of the five seedling types appears to be surprisingly similar in tropical forest sampled at eight sites on three continents (Figure 3.2; Appendix 3.1a), as first noted by Miquel (1987). Although the PEF type is usually most common in these woody tropical floras, ranging from 33 to 56 per cent, it is less dominant than in mostly herbaceous temperate floras, where it may reach 95 per cent of species (de Vogel, 1980). There are few species but many families in common among these sites, although different families predominate at each. For example, the ten most abundant families in the Malaysian, Gabonese and Panamanian samples (Figure 3.3) account for 40–50 per cent of all species; only the Leguminosae and Sapindaceae, accounting for 12–16 per cent of species, are among the top ten families at each site. As most families tend to be dominated by only one or two seedling types (Figure 3.3), it is surprising that an overall similarity emerges. The similarity in abundance of seedling types among tropical floras suggests that similar selection pressures may have been acting on seedling morphology and that studies of functional morphology in one region will be applicable to the tropics as a whole.

We should examine these patterns more rigorously to determine whether there are subtle but consistent differences among sites. I analyse the association between seedling type and other factors (such as floristic region or life form) with a log-likelihood ratio test of independence, using the G-statistic (Sokal and Rohlf, 1981), which compares actual and expected number of species for each combination of traits. Here, and in the next section, I discuss

64

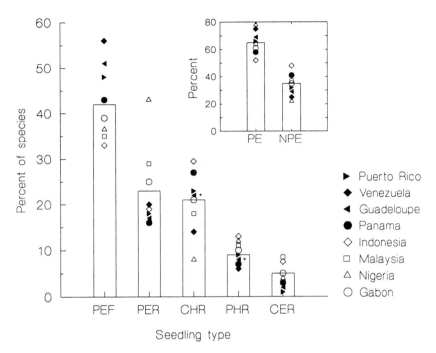

Figure 3.2 Distribution of seedling types in tropical floras, after Miquel (1987) and Hladik and Miquel (1990), with four additional sites. Bars show distribution across floras (*n* = 1,242 species from seven floras, excluding Guadeloupe). African sites: Gabon, 210 species (Miquel, 1987); Nigeria, 113 species (Okali and Onyeachusim, 1991); Asian sites: Malaysia, 210 tree species (Ng, 1978); Indonesia, 150 species (de Vogel, 1980); Neotropical sites: Guadeloupe, 102 species (Rousteau, 1983, cited in Miquel, 1987); Panama, 205 species (Garwood, 1979, 1983, and unpublished data); Venezuela, 194 species (Ricardi et al., 1987); Puerto Rico, 160 species (Duke, 1965). Rousteau (1983) did not separate CHR and PHR seedling types, which combined comprise 31 per cent of species: estimated percentages of CHR and PHR types (indicated by '+') are based on the average relative abundance of these types in the other six floras. Including Rousteau's Guadeloupe data in overall distribution across floras (bars) did not substantially change percentages of PEF, PER, and CER types (total *n* = 1345 species). Ng (1978) did not separate the 134 phanerocotylar-epigeal species into PEF and PER types; types were determined using more recently published descriptions and illustrations (Ng, 1975, 1976, 1991–1992; de Vogel, 1980). For Ricardi et al. (1987) and de Vogel (1980), I divided species into five types using their illustrations and descriptions; for Duke (1965), only illustrations were used. There is bound to be some disagreement with or error in assigning types to species without examining the seedlings themselves, but I hope this source of error is small. The inset shows the percentage of PE and non-PE type seedlings in the eight floras. Seedling types: PEF, phanero-epigeal-foliaceaous; PER, phanero-epigeal-reserve; PHR, phanero-hypogeal-reserve; CHR, crypto-hypogeal-reserve; CER, crypto-epigeal-reserve; PE, phanero-epigeal (PEF + PER); NPE, non-phanero-epigeal (PHR + CHR + CER). Values have been adjusted vertically by 1–2 per cent to minimize overlap of symbols

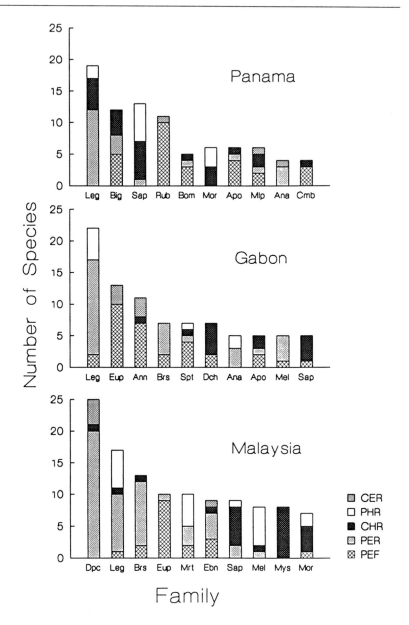

Figure 3.3 Distribution of seedling types among the ten most common families in three sites: Malaysia, Gabon and Panama. Data sources and seedling types as in Figure 3.2. Family abbreviations (Weber, 1982): Ana, Anacardiaceae; Ann, Annonaceae; Apo, Apocynaceae; Big, Bignoniaceae; Bom, Bombacaceae; Brs, Burseraceae; Cmb, Combretaceae; Dch, Dichapetalaceae; Dpc, Dipterocarpaceae; Ebn, Ebenaceae; Eup, Euphorbiaceae; Leg, Leguminosae; Mel, Meliaceae; Mlp, Malpighiaceae; Mor, Moraceae; Mys, Myristicaceae; Mrt, Myrtaceae; Rub, Rubiaceae; Sap, Sapindaceae; Spt, Sapotaceae

66

only the conclusions of these comparisons in the text, but a summary of the data tested, the statistical results, and a more technical description of the methods are included in the Appendices.

While superficially similar, there is still significant heterogeneity among the eight sites studied (Appendix 3.1b): that is, the number of species in each seedling type is not independent of the forest sampled. This significant association holds whether seedlings were divided into five, three, or only two morphological groups (Appendix 3.1b). We would like to know what factors account for this heterogeneity. Floristic province appears to be strongly associated with abundance of seedling types (Appendix 3.1b). Neotropical sites have more species with PEF type seedlings than Paleotropical sites, but fewer species with PER, PHR and CER types (Figure 3.2). There was still significant variation in the distribution of seedling types within both Neotropical and Paleotropical sites (Appendix 3.1b). Unfortunately, we cannot perform similar orthogonal tests to determine whether other factors such as climate, altitude or forest type would better explain differences among sites than floristic province because many studies sampled large ecologically variable regions (Appendix 3.1a). Instead, as an alternative means of exploring the heterogeneity among sites, I tested all possible pairs of sites for association between seedling type and site (Appendix 3.1c). The association was significant in 43 per cent of twenty-one pairs comparing five seedling types from seven sites and in 36 per cent of pairs comparing three seedling types from eight sites. In the first comparison (7×5), the Nigerian site, which had about twice as many PER type seedlings as other sites (Figure 3.2), differed significantly from five of the six other sites, and the Malaysian and Venezuelan sites each differed from three others. In the second comparison (8×3), the Nigerian site differed from six of the seven other sites, the Venezuelan site from five others. All other sites in both comparisons differed from at most two other sites (Appendix 3.1c). There was little pattern among these comparisons suggesting that other ecological factors were important. It is difficult to ascertain whether the studies represent comparable samples of their floras, without biases in species selection, because sampling methods are usually sparsely described. Therefore, we cannot rule out environmental or sampling differences among sites as the primary cause of these apparent floristic differences.

To separate the effects of floristic region and environmental factors on abundance of seedling types, we could compare forest types within one floristic region. We need to know whether the proportion of seedling types changes along large-scale environmental gradients, such as temperature gradients from lowland to montane forest or drought gradients from wet to dry forest to savannah. Preliminary data are available from seven forest types in Puerto Rico (Duke, 1965). Duke (1965) noted that the percentage of cryptocotylar species increased along a moisture gradient across four forest types, from dry thorn to evergreen rain forest, but did not quantify this. Depending on the calculation

Table 3.1 Percentage of cryptocotylar seedlings in woody species from seven forest types in Puerto Rico, calculated in two ways from data in Duke (1965). First, each species was assigned to its most typical forest type, using information from Duke's seedling keys to each forest type. The unique assignment of each species to one forest type allows a test of association between seedling type and forest type, which was not significant ($G = 7.33$, df $= 6$, $p = 0.291$). Second, each species was assigned to all forests types in which it is found, using distribution data in Duke's Appendix. This method better represents the species richness of each forest type and is more similar to ecological floristic surveys at the community-level than the first method. Non-native species were not excluded from either tabulation because it was difficult to eliminate recent from older neotropical introductions. Removing twelve Old World species did not alter the statistical results or change percentages by more than 3 per cent (except for the species-poor littoral forest, in which they increased from 30 per cent to 50 per cent and 26 per cent to 32 per cent). Approximate altitude, canopy height and tree species richness of each forest type are from Little and Wadsworth (1964).

	Vegetation characteristics			Percent cryptocotylar species (number of species)	
Forest type	Approximate altitude (m)	Canopy height (m)	Tree species richness (n)	Typical forest type	All forest types
Mangrove woodland	0	20	few	33 (9)	33 (12)
Littoral woodland	0	< 10	few	30 (10)	26 (23)
Dry limestone forest (thorn forest)	≤150	10–20		17 (24)	24 (46)
Dry coastal forest (deciduous seasonal forest)	≤150	10–20	200	30 (20)	29 (69)
Moist coastal and limestone forests (semi-evergreen seasonal forest)	≤150	10–25		32 (25)	37 (87)
Lower cordillera and Luquillo forests (evergreen rain forest)	150–600 (–1000)	35	170	42 (64)	33 (102)
Upper cordillera and Luquillo forests (mossy subtropical forest)	600–750 (–1000)	20	60	20 (20)	24 (25)
Dwarf forest	750–1300	< 6	few	—(—)	—(—)
All forest types	—	—	≈450	32 (172)	

method used (see Table 3.1), the percentage of cryptocotylar species along this gradient either sharply increases (17–42 per cent) and peaks in the evergreen rain forest, or only slightly increases (24–37 per cent) and peaks in the semi-evergreen seasonal forest (Table 3.1). The upward trend becomes less evident (using either method) if the other three forest types are included: the wetter mossy forest has a low percentage of cryptocotylar species, while the mangrove and littoral woodlands, where saline conditions or sandy soil should regularly cause moisture stress, have intermediate values (Table 3.1). While the trends in these preliminary data are suggestive, further work will be required to determine whether these patterns are caused by changes in one or more environmental factors along a simple or complex gradient rather than sampling biases. This will be difficult if the low amount of variation among forest types in Puerto Rico using the second method (24–37 per cent) is typical of tropical regions generally. The second method is probably more similar to many ecological floristic surveys, which draw random samples of species from those present in the community, than the first method (see Table 3.1), and may better reflect the range of variation that will be found.

Data from other forest types or tree-dominated vegetation types, which might offer insights into the ecological factors selecting for specific seedling types, are sparse. In the Brazilian cerrado, 60 per cent of twenty-five tree and shrub species have epigeal seedlings (Rizzini, 1965). This is a very small sample, and lacks comparative studies from moister Amazonian forest. De Vogel (1980) states that there is a lower proportion of species with PEF type seedlings (his *Macaranga* type) in closed rain forest compared to more open forest types, such as forests on limestone or beaches, heath forests, and monsoon forests, where the canopy is less dense due to poor soil or abundance of drought deciduous species. It is unclear whether these generalizations are meant to apply to all tropical areas or only the Indonesian region, but neither quantitative data nor references to other studies are given.

I conclude that, using data now available, we do not know the relative contribution of floristic region, forest type, or particular environmental factors to differences in the abundance of seedling types among tropical forests. Most useful at this point would be more regional studies along well-characterized environmental gradients of moisture and/or temperature. Consistent changes in abundance of seedling types along these gradients within many large, but not closely related genera or families would be extremely convincing. Comparing the same forest type in different floristic regions would require co-ordination between local research groups. In either case, large unbiased samples of the flora and unambiguous divisions between the somewhat arbitrary seedling types would be needed to test for differences. It is unclear whether the large effort needed to carry out such comparisons would not be better spent at this time on understanding other aspects of seedling morphology discussed in later sections.

DISTRIBUTION OF SEEDLING TYPES WITHIN FORESTS

A second method for probing the ecological relevance of the five seedling types is to compare the abundance of seedling types in different ecological components of the same forest. If seedling types are unique to or common in particular ecological groups, it will be easier to determine their functional significance. Ecological factors closely associated with seedling establishment and growth, such as regeneration strategy, seed size, or germination, are of special interest. Other factors, such as life form and dispersal mode, might also be informative. The limiting factor is the shortage of published studies with sufficient information.

In this analysis, I rely almost entirely on the earlier analyses and data of Ng (1978) from Malaysia and Miquel (1987) and Hladik and Miquel (1990) from Gabon, Africa, which are summarized in excellent tables. The Malaysian data are from the entire Malay Peninsula, which is primarily evergreen rain forest in both the lowlands and highlands; the Gabonese data are from a single site of lowland evergreen rain forest surrounding the Makokou field station. The distribution of seedling types did not differ between the two sites (Appendix 3.1c). If the same patterns are found at both sites, this would suggest that the relationships are general, at least for Paleotropical evergreen rain forest. Although the species included in each study may not be random samples of the flora, they are unbiased samples with regards to the factors analysed, as both authors sought to sample as much of the flora as possible. Where the authors have not provided specific analyses, I tested for association, regrouping the data when necessary to increase comparability. I summarize the results in Table 3.2, and present the detailed analyses and data in Appendices 3.2–3.7. For all comparisons, I first analyse the degree of association using all five seedling types. Because there were rarely significant differences among the CHR, PHR, and CER types and these comparisons usually suffered from an overabundance of sparse cells (Table 3.2), the CHR, PHR, and CER types were combined into one group (OTHER). I then analysed the degree of association among the three types (PEF, PER and OTHER).

Life forms

The Gabonese sample includes trees, lianas and a few other life forms (Miquel, 1987; Hladik and Miquel, 1990), whereas the Malaysian sample includes only trees (Ng, 1978). If the abundance of seedling types varies with life form, the two samples would not be comparable. This is not a major problem, as the distribution of seedling types in trees and lianas was not significantly different in the African sample (Table 3.2; Appendix 3.2b). Hladik and Miquel (1990) comment on the absence of CER liana seedlings in the African sample: I suspect that this can be attributed to sampling error, as only one or two species would have been expected given the relative rarity of the CER type. Lianas with CER type seedlings occur elsewhere in West Africa (e.g. at least three species of Hippocrateaceae, Hallé, 1962), as well as in the Neotropics (e.g. some *Strychnos* species, Loganiaceae, in Panama, Garwood, unpublished data). Although no differences were found between trees and lianas, studies including shrubs, vines and forest herbs are not available for any tropical forest, so differences between the woody canopy life forms and other life forms cannot be ruled out. In Brazilian cerrado woodland (Rizzini, 1965), 80 per cent of fifteen tree species but only 30 per cent of ten shrub species had

Table 3.2 Summary of tests of association between seedling type and life form, dispersal mode, regeneration strategy, seed size and germination time. The tabulated data, detailed statistical results and further explanation of methods are presented in the Appendices (Introduction and Appendices 3.2–3.5). Seed size was analysed using 2 or 4 seed size classes: where results differ, both are given (as results for 2-classes/4-classes, respectively). Germination time was analysed using two comparisons: fast versus slow (F–S) and rapid versus delayed (R–D); where results from Malaysia differ, both are given (as F–S/R–D, respectively). Only the F–S comparison is analysed for Gabon

| Comparison | Life form | Dispersal mode | Regeneration strategy | Seed size | | | Germination time | | |
| | | | | All species | | Non-pioneer species | All species | | Non-pioneer species |
Site	Gabon	Gabon	Malaysia	Gabon	Malaysia	Malaysia	Gabon	Malaysia	Malaysia
Overall associations:									
Five seedling types	ns	***	***§	***/***§	***	ns	**§	***	***
Three seedling types	ns	***	***	***/*	***	*/***	***	***	***
Non-orthogonal contrasts:									
PEF vs. PER	ns	*	*	*	*	ns/≈	ns§	*	*
PEF vs. OTHER	ns	*§	*	*	ns	≈/*	*	ns	ns
PER vs. OTHER	≈	*	ns§	ns	ns	ns	*	*	*
Among OTHER	ns§	≈§	ns§	ns§	ns§	ns§	ns§	*/ns	*/ns

Original data sources: Gabon (Miquel, 1987), Malaysia (Ng, 1978). Significance levels for overall tests of association: ***, $p \leq 0.001$; **, $0.001 < p \leq 0.01$; *, $0.01 < p \leq 0.05$; ns, not significant. Significance levels for non-orthogonal comparisons: *, $p \leq 0.0125$ (= 0.05/4, the more conservative Bonferroni significance level); ≈, $0.0125 < p \leq 0.05$ (the unadjusted significance level), marginally significant; ns, not significant. §, test with excessive number of cells with low expected frequencies; OTHER = CHR + PHR + CER types

epigeal seedlings: the distribution of epigeal and hypogeal seedling types was strongly associated with life form ($G = 6.42$, df $= 1$, $p = 0.011$), but whether such a small sample adequately represents the cerrado flora is uncertain. Needless-to-say, CHR and CER type seedlings are ubiquitous among all life forms in the monocots.

Regeneration strategy

Our primary interest in seedling morphology concerns the role that morphology plays in seedling establishment and early growth. Hence, we wish to compare species which differ in their early establishment requirements, one component of the regeneration niche (Grubb, 1977). To facilitate comparisons of tropical species, two regeneration strategies are commonly recognized (see Swaine and Whitmore, 1988; Whitmore, 1996). Pioneer species germinate, establish, and grow to maturity only in treefall gaps. Climax or non-pioneer species may germinate in the shade, and often establish there, although many species also require a later tree-fall gap to grow to maturity: there is a large continuum of response within this group, and further subdivision may be needed. Pioneer tree species typically have small seedlings with epigeal foliaceous cotyledons (the PEF type); but, primary species with foliaceous cotyledons are also a consistent if infrequent component of the understorey of tropical rain forests, often having long-persistent or large cotyledons (Ng, 1978; Hladik and Miquel, 1990; Okali and Onyeachusim, 1991)

In the Malaysian sample, Ng (1978) identifies twenty-three pioneer species, biological nomads (*sensu* van Steenis, 1958) found only in clearings and forest edges. Of these pioneer species, 78 per cent had PEF type seedlings, compared to only 29 per cent of the 186 non-pioneer tree species (Appendix 3.3a). Therefore, it is not surprising to find a highly significant association between regeneration type and seedling type in the Malaysian tree sample (Table 3.2; Appendix 3.3b). Although seedlings of pioneer tree species primarily have PEF type seedlings, most Malaysian tree species with PEF type seedlings (75 per cent) are non-pioneer species, as are the majority of species (89 per cent) in the sample. Thus, in spite of a strong association between regeneration strategy and seedling type, we gain few new insights into the significance of seedling morphology in the majority of Malaysian tree species. To understand the importance of seedling morphology in the large non-pioneer group, we will have to divide non-pioneer species into subgroups based on a better knowledge of the regeneration requirements, examine other traits correlated with regeneration strategies, or use different groupings of seedling morphology.

In contrast, Okali and Onyeachusim (1991) did not find a significant association between seedling type (phanero-epigeal versus other types) and four regeneration strategies in 113 Nigerian trees, using an earlier definition of pioneer based on Swaine and Hall (1983, 1986). Phanero-epigeal seedlings occurred in 82 per cent of small or large pioneers, 60 per cent of small primary species, and 78 per cent of large primary species. In ninety-seven species with emergent cotyledons (PEF, PER and PHR types), however, the distribution of foliaceous versus fleshy cotyledons was strongly associated with regeneration strategy, with foliaceous cotyledons occurring in 52 per cent of small and large pioneers, 25 per cent of small primary species, and only 13 per cent of large primary species (Okali and Onyeachusim, 1991).

The different results from the two studies probably reflect the relative abundance of 'pioneer' species in the samples: only 11 per cent of the Malaysian tree species were pioneers (*sensu* van Steenis, 1958), but 34 per cent of Nigerian tree species were small pioneers and 24 per cent large pioneers (*sensu* Swaine and Hall, 1983, 1986), about five times more than in the Malaysian sample. While this may in part be caused by different abundances of pioneer species in these forests, it is more likely caused by different sampling designs or the use of different definitions of pioneer species. As the pioneer guild (*sensu* Swaine and Whitmore, 1988) is probably relatively small, the proportions of non-pioneer species in the Malaysian sample are probably typical of many tropical forests.

While pioneer tree seedlings appear to be predominantly PEF types, other pioneer life forms need not be similar. Many of the large herbaceous monocots in the Musaceae, Zingiberaceae, and Marantaceae colonize gaps and other disturbed areas: some at least have seeds which germinate only in gap conditions and can persist in the soil for some time (N.C. Garwood, unpublished data), all have either CHR or CER type seedlings.

Seed size

Seed size, an oft-used measure of parental investment in individual offspring, is a trait closely associated with regeneration strategy. Pioneer species produce large numbers of seeds to colonize ephemeral and unpredictable treefall gaps, hence seeds are small, but the resulting small seedling can grow rapidly in the energy-rich gaps (Gómez-Pompa and Vázquez-Yanes, 1974). Non-pioneer species produce large seeds to provide large or reserve-rich seedlings capable of surviving in the dark energy-poor understorey, hence few seeds are produced (Foster, 1986). An association of seed size and requirements for understorey, small gap, or large gap conditions for establishment has been reported (Foster and Janson, 1985), although these results have been questioned on analytical grounds (Kelly and Purvis, 1993) and degree of shade tolerance was not related to seed biomass in wind-dispersed tree species (Augspurger, 1984a). We should examine the relationship between seed size and seedling type to determine whether it reveals further insights into the functional morphology of these types.

Ng (1978) first noted that the abundance of phanero-epigeal seedlings (PEF + PER) decreases with increasing seed size in Malaysian trees, from 100 per cent in seeds <3 mm long to about 50 per cent in seeds ≥20 mm long (Appendix 3.4a). A similar trend for phanero-epigeal seedlings occurs in the Gabonese sample (Miquel, 1987; Hladik and Miquel, 1990). The percentage of PEF-type seedlings drops even more sharply, to 5 per cent of species in seeds ≥40 mm long in Malaysia and to 19 per cent in seeds ≥20 mm long in Gabon (Appendix 3.4a). There is a highly significant association between seedling type and seed size class in both the Malaysian and Gabonese samples (Table 3.2; Appendix 3.4b). In both samples, seed size also differed between the PEF and PER types and between the PEF and OTHER (CHR + PHR + CER) types, but did not differ between the PER and OTHER types or among the OTHER type (Table 3.2; Appendix 3.4b).

In the Malaysian sample, the association of seedling type and seed size can be examined separately in pioneer and non-pioneer species. These two regeneration groups differ significantly in seed size (Appendix 3.4b). The twenty-three pioneer species are almost entirely small-seeded phanero-epigeal seedlings (Ng, 1978), a high but untestable degree of association. In the remaining 186 non-pioneer species, seedling type and seed size class are independent using all five seedling types (Table 3.2; Appendix 3.4b), but are significantly associated using only three seedling types (PEF, PER and OTHER). As found when all species were analysed, seed size did not differ between species with PER and OTHER type seedlings but did differ between PEF and OTHER types. In contrast, seed size between species with PEF and PER type seedlings was not significantly different when two seed size classes were analysed, and was only marginally significant when four classes were analysed (Table 3.2; Appendix 3.4b). This suggests that differences in seed size will explain less of the functional significance among seedling types within each regeneration strategy than would appear to be the case if all species were considered together. It would be of great interest to know whether the same result would be obtained if the Gabonese sample could be tested in the same way.

Germination

The time required for a seed to germinate after encountering suitable conditions is another trait sometimes thought to be associated with regeneration strategy. Seeds of pioneer species should germinate rapidly to gain a competitive advantage over other seedlings in treefall gaps; whereas, seeds of non-pioneer species might germinate more slowly because competition is less severe in the shaded understorey. As long as it does not include long periods of seasonal or other types of dormancy, time until germination is in some sense a measure of the length of the first stage of development. I would expect it to be correlated with other measures of early seedling development, such as time required for the first photosynthetic structures to expand or overall growth rates, although this has not been tested. Thus, it seems relevant to test for association between germination time and seedling type.

Germination data are available for both the Malaysian and Gabonese sites. Both are rather aseasonal forests, so the seasonal dormancy common in some semi-deciduous forests (Garwood, 1983) should not be a confounding problem. For Malaysian trees, Ng (1978) uses first and last day of germination of each sample to divide species into three germination groups: rapid (all seeds germinate in < 12 weeks), delayed (all seeds germinate in > 12 weeks), and intermediate. For Gabonese species, Miquel (1987) gives only the first day of germination. To compare both samples, I categorize germination as fast (< 6 weeks) and slow (≥ 6 weeks) based on first day only: the division at 6 weeks classifies 98 per cent of Ng's rapid group as fast, as well as 58 per cent of the intermediate group. Fast germination occurs in 81 per cent of the Malaysian but only 65 per cent of the Gabonese species, with a significant association of site sampled and time until germination (Appendix 3.5b). Whether the causes of this difference are methodological or ecological is unknown.

Seedling type is strongly associated with time until germination in both the Gabonese and Malaysian samples (Table 3.2; Appendix 3.5b). In the Gabonese sample, the germination times (fast–slow grouping) of species with PEF and PER type seedlings did not differ, but both types differed from the OTHER type (CHR + PHR + CER). In the Malaysian sample, in contrast, germination times (fast–slow and rapid–delayed groupings) of species with PEF and OTHER types did not differ, whereas both types differed from the PER type. This variation in response between sites makes it difficult to generalize about the importance of germination time and seedling types.

The presence of the fast-germinating pioneer species does not account for the strong association between seedling type and time until germination. When the twenty-three pioneer species were excluded from the analysis of seedling types and germination in the Malaysian sample, the results for non-pioneer species were nearly identical to those for all species, for both germination groupings (Table 3.2; Appendix 3.5b). This is not surprising for the rapid-delayed comparison, because there was not a significant association between regeneration strategy and time until germination (Appendix 3.6b). For the fast–slow comparison, however, this association was significant and supported the initial assumption of faster germinating pioneer species (Appendix 3.6b). Nevertheless, a strong association between seedling type and time until germination in non-pioneer species suggests that time until germination or some other developmental factor correlated with it, might be important for understanding differences between seedling types.

Dispersal mode

Hladik and Miquel (1990) suggest that there should be a relationship between dispersal mode and seedling type because dispersal should increase the probability of a seed landing in the microhabitat best suited for its seedling type. They categorize the Gabonese species as autochorous, anemochorous, or zoochorous. The nineteen autochorous species have almost exclusively PER and PHR seedlings, the twenty-four wind-dispersed (anemochorous) species have primarily PEF and PER seedlings, while the 116 animal-dispersed (zoochorous) species include all seedling types (Appendix 3.2a). This results in a strong association between dispersal mode and seedling type, with all three seedling types (PEF, PER and OTHER) differing from each other (Table 3.2; Appendix 3.2b). Hladik and Miquel (1990) discuss other patterns in a subset of eighty-five zoochorous species, concluding, for example, that PEF seedlings were dispersed by the widest range of animals and that the largest-seeded PEF species were dispersed by the largest animals – elephants. Because of overlap in animals dispersing each plant species, further statistical analyses were inappropriate.

A relationship of dispersal mode and seedling type might be a consequence of an association of dispersal mode and seed size, which was strongly associated with seedling type (see above). Seeds of zoochorous species do not differ in size from anemochorous and autochorous species combined (Appendix 3.7b). There is a tendency for anemochorous species to be smaller than autochorous species, but the sample sizes in all but the intermediate seed size category (0.5–2 cm) are too small for reliable comparisons (Appendix 3.7a).

Are these patterns general? Ng (1978) does not give dispersal mode for Malaysian trees. In contrast to the Gabonese forest, there are many examples of explosively-dispersed autochorous species in Panama with seedling types other than PER and PHR (N.C. Garwood, unpublished data), including PEF (Euphorbiaceae: *Acalypha, Adelia, Croton*; Violaceae: *Hybanthus*; Annonaceae, *Anaxagorea*), CER (Euphorbiaceae: *Hura*), and CHR (Violaceae: *Rinorea*). Likewise, there are many wind-dispersed species in Panama with seedling types other than PEF and PER, particularly CHR (Bignoniaceae, Hippocrateaceae, Leguminosae: Papilionoideae, Malpighiaceae, Sapindaceae, Verbenaceae), which are mostly lianas except for some legume canopy trees.

Habitat

Lastly, we can examine the functional significance of different seedling types by determining, within single forests, their relative abundance along environmental gradients. As in other areas of tropical forest biology, most attention has been focused on the gradient from shaded understorey to treefall gap or large clearing. The predominance of PEF seedlings in treefall gaps or clearings compared to the understorey is commonly emphasized (e.g. de Vogel,

76

1980), but rarely quantified. PEF seedlings occurred in 62 per cent of twenty-nine tree species colonizing 1–6-year-old abandoned fields from seed in Gabon, but in only 39 per cent of 210 species in the flora and in 40 per cent of ninety-two tree species > 5 cm dbh in a forest plot (Miquel, 1987; Hladik and Miquel, 1990). Duke (1970) found more phanerocotylar seedlings in large clearings (55–62 per cent of genera, 74–88 per cent of individuals) than in the understorey (47 per cent of genera, 35 per cent of individuals). Rousteau (1986) also reports that, in a study of fifty-three tree species from the rain forests of Guadeloupe, one-third of species in the understorey have PEF seedlings compared to two-thirds of species in large clearings. As it is well-established that small-seeded pioneer species colonizing gaps generally have small PEF seedlings, I am more surprised and interested in the third of species with other seedling types. Are they 'accidental' survivors in an adverse habitat, late arrivals establishing under environmentally less stressful conditions, or well-adapted gap species? The emphasis on gap–understorey comparisons is somewhat unfortunate, given that most of the variation in seedling morphology occurs among non-pioneer species (see above). We know nothing about the changing abundance of seedling types along other small-scale environmental gradients within forests, such as soil moisture gradients from seasonally inundated plains to dry slopes, or among more patchily distributed environmental factors, such as leaf litter depth or soil compaction. As seeds of species with all seedling types are likely to be dispersed into different patches or positions along a gradient, we need to determine whether seed germination or seedling morphology most influences establishment success. Such questions are extremely amenable to experimental manipulation, such as that used by Molofsky and Augspurger (1992) to separate the effects of habitat, leaf litter and seed size on seedling establishment success.

Conclusions

The above analyses have given us some, but not many, new insights into the functional morphology of tropical seedlings. This is caused, in part, by insufficient data. Even using two large data sets, it was not possible to test the generality of all conclusions because information was not available on regeneration strategy for Gabonese species (Miquel, 1987; Hladik and Miquel, 1990) and on dispersal mode for the Malaysian species (Ng, 1978). Large comparable data sets for other forests are not yet available. It is also caused by a number of more basic problems.

First, even if all five seedling types are found to have ecologically important differences in functional morphology, species with the CER and PHR types are so uncommon in any forest sample that it is rarely possible to perform meaningful analyses of their association with ecological variables. In almost all of the comparisons of CER, PHR and CHR type seedlings discussed above, the rarity of these two types resulted in too many cells with low expected frequencies and no differences being found among the three types (Table 3.2; Appendices 3.2–3.5). The rarity of these two types also led to low expected frequencies in some analyses of all five seedling types, even though more than 100 species were usually analysed (Table 3.2; Appendices 3.2–3.5).

Second, the analyses presented compared numbers of species with particular traits, without weighting species by their abundance in the forest studied or their regional distribution. For example, while CER was the rarest seedling type in all forests sampled, it does not necessarily occur in rare or narrowly distributed taxa. Species with CER type seedlings account for 20 per cent of individual trees over 5 cm dbh in the Gabonese forest, but comprise only 5 per cent of the species (Miquel, 1987; Hladik and Miquel, 1990). The Neotropical genus *Virola* (Myristicaceae) is a relatively diverse genus of about sixty species characteristic of lowland tropical forests, although rarely dominant in them: where known, all have CER type seedlings (see Figure 3.1; and Duke, 1969; Maury-Lechon and Poncy, 1986; Flores and Rivera, 1989; Flores, 1992). What part seedling morphology plays in determining the abundance of adults is not known.

Third, many of the traits examined above, such as seed and regeneration strategy, are likely to be correlated. In principle, this could have been addressed by more complex three- or four-way comparisons. In practice, data were not available for all traits of all species and there would be so many empty cells for the rarer CER and PHR seedling types that the analyses would be invalid. Other types of multivariate analysis might be more appropriate. Kitajima (1992a) has used both multivariate regression and canonical discriminant analyses to explore these relationships (see below).

Fourth, we must be extremely cautious in using this simple comparative approach at the community level. Many seedling traits, such as fleshy or leafy cotyledons, are phylogenetically conservative and found throughout large taxa. Where such taxa are abundant, perhaps for reasons unrelated to seedling ecology, they could easily bias ecological conclusions based solely on abundance of particular morphologies. An appropriate comparative study (e.g. Harvey and Pagel, 1991; Kelly and Purvis, 1993) would have to compare traits within families or map seedling traits onto a phylogeny of the angiosperms derived independently of seedling traits. Such a phylogenetic analysis is beyond the scope of this review. Since higher-level phylogenies based on morphological data incorporate seed characters, many of which are highly correlated with seedling characters, an appropriate analysis may need to be built on a molecular-based phylogeny such as Chase et al. (1993).

Knowledge of the phylogenetic distribution of seedling traits is also essential for addressing evolutionary or biogeographical questions. How many separate times have particular seedling morphologies or traits evolved? Are they relatively old or recent? Have they contributed to the success or failure, i.e. adaptive radiation or decline, of the taxa in which they occur? Do regionally endemic families, such as the Dipterocarpaceae, have seedlings types different from presumably older pantropical families, such as Myrtaceae or Annonaceae?

Fifth, there are several major problems in using this classification scheme of five seedling types, or other seedling classifications (e.g. Bokdam, 1977; de Vogel, 1980; Ye, 1983), to study the functional morphology and ecology of tropical seedlings.

(1) Our understanding has been constrained by a narrow focus. Attention has centred on one morphological feature, the cotyledon, and the two functions associated with it, photosynthesis and reserve storage. Although the cotyledon is the part most unique to the seedling stage and the photosynthetic and reserve functions are extremely important, we have neglected other parts, such as roots and leaves, and other functions, such as water balance and anchorage, which must also play a vital role in early seedling establishment (Table 3.3).

(2) The five 'traditional' seedling types probably do not represent good functional groups even with regard to the two most-studied seedling functions, photosynthesis and reserve storage. If we partition each function into categories according to the initial seedling parts which perform them (Table 3.4A), we find that each 'traditional' seedling type is not uniquely associated with one group defined by these two divisions. For example, the PEF type occurs in two groups which have the cotyledon as first photosynthetic organ, one with no seed reserves and one with seed reserves stored in the endosperm (Table 3.4A). Conversely, the group categorized by having the leaf as first photosynthetic organ and reserves stored in cotyledons contains three seedling types, CHR, CER and PHR (Table 3.4A).

(3) Seedling development and establishment are dynamic processes, with functions waxing and waning and shifting between parts. A static classification, based on only one developmental stage, will obscure much of the functional morphology we need to understand.

(4) One simple seedling classification is unlikely to be appropriate for addressing all of the interesting questions in seedling functional morphology, unless all morphological traits are highly correlated. We need to refocus study on functions, and how these change through development and establishment.

Table 3.3 Distribution of functions among seedling parts. Stems (S) include hypocotyls (H), epicotyls (Ep), and later internodes (I); attached diaspore parts (excluding storage reserves) include parts of fruit (F) and testa (T). –, absent or rare; +, common; ++, typical; ?, possible but usually not considered

		Distribution in seedling parts (part symbol)					
Function	*Function symbol*	*Attached diaspore* (F/T)	*Endo-sperm* (E)	*Root* (R)	*Stems* (S)	*Coty-ledons* (C)	*Leaves* (L)
Photosynthesis	P	–	–	–	+	++	++
Reserve storage	R	–	++	+	+	++	–
Haustorium	H	–	–	–	–	++	–
Support of photosynthetic organs	S	–	–	–	++	–	–
Uptake of nutrients	U	–	–	++	–	?	+
Water balance	W	?	–	++	++	++	++
Anchorage and stability	A	?	–	++	+	–	–
Capture of symbionts	C	–	–	++	+	–	+
Defence	D	+	–	+	+	+	+

Table 3.4 Two independent seedling functions, photosynthesis and storage of energetic reserves, the seedling parts which initially perform these functions, and the distribution of the seedling types or groups in the resulting categories. A. Distribution of the five 'traditional' seedling types (Figure 3.1), and cotyledon functional groups (Kitajima, 1992a,b, 1996). Seedling types: PEF, phanero-epigeal-foliaceous; PER, phanero-epigeal-reserve; PHR, phanero-hypogeal-reserve; CHR, crypto-hypogeal-reserve; CER, crypto-epigeal-reserve; 'CHR', seedlings usually assigned to the CHR type which store reserves in the hypocotyl; ?, unrecognized combinations. Cotyledon functional groups: P, photosynthetic; PS, dual photosynthetic–storage; S, storage. B. Distribution of 'morpho-functional' groups, discussed in text: function and part symbols in parentheses in headings. Two of the eight potential 'morpho-functional' groups appear to be absent or rare among woody tropical species and are not discussed in the text. I know of no examples of $P_L R_0$, but $P_C R_H$ may occur in *Chrysochlamys eclipes* (see Figure 3.5)

First photosynthetic organ (P)	Presence and initial location of energetic reserves (R)			
	Absent (0)	*Endosperm* (E)	*Cotyledon* (C)	*Hypocotyl* (H)
A. Distribution of five 'traditional' seedling types (Cotyledon functional groups)				
Cotyledon	PEF (P)	PEF (P)	PER (PS)	? (–)
Leaf	? (–)	CHR CER (S)	CHR PHR CER (S)	'CHR' (S)
B. Distribution of 'morpho-functional' groups				
Cotyledon (C)	$P_C R_0$	$P_C R_{E(C)}$	$P_C R_C$	$P_C R_H$
Leaf (L)	$P_L R_0$	$P_L R_{E(C)}$	$P_L R_C$	$P_L R_H$

TOWARDS A BETTER UNDERSTANDING OF SEEDLING FUNCTIONAL MORPHOLOGY

We need a better understanding of the diverse and changing functions of seedling parts during development, more integration of physiology and morphology, reassessment of functional groups of species, a finer division of environmental heterogeneity within the forest, and an assessment of success of different morphologies in these environments.

Seedling morphology and functions

The major functions that must be carried out by the developing seedling are summarized in Table 3.3, along with the major parts most likely to contribute to these functions. Many of the functions of the principal seedling parts are similar to those in later stages of development, while some are unique to or carried out by special structures during the seedling stages. Within one species, a single structure may have multiple simultaneous functions, change function during seedling development, or share functions with other parts. One part may serve very different functions in different species. Anatomical and physiological specializations for one function may limit the ability of that part to carry out a second function. I will discuss the distribution of functions among seedling parts in more detail below, and briefly note where other life forms may differ from tropical tree seedlings.

To facilitate discussion and comparison of seedling functions, I would like to introduce a system of notation that primarily emphasizes seedling functions, identifies which parts carry them out, and how they change during development. Functions are identified by capital letters, e.g. photosynthesis (P), reserve storage (R), etc.; parts carrying out each function are also represented by capital letters: e.g. cotyledon (C), leaves (L), etc. (see Table 3.3). By combining the two, and subscripting the part, we have a simple descriptor of functional morphology of the seedling. For example, $P_L R_C$ would be a 'morpho-functional' seedling group composed of species with reserves stored in cotyledons and leaves as the initial photosynthetic organs. I will use this notation in the discussion below on specific seedling functions to clarify which contrasts are being addressed.

The advantages of this system for comparative study are many. First, for any combination of functions and the parts which perform them, there is only one 'morpho-functional' group describing each category (Table 3.4B), unlike the 'traditional' seedling types which are not uniquely associated with each category (Table 3.4A). Functions that are lacking can be scored as absent (0), e.g. $P_C R_0$. Second, the notation can be easily extended. Suspected but untested contributions can be indicated, e.g. $P_{?H} R_C$. Unknown functions of conspicuous parts, such as the persistence of the seed coat on the lower surface of the semi-exposed fleshy cotyledons of some species, can also be noted, e.g.

81

$P_LR_C?_T$ (T = testa). Co-involvement of two structures can be easily noted, such as the obligatory presence of a haustorial cotyledon when endosperm reserves are present, $P_LR_{E(C)}$. The relative importance of two parts to the same function can be ordered as primary to secondary contributions or weighted by percentage contribution, e.g. $P_{1L,2C}R_C$ or $P_{L70\%, C30\%}R_C$. Third, changes that occur during one developmental stage can be concisely recorded, e.g. $P_{0\rightarrow H}R_{E(C)\rightarrow R}$. Specific developmental stages, such as the expansion and seed-reserve stages (described below), could be annotated separately or combined into one expression, e.g.:

$$[P_0R_{E(C)}]^{exp} + [P_CR_H]^{res} = P_{0/C}R_{E(C)/H}$$

The combined form is particularly good for emphasizing the changing role of one part, such as the cotyledon, or the ephemeral nature of some functions, such as reserves. This more complex notation might be useful in comparative studies of several species to summarize the dynamic changes that occur during development, but would not be suitable for large-scale community studies. Including too much detail in a particular notation, e.g.: $P_{H\rightarrow 1C,2H/C90,L10\rightarrow C20,L80}R_{E(C)\rightarrow H/H\rightarrow 0}$, however, should be discouraged.

I am not advocating use of this particular terminology in broad community surveys of seedling ecology. Rather, I hope that it will encourage tests of the functional significance of different morphologies by making the comparisons more explicit. The results of such tests could then be used to construct groups which are ecologically relevant and functionally distinct, that can be used with confidence in community surveys. In contrast, the assumptions underlying recognition of seedling groups currently in use are largely untested.

Seedling development

Because the function of various seedling parts often changes during ontogeny, it is essential to clarify which stages are being discussed and to compare seedlings with different morphologies at the same stage of development. These functional stages do not always coincide with morphological stages, such as the cotyledon and eophyll stages of Bokdam (1977), which are based on the expansion of particular structures. Given the various meanings of 'seedling' among disciplines, it is not surprising that terms used to describe seedling developmental stages vary greatly in the literature, but it is unfortunate that criteria used to separate stages are not more clearly stated. The developmental stages used in this paper are described below and illustrated in detail for *Anacardium excelsum* (Figure 3.4) and in part for other species (Figures 3.1, 3.5–3.7). Further subdivisions can be used to test particular hypotheses (see Kitajima, 1992a). Any division into stages is arbitrary because development and growth are continuous processes. Even if arbitrary, these seedling stages are independent of specific seedling morphologies and size and thus provide a necessary framework for comparing morphologies.

Seed stage

Although not strictly within the remit of the Workshop, this stage is relevant for understanding the three seedling stages. First, the morphological structure of the mature seeds reveals much about the morphology of the early seedling (compare Figure 3.4B and Figure 3.4D), as has long been known (e.g. Lubbock, 1892), and the biochemical makeup of any seed storage reserves foreshadows that in the seedling. Second, strong selection on the seed stage will have major repercussions at the seedling stages: for example, selection for increased numbers of seeds would result in smaller seeds and smaller seedlings. Third, on an evolutionary scale, developmental canalization of seed morphology may preclude certain seedling morphologies in a lineage, but al-low elaboration of others. The seed stage ends at germination, defined as the extrusion of the radicle from the seed (Figure 3.4C).

Seedling expansion stage

This occurs after germination (Figure 3.4D,E) and ends with the full expansion of the initial entirely photosynthetic organs, the stems that support them, and the first roots (Figures 3.1A–E, 3.5A,B, 3.7A). This is the 'initial morphology' of the seedling. Unless respiratory losses are compensated by photosynthetic gains, overall biomass of the expanding seedling often decreases, relative to initial seed mass, during this stage (Kitajima, 1992a). Although the end of the expansion stage is unambiguous for above-ground structures, we know little of early root expansion. Expansion is an important phase, but frequently neglected because seed ecologists and physiologists often lose interest after germination and seed-ling ecologists rarely take note before the seedling has expanded.

Seedling seed-reserve stage

After expansion, seedlings may utilize reserves still present and stored in the attached seed (Figure 3.1A,B) or hypocotyl (Figure 3.5A,B) or those pre-viously transferred from seed to seedling during expansion. New structures produced entirely from these reserves do not represent growth, but a transfer or reallocation of reserves between parts of the seedling without overall in-crease in seedling biomass or nutrient levels. When seed reserves are minimal or absent, or completely consumed during expansion (as in Figure 3.4), this stage can be inconspicuous or lacking. This stage ends when reserves are de-pleted or no longer exploitable. Because the transition from reserve to newly acquired resources can occur at different times for different nutrients (Fenner,

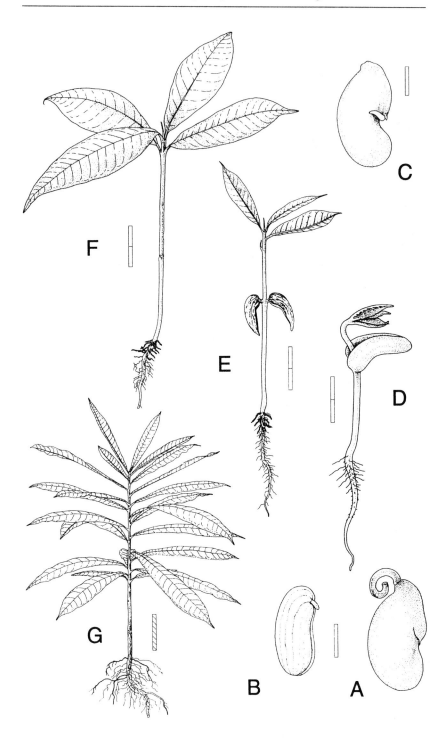

1986) or for nutrients and carbon (Kitajima, 1992a, 1996), passage from this stage to the next can be gradual.

Seedling autonomous stage

Without further seed reserves (Figures 3.4F, 3.6, 3.7A–C), the seedling must rely on its own ability to photosynthesize and capture nutrients. If its capacity exceeds maintenance needs, new growth and further differentiation are poss-ible and the overall biomass of the seedling can increase. Gradually, this new growth will predominate. When the photosynthetic organs formed in the pre-vious two seedling stages become physiologically inactive or abscise, and root and shoot tissues produced in those stages are incorporated into the conduct-ing and supporting internal structure of the plant, the young tree has passed into the juvenile stage (Figure 3.4G).

Juvenile stage

For most tree species, this stage will be much longer than the preceding stages. While this stage will include many large individuals, including what are often called saplings, it will also include small individuals of many spe-cies, especially pioneer trees.

Seedling establishment

I deliberately described the developmental stages independently of seedling establishment, a process that many (including myself) profess to study, be-cause I feel it is more useful to discuss specific factors that influence survivor-ship and growth throughout the seedling stages than to try and pinpoint the time of establishment *per se*. Many workers would probably concur that es-tablishment occurs sometime in the autonomous stage, after the seedling is in-dependent of seed reserves and has grown sufficiently to have a relatively high survivorship (at least in the short term), and that seedlings persisting at

Figure 3.4 Seedling development in *Anacardium excelsum* (Bertero & Balb.) Skeels (Ana-cardiaceae), a canopy tree common from Costa Rica through Ecuador and Venezuela, with phanerocotylar-epigeal-reserve (PER) type seedlings and storage–photosynthetic cotyledons. A, mature single-seeded diaspore (an indehiscent fruit); B, embryo from mature seed, composed pri-marily of large fleshy cotyledons, with a small radicle; C, germinating seed, with the radicle pro-truding from the fruit; D, expanding seedling, after the cotyledons have been pulled free of the fruit by the elongating hypocotyl; E, expanding seedling, with the first leaves (usually four) half-expanded and the cotyledon reserves partially depleted; F, fully expanded seedling in autonomous stage, immediately after the shrivelled fleshy cotyledons have fallen; G, seedling in juvenile stage, after the four initial seedling leaves have abscised. Scale bars: open bars, 1-cm units; hatched bar, 10-cm units

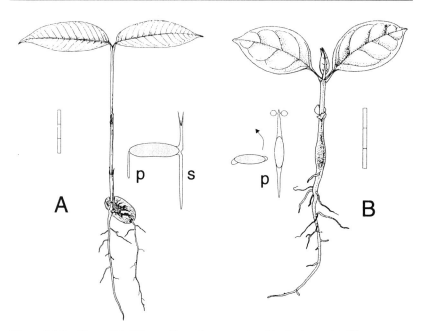

Figure 3.5 Seedlings of Guttiferae with seed reserves stored in the hypocotyl. Diagrams show seedling expansion: the seed primarily consists of the thick hypocotyl (shaded), the stem extends from the apex of the hypocotyl and the primary root (p) from the base, although the primary root is sometimes superseded by a larger secondary root (s) growing down from the apex. A, *Garcinia madruno* (Kunth) Hammel (= *Rheedia acuminata* (R. & P.) Planch. & Tr. in Croat, 1978) small tree: cotyledons are absent; B, *Chrysochlamys eclipes* L.O. Williams (= *Tovomitopsis nicara-guensis* Oerst. ex Planch. and Tr. in Croat, 1978), small tree: it is not yet known whether the small foliar organs are cotyledons or reduced leaves. Scale bars: 1-cm units

their compensation point with no new net growth are not established. However, the oft-used term has not been defined in a way that is practical to use in comparing an array of morphologically diverse seedlings in the field (Fenner, 1987). Even studies of seedling establishment usually report habitat-specific differences in growth and survivorship through time, rather than the proportion of seedlings establishing or the time required to do so. Unless there is a simultaneous change in some measurable parameter of growth and the probability of surviving, applicable across species, a precise definition of the time of establishment will remain elusive. Establishment is most likely a gradual process, as the common use of well-established or poorly established suggests. Further progress in understanding establishment will depend on combining physiological and demographic studies of growth and survivorship for many species of diverse morphology. We need better ways of measuring growth in the field that reflect below-ground processes. We must also identify the appropriate time-scale: the period available for establishment is often

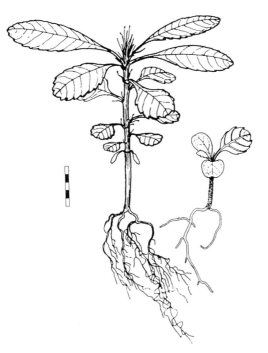

Figure 3.6 Seedlings of *Cespedezia macrophylla* Seem. (Ochnaceae), medium-sized tree, shown at the beginning and end of the autonomous stage. Seedlings are phanerocotylar-epigeal-foliaceous (PEF), with entirely photosynthetic cotyledons, Scale bar: 1-mm units

constrained by seasonal cycles of drought, flooding, or cold or by similar but unpredictable stresses.

Energetic reserve utilization *versus* first photosynthetic organs

Photosynthesis and storage of energy reserves are two independent seedling functions, which may occur in the same or different seedling parts (Tables 3.3, 3.4). Photosynthesis, the autotrophic source of new carbon for growth, occurs primarily in leaves and cotyledons, but also in stems (hypocotyls, epicotyls, or later internodes), stipules, or petioles. Stored energy reserves, the heterotrophic source of energy which allows the seedling to remain independent of external supplies early in development, are usually stored in the cotyledons or endosperm of the attached seed, but are sometimes stored in the hypocotyl or root or dispersed throughout the seedling. We need to understand the ecological and phylogenetic constraints that determine which function predominates in the early stages of seedling development and in what part it occurs. Press et al. (1996) review the photosynthetic response of leaves of older seedlings to different light regimes and nitrogen and water availability.

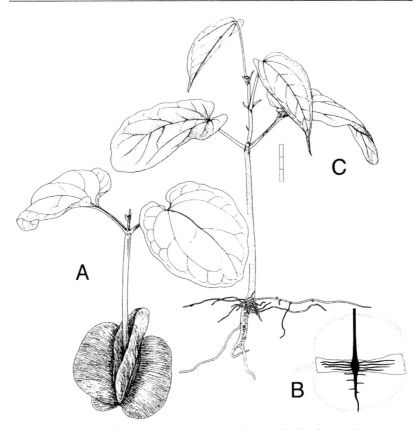

Figure 3.7 Seedlings of *Cavanillesia platanifolia* (H. & B.) H.B.K. (Bombacaceae), canopy tree, shown in the autonomous stage. Seedlings are phanerocotylar-epigeal-foliaceous (PEF), with entirely photosynthetic cotyledons. The central portion of the large wind-dispersed fruit, surrounding the single seed, is packed with water-absorbing mucilage (Garwood, 1985). A, Seedling with cotyledons fully expanded, primary root not yet extending out of fruit; B, diagram of root development within fruit, showing proliferation of small roots from collet (junction of the hypocotyl and primary root) into mucilage-rich central part of the fruit, as primary root grows out of fruit wings; C, seedling with first leaves expanding and fruit remains removed to show persistence and further development of roots within the mucilage-rich fruit. Scale bar: 1-cm units

Comparative work has focused on the photosynthetic function (P_C) or reserve function (R_C) of the cotyledons, such that it is the best understood aspect of functional morphology of young seedlings. Early work on temperate herbs (Lovell and Moore, 1970, 1971) and temperate trees (Marshall and Kozlowski, 1974a,b, 1975, 1976a,b, 1977; Ampofo et al., 1976a,b), which influenced my early thinking on tropical seedlings, established a continuum of response in green epigeal cotyledons from mostly photosynthetic to mostly storage. Green hypogeal cotyledons, in spite of having chlorophyll, had few stomates and nil rates of photosynthesis. The importance of these different cotyledon functional morphologies for successful establishment in different environments was not discussed.

Kitajima (1992a,b, 1996), in the largest comparative study of cotyledon function, has extended coverage to tropical woody species. Photosynthetic rate on a dry mass basis rapidly decreased as a function of cotyledon thickness in ten species, with gross photosynthesis in green epigeal cotyledons >0.6 mm thick barely exceeding respiration. Thin green epigeal exposed cotyledons were primarily photosynthetic, while thicker exposed green cotyledons were primarily storage and secondarily photosynthetic; hidden cotyledons had an entirely storage function. Hence, three cotyledon functional groups were recognized: photosynthetic, photosynthetic–storage, and storage. (These roughly correspond to the PEF, PER and CHR + PHR + CER seedling types, respectively.) Cotyledon thickness and exposure were used to identify the cotyledon functional group of eighty-four species and examine the correlation among many seed and seedling traits. These relationships and the importance of these cotyledon functional groups for understanding seedling growth (Kitajima, 1992a) suggest that these groups differ by a number of highly correlated co-evolved traits and reflect strategies for establishment in different forest environments, which will be discussed in more detail in the last section.

Nevertheless, the three cotyledon functional groups were not entirely homogeneous for several potentially important ecological traits (Kitajima, 1992a,b, 1996). About 60 per cent of species with primarily photosynthetic cotyledons germinated from seeds with abundant endosperm and 40 per cent from seeds with no or negligible endosperm; whereas, about 85 per cent of species with primarily storage cotyledons (or hypocotyls) or storage-photosynthetic cotyledons germinated from seeds with no or negligible endosperm. In addition, cotyledons that were primarily photosynthetic were also long-persistent (≥ 10 weeks in 97 per cent of species); those that were photosynthetic–storage were short-persistent ($\ll 10$ weeks in 92 per cent of species); whereas, those that were primarily storage were equally split between long- and short-persistent. The cotyledon functional groups are also heterogeneous when compared to the eight 'morpho-functional' groups defined by initial photosynthetic organ (cotyledon or leaf) and absence or presence of stored reserves in the cotyledon, endosperm or hypocotyl (Table 3.4). Primarily photosynthetic cotyledons occur in two 'morpho-functional' groups (P_CR_0 and $P_CR_{E(C)}$), photosynthetic–storage cotyledons in only one group (P_CR_C) and hidden reserves with non-photosynthetic cotyledons in three groups (P_LR_C, P_LR_E and P_LR_H).

Is this heterogeneity within cotyledon functional groups ecologically important? If so, we need to determine whether the heterogeneity represents minor variations within each cotyledon functional group or whether alternative ways of clustering species into other functional groups produces groupings that are more homogeneous. Are the 'morpho-functional' groups more homogeneous than the cotyledon functional types? Are other ecologically important traits concerning photosynthesis or reserve storage overlooked by focusing on these cotyledon functional groups or 'morpho-functional' groups? These questions, and the research needed to answer them, are discussed below.

First, about half of the species in Kitajima's sample with thin photosynthetic cotyledons develop from seeds with negligible endosperm (P_CR_0) and half from seeds with abundant endosperm ($P_CR_{E(C)}$). In the former group, cotyledons have presumably completed most of their morphogenesis into photosynthetic organs before germination, except for final expansion; in the latter group, cotyledons function as haustorial organs throughout germination and much of seedling expansion before undergoing morphogenesis into photosynthetic structures. Are there differences in the gross morphology or anatomy of cotyledons or other seedling parts in these two groups? In particular, are storage reserves more widely dispersed throughout the seedling in the former group (P_CR_0), compared to that of the latter group ($P_CR_{E(C)}$)? If so, are there differences in the amounts of dispersed reserves stored throughout the seedling compared to that concentrated in the endosperm? If reserves are widely dispersed, rather than absent, use of P_CR_0 is inappropriate and should be changed to P_CR_D (where D = dispersed through seedling). We must then ask if both groups (P_CR_0 and P_CR_D) occur among tropical species and, if so, is the distinction of ecological importance.

Are cotyledons which are entirely photosynthetic (P_CR_0) more efficient photosynthetically at maturity than those which are sequentially haustorial then photosynthetic ($P_CR_{E(C)}$)? Or, are they similar physiologically and morphologically, but the entirely photosynthetic cotyledons reach maturity faster than those that are haustorial then photosynthetic? There are no quantitative data on this contrast for either photosynthesis or cotyledon expansion; but, when species with conspicuously tardily emergent cotyledons are reported, they are from families with abundant endosperm, such as Annonaceae and Rubiaceae (Duke, 1969; Garwood, 1979). Within Panamanian Rubiaceae, cotyledons of larger-seeded genera, such as *Tocoyena* (Figure 3.1D), *Genipa*, *Coussarea* and *Randia*, emerge more slowly than cotyledons of smaller-seeded genera, such as *Alseis*, *Macrocnemum*, or *Palicourea* (N.C. Garwood, personal observation). Whether rate of cotyledon emergence within families with abundant endosperm is related to absolute amount of endosperm present or the relative size of endosperm and embryo is unknown.

Second, although most species with non-photosynthetic cotyledons in Kitajima's sample had reserves stored in the cotyledons (P_LR_C), about 15 per cent of species had them stored in the endosperm ($P_LR_{E(C)}$) or hypocotyl (P_LR_H). Endospermic reserves with strictly haustorial cotyledons occur in a limited number of dicot families, but are ubiquitous in monocots; the accompanying haustorial cotyledon can be specialized or not. For example, all Myristicaceae

(Figure 3.1E) and Palmae are cryptocotylar and have specialized non-foliaceous haustorial cotyledons. Cryptocotylar species of Annonaceae have unspecialized foliaceous haustorial cotyledons, which resemble those of phanerocotylar species except that they do not emerge and become photosynthetic (Garwood, 1995). Among species with strictly haustorial cotyledons ($P_LR_{E(C)}$), are the most specialized haustorial cotyledons more efficient at breaking down and translocating reserves than the less specialized ones? Are strictly haustorial cotyledons more efficient than those that are sequentially haustorial then photosynthetic ($P_CR_{E(C)}$)? Are reserves translocated faster to the growing seedling axis in species with cotyledon reserves (P_LR_C) than in those with endosperm ($P_LR_{E(C)}$), which must be broken down and absorbed by the exclusively haustorial cotyledons before being exported? In spite of frequent declarations that these two groups (P_LR_C and $P_LR_{E(C)}$) are functionally equivalent in tropical species, and should therefore be combined in the same seedling type, I am not aware of comparative data that test this assumption. Hypocotylar reserves occur frequently in the Guttiferae (Figure 3.5) and Rhizophoraceae (de Vogel, 1980), but rarely in other families. Are there any advantages to packing the reserves in the hypocotyl in the seed rather than the cotyledons? If so, why is it not very common? Species with such endospermic or hypcotylar reserves are usually included with CHR type seedlings, but we do not know if the nature of the reserves or the rate at which they are translocated out of the expanding seedling are similar.

Third, species in Kitajima's sample with strictly storage cotyledons or parts (P_LR_C, $P_LR_{E(C)}$ and P_LR_H) were equally divided between those with short- and long-persistent reserves, whereas those with storage-photosynthetic cotyledons (P_CR_C) were mostly short-persistent. Among species with photosynthetic cotyledons, the cotyledons were usually long-persistent, but reserves were absent from about half the species which lack endosperm (P_CR_0) and short-persistent in the remainder with endosperm ($P_CR_{E(C)}$). The change in reserve use during development (where '→' indicates a change from the expansion stage to the post-expansion stage) can be summarized in the following way: reserves always absent, $R_0 \rightarrow R_0$; reserves short-persistent, $R_+ \rightarrow R_0$; reserves long-persistent, $R_+ \rightarrow R_+$. Short-persistent reserves probably contribute only to the development of the initial morphology of the seedling during the expansion stage, whereas long-persistent reserves may contribute to post-expansion growth or survival. It would be useful to know, for any seed size class, whether short-persistent reserves are associated with shorter expansion times or larger initial size, compared to species with long-persistent reserves. I suspect that the timing of reserve utilization during development will prove more important for understanding the ecology of tropical seedlings than either the location of the reserves or the single or dual function of the cotyledons. To reflect this suspicion, I show one alternative division of seedling functional morphologies based primarily on reserve persistence and secondarily on

Table 3.5 An alternative classification of seedling functional morphologies using timing of reserve utilization during seedling development as the primary criterion dividing species into functional groups and the location of reserves as the secondary criterion. Changes in functional morphology of seedlings shown are from expansion stage (the initial morphology) to post-expansion stages (e.g. $R_+ \to R_0$). 'Traditional' seedling types are the five types described in the text (see Table 3.4 and Figure 3.1). Symbols as in Tables 3.3, 3.4; +, present

Primary division: timing of reserve utilization		Secondary division: reserve location			
Reserve status	Developmental changes	Location	Developmental changes		'Traditional' seedling types
Absent	$R_0 \to R_0$	absent	P_cR_0	$\to$ P_cR_0	PEF
Short-persistent	$R_+ \to R_0$	endosperm	$P_cR_{E(C)}$	$\to$ P_cR_0	PEF
		endosperm	$P_LR_{E(C)}$	$\to$ P_LR_0	CER
		cotyledon	P_cR_C	$\to$ P_LR_0	PER
		cotyledon	P_LR_C	$\to$ P_LR_0	CHR,PHR
		hypocotyl	P_LR_H	$\to$ P_LR_0	'CHR'
Long-persistent	$R_+ \to R_+$	endosperm	$P_LR_{E(C)}$	$\to$ $P_LR_{E(C)}$	CER
		cotyledon	P_LR_C	$\to$ P_LR_C	CHR, PHR
		hypocotyl	P_LR_H	$\to$ P_LR_H	'CHR'

reserve location (Table 3.5). Note that these functional groups cannot be recognized on the basis of initial morphology alone, whether the 'traditional' seedling types or 'morpho-functional' groups are used: later developmental stages must also be studied. Unfortunately, determining whether reserves are short- or long-persistent is more time-consuming than describing the initial morphology alone or using Kitajima's criteria for classifying seedling into the three cotyledon functional groups (Kitajima, 1992a). Would the extra effort involved yield a better understanding of seedling functional morphology?

Fourth, whatever functional groups are used, we will also want to contrast the quality of reserves utilized, that is, whether reserves are primarily energy-rich lipids or lower energy carbohydrates and proteins, and determine whether these reserves are metabolized and translocated at the same rate. The concentration of lipids in seeds varies widely among species, is not correlated with seed mass (Levin, 1974), and is positively correlated with protein concentration in some herbaceous families, but not others (Barclay and Earle, 1974). In twelve tropical species in three families, seed energy concentration was not related to cotyledon functional type or seed mass, but did differ among families (Kitajima, 1992a). The proportional loss of energy during early seedling expansion was similar across these species; whereas, the proportional loss of biomass decreased with increasing seed energy concentration, but was not related to seed mass or cotyledon functional type.

The energy concentration per unit biomass of the cotyledon might also be a useful way of distinguishing the relative role of photosynthesis and storage in fleshy or somewhat fleshy cotyledons. Although cotyledon thickness was correlated with photosynthetic rate (Kitajima, 1992b), it is likely that absolute thickness will increase with seedling size even if cotyledons contribute the same proportion of energy toward seedling expansion. Given these types of expected allometric relationships, a size-independent measure of storage would be useful.

Fifth, we need to identify the primary functions of long-persistent reserves. Do they supply energy or nutrients to prolong survival in suboptimal habitats, develop new structures such as leaves or roots to improve carbon or nutrient gain, differentiate existing structures (such as lignifying stems), or provide insurance against damage by falling branches or herbivores? While there is much speculation about possible functions (Foster, 1986), there have been few experimental studies to test them. Persistent reserves produce new shoots after damage in some species, but may carry out other important functions when the initial shoot remains undamaged (Denslow, 1980; Kiew, 1982; McHargue and Hartshorn, 1983). Are long-persistent reserves general purpose bet-hedging structures, or are there different kinds of reserves which best carry out specific functions?

Sixth, comparative work on seedling functional morphology has focused on the photosynthetic or reserve status of the cotyledons, in spite of the diverse parts which can participate in these functions. This has diverted attention from general problems of utilization of reserves and nature of first photosynthetic organs. For photosynthesis, the potential role of the hypocotyl (P_H) during the expansion stage has not been adequately explored. In several temperate tree species, hypocotyls were photosynthetically active five days after seedling emergence, but nearly inactive five days later (Marshall and Kozlowski, 1974a). Because hypocotyls and young stems are so often green in tropical species, we should determine whether photosynthetic contributions from the hypocotyl in early development balance respiratory demands of the expanding seedlings, as photosynthetic contributions of epigeal storage cotyledons balanced respiration (Kitajima, 1992b). As expansion progresses, the primary site of photosynthesis would probably shift from the hypocotyl to the expanded cotyledon or leaf ($P_{H \to C}$ or $P_{H \to L}$). An early photosynthetic contribution from the hypocotyl might be extremely important in small PEF type seedlings, especially those with little endosperm reserves.

Lastly, in species with abundant endosperm, the cotyledon acts as a haustorial organ, translocating reserves into the developing seedling. These reserves sometimes accumulate in conspicuously swollen hypocotyls or roots ($R_{E(C) \to H}$ or $R_{E(C) \to R}$), from which they are later mobilized. Whether these reserves are depleted during expansion or persist into the seed-reserve stage, and to what extent depletion and persistence are associated with the retention of photosynthetic cotyledons versus abscission of the exclusively haustorial cotyledons, have been little studied. If there are significant amounts of long-persistent reserves in these hypocotyls or roots, such species would be functionally similar to cryptocotylar species with long-persistent reserves. This seems to be the case for the Malaysian *Styrax benzoin* (Styracaceae), as reserves typically persist in the hypocotyl for four to six months (Kiew, 1982). Reserves stored below ground might also be safer from herbivores than those stored above ground.

Panamanian species of Annonaceae, whose epigeal seedlings are derived from large endospermous seeds with small embryos, illustrate the spectrum of variation (Garwood, 1995). Among species with haustorial–photosynthetic cotyledons, *Anaxagorea panamensis* has negligible amounts of stored reserves in the seedling, *Guatteria amplifolia* has at least some short-persistent reserves in the hypocotyl, and *Xylopia macrantha* has abundant possibly long-persistent reserves in the root. Along this species gradient, there is a gradual progression from broad to narrow photosynthetic cotyledons. In species with exclusively haustorial cotyledons, *Desmopsis panamensis* and *Unonopsis pitteri* have abundant, possibly long-persistent reserves in the root; the thin, leaf-like cotyledons expand into and absorb the endosperm in much the same way as the haustorial–photosynthetic cotyledons. The latter species are typical examples of the CER or durian seedling type, which is often considered maladapted because the photosynthetic potential of the cotyledons, and the energy used to lift them and the attached seed, is wasted (Ng, 1978). On the other hand, given the phylogenetic constraint of small embryo and abundant endosperm shared by all Annonaceae, this may be the only evolutionary path available to the functional condition of long-persistent reserves.

Other seedling functions

Much less study has been directed to the other important functions tropical seedlings must carry out to become established (Table 3.3). I briefly consider these below.

Nutrient stored reserves

Like energy reserves, nutrient reserves allow the seedling to remain independent of external supplies early in development and can be stored in the cotyledons, endosperm, hypocotyl, or roots or dispersed throughout the seedling. For several tropical species, Kitajima (1992a, 1996) found that seedlings became independent of stored energy reserves before they became independent of nitrogen reserves. Although seed reserves of herbaceous species may contain all the trace elements necessary for the adult (Fenner, 1987), this is unlikely to be true for tropical trees. Little is known of the abundance of

94

particular nutrients in stored reserves of seedlings of different functional groups or species characteristic of specific habitats or forest types.

Anchorage and nutrient uptake

Functions primarily carried out by roots have been little studied in tropical tree seedlings from a morphological or physiological viewpoint. Anchorage in the substrate and stability of the developing stem are important functions of the primary and secondary roots, as well as stilt or adventitious roots. For most tree seedlings, the seedling substrate will be soil of various compositions, but some species initially root on dead fallen trees (Swaine, 1983; Lack, 1991), or water-logged or flooded soils (McHargue and Hartshorn, 1983; Farrant et al., 1987), and strangling fig species typically root in humus-filled crotches within the crown (Putz and Holbrook, 1989). During expansion, associated fruit or seed parts, especially if winged or heavy, may stabilize the stem before the roots are well-developed or provide a counter-thrust or force that allows the roots to penetrate the substrate. For example, when the single seed is removed from the large wind-dispersed fruit of *Cavanillesia platanifolia* (see Figure 3.7) and sown separately, the primary root has great difficulty penetrating the soil during seedling expansion and the cotyledons often do not emerge completely from the seed. Nutrient and water uptake is also primarily a function of roots, particularly by root hairs, young fine roots, or mycorrhizal symbionts, although nutrient uptake through the leaf surface might be of secondary importance in some species.

Root architecture among tropical trees displays considerable diversity (Jeník, 1978), but there are only scattered descriptions of root systems of seedlings (see references in Jeník, 1978), most often for species with stilt roots or pneumorrhizae (pneumatophores or 'breathing roots'), or older 2–3 m tall saplings (Becker and Castillo, 1990), and few accounts of root development from seedling to juvenile to adult. When roots are considered at all, it is usually the relative biomass allocated to roots rather than leaves and shoots (discussed below), and not the structure and functions of the root system itself. Root systems in tropical tree seedlings vary from mostly fibrous to mostly tuberous (N.C. Garwood, personal observation). Although only some species of tropical trees develop large tap roots as adults, tap roots are commonly present in tropical tree seedlings and develop from the primary, secondary, or adventitious roots: the size and distribution of smaller roots along the tap root vary greatly (Figures 3.1, 3.4, 3.5 and 3.7). In *Cochlospermum vitifolium*, a small tree, the tap root becomes a tuberous water-storage organ (xylopodium), first formed in seedlings about 20 cm tall (Garwood, 1994) and well-developed in adults (Poppendieck, 1980). A tuberous tap root of unknown function is also present in seedlings of *Spondias* spp. (N.C. Garwood, unpublished data), but I do not know if this persists in the adult canopy trees.

Other species lack a tap root during the seedling stages. In some, a highly branched fibrous root system develops rapidly (Figure 3.6); in others, several stout roots are produced. For example, the mangrove species *Avicennia marina* lacks a primary root and tap root, but up to nine stout adventitious roots are produced on the hypocotyl in three phases (Farrant et al., 1987). This phasic production of roots was interpreted as an adaptation to the unstable mangrove environment, where the first roots might easily become desiccated at low water or broken during movement by the tides.

We need to determine whether there is an association of particular systems with specific conditions of light, nutrient and moisture availability, soil texture or aeration; how rapidly these systems differentiate during seedling development; and whether they correlate well with other seedling traits. For example, Ng (1978) suggested that initial root size is related to seed size and the ability to establish in compact soil, with seedlings germinating from small seeds (<3 mm long) having fine roots, which can penetrate tiny crevices in compacted soil, and seedlings from larger seeds having thicker roots, which have more difficulty anchoring in a hard substrate. This area is wide open for further observational and experimental work.

Water balance

The amount of water present in the soil, the ability of roots to extract it, and capacity of leaves and cotyledons to control loss will determine the overall water balance of the seedling. The importance of predictable seasonal droughts in controlling the timing of seed germination and early seedling growth is well-established (Garwood, 1983, 1986). More recently, it has been recognized that seedling survivorship and growth are also strongly influenced by unpredictable droughts in forests that do not experience a regular dry season and by local variations in moisture availability associated with gap and understorey conditions in a variety of forest types (see Whitmore, 1996; Press et al., 1996). The converse problem of excessive moisture for seedlings has been recognized for monsoon forests that receive prolonged periods of high rainfall (Aiyar, 1932) and for seasonally flooded igapó and várzea forests (Coutinho and Struffaldi, 1971; Scarano and Crawford, 1992).

Susceptibility to drought varies among species and among size classes within a species for seedlings of the few tropical trees studied (see Whitmore, 1996; Press et al., 1996; Burslem, 1996). Susceptibility to flooding was greater in seedlings of *Parkia pendula*, characteristic of the terra-firme forest (Scarano and Crawford, 1992), than in those of *Parkia auriculata*, characteristic of the seasonally flooded igapó forests (Coutinho and Struffaldi, 1971). We need to determine whether the degree of susceptibility to drought and flooding is caused by differences in physiology or morphology. For seedlings in the early stages of development, physiological measures of water balance, such as stomatal conductance and water-use efficiency, have not been compared between photosynthetic cotyledons and the first leaves. For seedlings in later developmental stages, leaf stomatal conductances differ widely among dipterocarp species (see Press et al., 1996), but it is not known whether this is the basis for differences in drought tolerance. As noted above, information on root architecture that would be relevant to understanding water relations, such as depth of rooting, the distribution and abundance of secondary and higher-order roots, or presence of water-storing tuberous roots, is totally lacking for tropical seedlings. Root/shoot ratios, where known, are usually interpreted as responses to the light environment, not to stresses of periodic drought which might occur in either understorey or gap environments.

In general, seedlings in the expansion stage would be expected to be more susceptible to short-term drought than those in later stages, which have developed a substantial root system and mature leaves or cotyledons. Also, species which require longer to develop would be susceptible to short-term drought for longer periods than those that expand more rapidly. Exposed fleshy storage reserves might also be more vulnerable than those that are enclosed by the fruit or seed coat. For example, in *Gustavia superba*, which has large exposed fleshy cotyledons, fewer seedlings emerged in sun versus shade environments, except where deep litter covered the germinating seeds and prevented desiccation (Molofsky and Augspurger, 1992).

Other seedling-associated structures, such as fruit or seed parts, may occasionally contribute to the water balance. For example, the mucilage-rich fruits of *Cavanillesia platanifolia* persist about the expanding seedlings (Figure 3.7A), absorbing and holding abundant moisture after a rain (Garwood, 1985). Several small roots grow into the moisture-rich mucilage (Figure 3.7B), allowing the 10-cm diameter foliaceous cotyledons to expand before the radicle pushes through the fruit into the ground and secondary roots develop in the soil, and enhancing survival during short unpredictable droughts following germination.

Initiation of symbiotic relationships

Capture or attraction of symbionts often occurs in the seedling stage. Temperate legume seedlings fix nitrogen within 2 weeks of germination (Halvorson et al., 1991). Tropical *Shorea* seedlings had ectomycorrhizal infections within twenty days of germination (Alexander et al., 1992). Seedlings of many tree species show enhanced growth or survival within 1 year of inoculation with vesicular-arbuscular (VA) mycorrhizae (Janos, 1980b). R.A. Herrera (personal communication) found that reliance upon VA-endomycorrhizae at the seedling stage decreased from pioneer to climax species, with large seed reserves compensating for lack of infection at this early stage of development. For continued seedling growth, however, large seeds allow development of extensive root systems, which are needed to encounter mycorrhizal inocula, and substantial photosynthetic shoots, which provide the symbiont with carbon (Janos, 1977, 1980b). Janos (1980a,b) suggested that many tropical pioneer species are non-mycorrhizal or facultatively mycorrhizal, depending on soil nutrient levels, while more climax species, particularly those with large seeds, would be obligately mycorrhizal. We should establish at what stage roots of tropical tree seedlings are susceptible to or require mycorrhizal infection and rhizobial nodulation, and whether there are particular root architectures or root system sizes that enhance encounter rates.

Nectaries, domatia, or food bodies to attract mutualistic ants or mites are produced during the seedling stages in some species but not others. For example, nectaries on the leaf petioles of *Paquira aquatica* are active during the seed-reserve stage, but the food bodies of *Cecropia* spp. are generally not produced until the juvenile stage (N.C. Garwood, personal observation). Leaf domatia in *Annona* species generally develop in the autonomous or juvenile stages (Garwood, 1995).

Seed coats and fruit parts around stored reserves

Phanerocotylar and cryptocotylar seedlings are distinguished by whether the cotyledons emerge from the seed coat or not. Because the seed coat and any persistent fruit parts vary from extremely thin and weak to very thick and strong, they are unlikely to play only one functional role across species. While the emergence of thin, photosynthetic cotyledons from the seed coat needs no explanation, many storage–photosynthetic cotyledons, which are usually short-persistent, and some exclusively storage cotyledons also emerge or partially emerge from the envelopments. If short-persistent storage cotyledons metabolize and translocate reserves faster than those with long-persistent cotyledons, the higher respiratory demands of the former group may require greater oxygen availability. Thick or impermeable seed coats or endocarps, which would reduce gas exchange, would be disadvantageous in such species unless anaerobic metabolic pathways are utilized. This could be experimentally tested by covering phanerocotylar storage cotyledons with impermeable coats.

Thick envelopments, such as the heavy endocarps surrounding the edible endosperm in many palms, are usually interpreted as mechanical protective structures. Thin envelopments have received little attention. Do they offer protection by camouflaging the usually pale-colored cotyledonary reserves in the leaf litter, repelling predators chemically, or retarding moisture loss from the reserves? The importance of these functions could be tested by removing thin envelopments from around the reserves.

Defence

Defences against herbivores and pathogens may be chemical or structural and can be expected among all seedling parts. Although herbivory on seedlings has not been included in the Workshop, it should be mentioned at least briefly. Chemical defences are well known in seeds (Janzen, 1969) and can be expected to be retained in attached seeds, but their concentration in short- versus long-persistent reserves or exposed versus hidden reserves has not been compared. Dispersement of defensive chemicals from the seed into the seedling, or the breakdown and mobilization of toxins into nutrients, are also poorly known. In seeds of scatter-hoarded species, where the reserves themselves are the dispersal attractant, we might expect changes in the chemical composition or odours emitted from germinating seeds and developing seedlings that make them less attractive to predators compared to the ungerminated seed awaiting dispersal. Germinated seeds and seedlings of *Vouacapoua* are less attractive to caviomorph rodents than ungerminated seeds (Forget, 1990), but hypocotyls of *Virola* are preferred over the fresh seeds (Howe et al., 1985; Larson and Howe, 1987; Forget and Milleron, 1991). It is unknown whether such preferences are based on changes in nutritional value or secondary chemicals during development.

Structural defences around the seed reserves were discussed above. Physical defences such as spines and prickles tend to develop later, often not until the juvenile stage (N.C. Garwood, personal observation), whereas defensive mutualisms sometimes develop early (as noted above). Lignification of the hypocotyl and epicotyl, which decreases susceptibility to attack by pathogenic fungi, may also occur early in seedling development (Augspurger, 1983, 1984b; Augspurger and Kelly, 1984).

Supportive stems and seedling height

A major function of the hypocotyl and epicotyl is to carry the first photosynthetic organs to a position suitable for photosynthesis, as well as conduct water and nutrients to the leaves from the roots and transfer energy back to the roots. The height of the initial stem, and any extra height added by the petioles, will be of functional significance when conditions near the soil surface are unfavourable for photosynthesis or when seeds have been buried in the soil. Initial height depends upon seed mass, patterns of biomass allocation to stems, leaves and roots, and the degree of plasticity occurring in different environments. Seed size and initial height are correlated among and within species (e.g. Augspurger, 1984a and Howe and Richter, 1982, respectively). Unfortunately, potential height is often inferred from seed mass, rather than measured directly; but, for any seed mass, height will vary considerably among species, depending on the pattern of biomass allocation.

For any one seedling type, Rousteau (1986) envisioned a range of heights of species within that type, but expected average height to increase from the PEF type to the CHR type. In Panamanian species, initial heights of PEF type seedlings were typically less than that of other seedling types (Garwood, 1983; Kitajima, 1992a), but heights of PER type seedlings did not differ on average from other types with seed reserves (CHR, PHR and CER combined). These differences in initial height parallel differences in seed size among types (Ng, 1978; Miquel, 1987; Hladik and Miquel, 1990; Kitajima, 1992a). As the PER type seedlings do not have persistent reserves, the functional significance of initial height should be independent of the presence or absence of long-persistent reserves.

In temperate crop species, it has long been known that the ability of seedlings to emerge from buried seed is closely related to seed size and the length of the hypocotyl produced (Harper, 1977). In tropical species, we would also expect species that are typically buried to have taller stems, or greater phenotypic plasticity, than those that usually germinate on the surface. The extra height could be achieved either through additional seed biomass or differential allocation of biomass to height. Two groups of tropical tree species typically germinate from seeds buried in the soil: small-seeded pioneer species, which are buried after dispersal by factors such as rainfall; and larger-seeded species, which are dispersed and buried by scatter-hoarding rodents, sometimes to 8 cm deep (see references in Garwood, 1989). In tropical pioneer species, light quality or temperature usually limit germination to seeds from shallow depths (Vázquez-Yanes and Orozco Segovia, 1984), unlike most temperate crop species tested; therefore, large differences in initial height between species that are typically buried and those that typically germinate on the surface might not be detected. There seems to be no comparative data on height of species buried or not by scatter-hoarding rodents.

Litter is a frequently mentioned factor possibly favouring taller tropical seedlings (Ng, 1978; de Vogel, 1980; Foster, 1986). Aspects of the physical structure of litter which may impede emergence or establishment and favour particular seedling heights or morphologies include depth, degree of compaction, connection of parts by fungal hyphae, and shape, size and thickness of components (Facelli and Pickett, 1991). Litter also alters the microenvironment and releases beneficial and detrimental chemicals during decomposition (Facelli and Pickett, 1991). The amount of litter and its physical structure will be extremely heterogeneous in both time and space within a forest. In less seasonal forests, litter fall and decomposition are high throughout the year (Burghouts et al., 1992), but spatially heterogeneous; in seasonal forests, litter fall is often greatest toward the end of the dry season. Litter fall, particularly branches and trunks, is an important cause of mortality for seedlings and juveniles of many tropical tree species (Clark and Clark, 1989, 1991); but, in two species with initially tall seedlings (>11 cm), leaf litter fall alone caused little mortality in post-expansion seedlings compared to other causes (Denslow, 1980; Kiew, 1982).

If litter depth is an important factor limiting seedling establishment, we would expect species germinating when or where litter was deep to be taller. Although litter should be deeper at the beginning of the rainy season in Panama, when most species germinate, seedlings of species germinating early in the rainy season were not taller on average than those germinating later in the rainy season (Garwood, 1983). This very crude test does not rule out a relationship between litter depth and seedling height, as long-term persistence of slow-growing seedlings in the understorey depends on survival through the annual cycle of litter accumulation and decomposition. Spatial heterogeneity in litter depth may overwhelm effects of temporal variability. In Panama, about 16 per cent of the surface was bare ground in July, several months after the rainy season had begun and litter decomposition was well under way, another 17 per cent was covered by medium to deep litter (corresponding to ≥ 6 cm of dry intact leaves), and the remainder was covered by shallow litter (Molofsky and Augspurger, 1992). Changes in litter depth occurred rapidly over very short distances, but did not differ systematically between gaps and understorey. Within treefall gaps, short pioneer seedlings establish more frequently on the bare soil surrounding upturned roots than in litter-covered areas (Putz, 1983; Riera, 1985). Given that bare ground should be equally common in gaps and shaded understorey (Molofsky and Augspurger, 1992), are there species with short seedlings that primarily establish in these litter-free patches in the shaded understorey? Likely candidates might be found among the small-seeded understorey shrubs and trees, common in the Rubiaceae and Melastomataceae, whose seedling and juvenile stages are commonly encountered throughout the understorey. This group of species has been neglected in discussions of seed size and establishment requirements. D. Metcalfe (personal communication) is currently examining how and where seedlings of this group of species become established in the forests of Singapore.

The effects of litter depth on tropical tree establishment and growth has been studied experimentally (Guzmán-Grajales and Walker, 1991; Molofsky and Augspurger, 1992), apart from initial effects on germination, but these do not particularly address the relationship between morphological attributes of seedlings and success in particular depths. In small-seeded shade-intolerant species with PEF type seedlings, which require gaps to become established, *Luehea seemmanii* (seed mass, 2 mg; seedling height, 2 cm) had poor germination and emergence even in shallow litter; *Ochroma pyamidale* (6 mg; 4 cm) and *Cordia alliodora* (3 mg; 5 cm) germinated at all litter depths, but could not emerge above deeper litter; and *Ceiba pentandra* (45 mg; 10 cm) had reduced emergence only in the deepest litter (Molofsky and Augspurger, 1992). (Seed mass from Molofsky and Augspurger (1992); seedling heights are approximate maxima from well-formed seedlings in my herbarium collections, N.C. Garwood, unpublished data). The decreasing severity of litter on early establishment in these species corresponds to their increasing seed mass and initial heights. Of three species tested, overall emergence and survival were generally higher in gaps than understorey at each litter depth. Thus, in gap conditions, taller species had a clear advantage in deeper litter. We do not know the degree of plasticity within these species, or whether shade-induced

101

elongation of the hypocotyl (etiolation) occurs and primarily reduces the photosynthetic area of the cotyledon or the development of the root system. For two large-seeded species, there was no evidence that having tall seedlings enhanced establishment in deep litter. In *Gustavia superba* (seed mass = 6,900 mg, seedling height = 16 cm; data sources as above), litter depth in the shade treatment had no effect on emergence, but emergence increased with litter depth in sun treatments, probably by preventing seed dissication (Molofsky and Augspurger, 1992). In *Aspidospermum cruenta* (684 mg, 10 cm), emergence was higher on bare soil than in litter and higher in shade than sun at each litter depth (Molofsky and Augspurger, 1992). Whether these species reallocate biomass not used in stem production to increased root or leaf development in shallow litter was not determined.

If a primary effect of litter is impeding penetration of roots into the soil (Ng, 1978), rather than preventing the first photosynthetic organs from reaching sunlight, we would not expect successful establishment to be explained by seedling height and litter depth. Rather, the position of the seed above or below the litter (which depends on the phenology of litterfall and seed dispersal), the ability of the developing shoot to push aside the litter, and the architecture of the roots would determine success.

Other conditions near the soil surface impeding photosynthesis include neighboring seedlings limiting the amount of light received by the seedling in either tree-fall gaps or shaded understorey; high temperatures near the soil surface, especially on bare soil in gap environments, limiting water availability or the activity of photosynthetic enzymes; and flood waters covering the leaves or photosynthetic cotyledons. The possibility that such factors selected for large seeds in tropical species was reviewed by Foster (1986). There is still little experimental evidence to test these predictions, but natural history observations suggest that they should be pursued. For example, in large-seeded littoral or swamp species such as *Carapa guianensis, Xylocarpus (= Carapa) moluccensis* (Meliaceae), and *Heretiera fomes* (Sterculiaceae), tall stems develop rapidly and may lift the first leaves above water level (Troup, 1921; de Vogel, 1980, McHargue and Hartshorn, 1983). (If, as argued, this behaviour allows photosynthesis to begin before the flood waters recede, physiological mechanisms supplying oxygen to the submerged roots and seed storage reserves should be studied.) In the mangrove members of the Rhizophoraceae, a tall stem is developed before the seedling is shed from the parent (de Vogel, 1980).

Special adaptations

Seedlings of tropical savannah trees are subject to almost yearly fires during the long dry seasons. In both Africa and America, various special adaptations have evolved in some species to bury the plumule at a safe distance in the soil but leave the cotyledons above ground (Rizzini, 1965; Burtt, 1972; Jackson,

1974). Frequently, the plumule is pushed downward by elongating, sometimes fused, cotyledon petioles. In the rain forest as well as savannah, the apical meristem of many palm seedlings is also buried, either pushed downward by the cotyledonary petiole or growing directly down into the soil (Tomlinson, 1990). No morphological adaptations for plumule burying have been reported in rain forest tree seedlings of dicots, although it would allow young seedlings to resprout from buried cotyledonary buds and recover after heavy herbivory or physical damage from falling debris, two known causes of high seedling mortality in tropical tree seedlings (e.g. de Steven and Putz, 1984; Sork, 1987; Schupp, 1988; Clark and Clark, 1989, 1991; Howe, 1990; Forget and Milleron, 1991). Seed burial by scatter-hoarding rodents (Smythe, 1978; Hopkins and Graham, 1983; Sork, 1985, 1987; Hallwachs, 1986; Forget, 1991) may protect the plumule or allow resprouting in a similar manner.

Growth, biomass allocation and plasticity

The growth of tropical tree seedlings in particular environments, and their ability to adapt to changes in that environment, depends on the complex inter-action of morphological and physiological attributes of each species. Gross morphological traits include leaf area, thickness and number; total biomass al-location to roots, shoots and leaves; stem width, height and density; and the spatial arrangements of leaves and branches. These are often expressed as root–shoot ratios, specific leaf weight, leaf area ratio or other derived parame-ters. Physiological traits include photosynthetic rate, respiration rate, light compensation points, stomatal conductance, and water use efficiency. Leaf anatomical traits, such as number of stomata and thickness of the spongy mesophyll, and nutrient composition of roots, stems and leaves, are also im-portant determinants of growth. (For general reviews of tropical ecophysiol-ogy, see Bazzaz and Pickett, 1980; Medina et al., 1984; Bazzaz, 1991, as well as Whitmore, 1996, and Press et al., 1996; for a review of tropical tree archi-tecture, see Oldeman and van Dijk, 1991.)

Growth rates of tropical seedlings and saplings, variously measured as height increments, biomass accumulation, relative growth rates or unit leaf rates, have been measured in field or laboratory conditions for quite a few species (e.g. Coombe, 1960; Coombe and Hadfield, 1962; Okali, 1971, 1972; Sasaki and Mori, 1981; Fetcher et al., 1983, 1987; Whitmore and Bowen, 1983; Whitmore and Gong, 1983; Augspurger, 1984a; Brokaw, 1985, 1987; Oberbauer and Donnelly, 1986; Bongers et al., 1988; Popma and Bongers, 1988, 1991; Kitajima and Augspurger, 1989; Turner, 1990a,b; Brown and Whitmore, 1992; Osunkoya et al., 1993). Most studies also measured at least some morphological components of growth; only a few measured physiologi-cal ones (Fetcher et al., 1983, 1987; Oberbauer and Donnelly, 1986; Kitajima and Augspurger, 1989). Other studies have measured physiological traits but not growth (e.g. Langenheim et al., 1984; Oberbauer and Strain, 1986; Hogan, 1988; Ramos and Grace, 1990; Riddoch et al., 1991; see also earlier reviews in Medina et al., 1984). Most physiological studies of tropical tree species have been of seedling or saplings, not adults, because the canopy has been inaccessible until very recently (Parker et al., 1992).

These studies have shown that there is a wide range of growth rates among tropical tree seedlings, with pioneer species growing faster in large gap environments than most climax species, as expected. All species had no or low growth in the shaded understorey and grew faster at higher light intensities, although maximum growth rates of some climax species did not occur in the largest gap environments. All species showed some degree of plasticity in morphological and physiological traits in response to sun or shade environments, but species varied greatly in the amplitude and rate of change of particular traits. While species displayed similar directional shifts in most traits, such as increases in root–shoot ratios or specific leaf weights in high light environments, the magnitude of these shifts varied greatly among traits and among species. Growth and biomass allocation is further discussed by Whitmore (1996).

At present, we understand only poorly how species-specific differences in these traits, including the degree of plasticity, determine growth in particular environments, and the success of individuals or species. This is an active area of research, addressed by many papers in this Workshop. The much-studied sun–shade contrast is extended to include differences in soil nutrient levels (Gunatilleke et al., 1996; Press et al., 1996), soil nutrient and moisture levels (Burslem, 1996), and effects of seed size (Boot, 1996). Press et al. (1996) also aim to integrate physiological and morphological determinants of plant growth to understand niche differentiation within the dipterocarps.

It is difficult to disentangle the relative importance of different seedling traits on growth, and when and how each trait acts. For example, seed size was highly correlated with many early seedling traits, including non-cotyledon biomass and cotyledon thickness in expanded seedlings (Kitajima, 1992a), and height of several month-old seedlings in gap and understorey environments and of year-old seedlings in understorey environments, where growth is negligible (Augspurger, 1984a; Osunkoya et al., 1993; Boot, 1996). Seed size was not correlated with relative growth rates or survival measured during the first four to sixteen months in gap or understorey conditions (Augspurger, 1984a; Osunkoya et al., 1993; Boot, 1996), but was correlated with survival in total darkness (Boot, 1996); and was negatively correlated to the degree of plasticity, measured as the ratio of biomass in gap to understorey environments (Osunkoya et al., 1993). Initial seedling morphology is not independent of seed size: seed mass of species with photosynthetic cotyledons was smaller than that of species with storage or storage–photosynthetic cotyledons (Kitajima, 1992a). As discussed earlier (Table 3.2), seedlings with PEF type seedlings had smaller seeds than species with PER or other (CHR + PHR + CER) seedling types when both pioneer and climax species were analysed; however, within the more abundant climax species, species with PEF types did not have smaller seeds than those with PER types, but they were smaller than the combined other types (CHR + PHR + CER). As different initial seedling morphologies reflect considerable differences in early biomass allocation patterns, they may contribute substantially to later differences in growth beyond that contributed by initial differences in the amount of reserves in the seed.

Nearly all the studies discussed above concern growth of autonomous-stage seedlings or juvenile plants, whereas seedlings in the expansion or seed-reserve stage, and the effects of initial seedling morphology, have rarely been studied. Kitajima, (1992a) divided early seedling growth of about sixty species into three post-germination stages, ending with fully expanded cotyledons, fully expanded first leaves, and the abscission of the cotyledons (or ten weeks, whichever came first). In sun and shade, relative growth rates (RGR), cotyledon-specific area (CSA), and leaf plus cotyledon area ratio (LAR) were greater in seedlings with photosynthetic cotyledons than in seedlings with photosynthetic–storage or solely storage cotyledons for each early developmental stage in which they were compared. (Species with storage cotyledons were excluded from comparisons of CSA at all stages and LAR at the first stage.) Cotyledons expanded to their full size at the same rate, whether they were photosynthetic or storage. Although seedlings with storage or storage–photosynthetic cotyledons expanded their first leaf before those with photosynthetic cotyledons, this did not compensate, in terms of relative growth rate, for the early photosynthetic contribution from the cotyledons. When species with storage–photosynthetic cotyledons differed from those with storage cotyledons, they were usually intermediate between the other two groups. Lastly, the difference in growth rate, CSA and LAR between sun and shade, a measure of the plasticity of each response, was greater for species with photosynthetic cotyledons than those with storage or storage–photosynthetic cotyledons.

In a subsample of forty-eight species, Kitajima (1992a) also found that these three cotyledon functional groups were well-separated by canonical analysis for multiple seed and seedling traits, including seed mass and seedling growth characteristics, indicating that the three groups differ by a number of highly correlated, probably co-evolved characters. In a similar analysis, it was found that regeneration guilds, based on sapling spatial distribution and an index of heliophily (Hubbell and Foster, 1986) were poorly separated using the same seed and seedling traits, but well-separated using other sapling growth and recruitment characteristics (Welden et al., 1991). In the regeneration guild analysis, there was a high correlation across species between the first canonical variable using seedling traits and the first canonical variable using sapling traits, as well as between pairs of the second and third variables. This suggests that early seedling growth and morphological traits are closely related to later sapling performance in gaps and understorey, but will not be easily explained or predicted by a few selected traits.

We need to determine how these differences in growth rates, occurring in the expansion and seed-reserves stages, and the associated morphological and physiological traits, determine changes in abundance at later seedling, sapling and adult stages as reported by Hladik and Mitja (1996). We should also compare the early growth and various traits of vegetative propagules, as reported by Sagers (1996) for a number of shrubs, with their respective seedlings to understand what advantages accrue to vegetative propagation versus reproduction by seeds.

The timing of biomass allocation during the seedling expansion stage may also be indicative of later seedling or sapling traits, but has not been studied. In many species with hypogeal storage cotyledons, the tap root is often described as developing substantially before the shoot is initiated (e.g. Figure 3.1A) and remaining relatively large compared to the shoot at the end of the expansion stage (Burtt, 1972; De Vogel, 1980; N.C. Garwood, personal observation). In contrast, in many species with epigeal photosynthetic or storage-photosynthetic cotyledons, the tap root is often described as poorly developed when the shoot is initiated and relatively small compared to the shoot (e.g Figure 3.7A). The exception to the latter pattern occurs in species with photosynthetic cotyledons that are initially haustorial for absorbing the abundant endosperm; here, the tap root is often substantial and well-developed before the hypocotyl completes development and the cotyledons emerge (e.g. Figure 3.1D).

Root–shoot ratios at the end of the expansion stage may also be indicative of habitat specialization. Many savannah trees develop deep tap roots before shoots grow extensively (Rizzini, 1965; Jackson, 1974), presumably an adaptation to both low rainfall and frequent fires. Therefore, high root–shoot ratios in forest tree seedlings at the expansion stage might indicate they are better able to establish in drier habitats, such as ridge-tops or rapidly drained sandy soil, or in drier forest types. In growth experiments with tropical tree seedlings at later stages, emphasis has been on the shift to higher root–shoot ratios in large gap versus understorey conditions which occurs in most species (Popma and Bongers, 1988), rather than on initial root–shoot ratios at the expansion stage or the varying degrees of plasticity for this trait shown among species. Quantifying these root–shoot changes during initial seedling expansion and degree of plasiticity at later stages may provide other characters to differentiate the early morphologies of tropical tree seedlings in an ecologically meaningful way.

More complex architectural analyses of tropical saplings include not only biomass allocation between parts, but the spatial distribution of leaves and stems as means of optimizing growth in understorey or sunny environments and mechanical properties of supporting stems (King, 1990, 1991; Kohyama, 1987, 1991; Kohyama and Hotta, 1990). There are architectural trade-offs between maximizing height growth to reach high light levels in the canopy and maximizing lateral growth to survive in the understorey by intercepting much of the available light (see further discussion by Whitmore, 1996). We do not know when during seedling development these trade-offs first occur. How much of the variation among species in initial seedling size and morphology or the number, shape and arrangement of leaves is explained by an early commitment to one architectural path or the other? In tropical trees with compound leaves, the first seedling leaves are compound in some species but simple in others. Are these phylogenetic traits or ecological traits? For many species with initially simple leaves, such as species of *Guarea* or *Cupania*, there is a progressive increase in size of the simple leaves produced, then a sudden switch to compound leaves. What factors trigger the switch?

Lastly, we need to determine the degree of plasticity in seedling traits at early compared to later developmental stages within species, as well as the amount of plasticity in early seedling traits among species with different seedling functional morphologies. For example, how plastic are photosynthetic cotyledons compared to true leaves, in terms of the ability to vary area, thickness, or other physiological traits during expansion in response to environmental conditions present during germination? Within some species, sun or shade leaves are produced depending on environmental conditions during leaf expansion (see Press et al., 1996; Table 2.1). In species with leafy cotyledons, are sun or shade morphs produced in similar conditions or is the apparent degree of plasticity of cotyledons a simple consequence of increased biomass allocation to stems in low light (etiolation)? Are the first leaves produced less plastic than leaves produced later on the same plant? Are the first leaves or cotyledons less able to acclimate to changing environmental conditions than leaves produced at later stages of development? For species with storage or storage–photosynthetic cotyledons, are leaves of species which produce rapidly maturing shoots less plastic than leaves of species which produce slowly maturing shoots? Is the degree of plasticity at the youngest seedling stages correlated with plasticity of older juveniles or adults? Species that are less plastic morphologically at the seedling stage must be more plastic physiologically or be restricted to fewer suitable environments as seedlings.

CONCLUDING REMARKS

Further understanding of the functional significance of the diverse morphologies of tropical tree seedlings will require studies utilizing a variety of approaches. Intensive studies on a few species are needed that integrate the changing biochemical, physiological and structural attributes of developing seedlings and saplings with environmental conditions in which establishment and growth occur. Experimental field studies are needed to test predictions of the functional significance of particular seedling morphologies, sizes, or developmental patterns: species will have to be chosen carefully to control for factors not being investigated. For example, when comparing seedling morphologies, species could be chosen from those with similar seed sizes, preferably from the same higher taxonomic group (e.g. genera or families); alternatively, pairs of species in two higher taxa could be matched across a range of seed sizes. Broad surveys are still needed to identify the establishment conditions of most species and test the generality of conclusions drawn from more intensive studies of a limited number of species. Whether the diversity of functional morphologies among tropical tree seedlings contributes to the high species diversity of tropical forests through morphological specializations relating to establishment requirements is still not known.

ACKNOWLEDGEMENTS

This review is an offshoot of the Seedling Flora Project for Barro Colorado Island (BCI), Panama, which has been generously supported by the NSF (BSR-8517395), the NERC (GR3–6951), the Smithsonian Tropical Research Institute (STRI), and the Natural History Museum (NHM). I am very grateful for this support, for permission from INRENARE to work in Panama, and for the assistance of many people from BCI, STRI, NHM and the Field Museum who have helped the Project in various ways but are too numerous to mention here individually. For this review, I especially thank M. Tebbs for illustrating the seedlings; M. Beasley and J. Upton for obtaining much-needed references; J. Dalling and K. Kitajima for comments on the manuscript; K. Kitajima for thoroughly investigating cotyledon functional morphology and providing me with a copy of her thesis; R. Dempsey for proof-reading the manuscript, and M.D. Swaine and UNESCO for inviting me to participate in the Seedling Workshop held in Aberdeen.

REFERENCES

Aiyar, T.V.V. (1932). The Sholas of the Palghat Division, A study of the ecology and silviculture of the tropical rain-forests of Western Ghats. Parts I–II. *Indian Forester*, **58**, 414–32, 473–86.

Alexander, I., Ahmad, N. and Lee, S.S. (1992). The role of mycorrhizas in the regeneration of some Malyasian forest trees. *Philosophical Transactions of the Royal Society of London*, Series B, **335**, 379–88.

del Amo, S. (1979). Clave para plántulas y estados juveniles de especies primarias de una selva alta perennifolia en Veracruz, México. *Biotica*, **4**, 59–108.

Ampofo, S.T., Moore, K.G. and Lovell, P.H. (1976a). Cotyledon photosynthesis during seedling development in *Acer*. *New Phytologist*, **76**, 41–52.

Ampofo, S.T., Moore, K.G. and Lovell, P.H. (1976b). The role of the cotyledons in four *Acer* species and in *Fagus sylvatica* during early seedling development. *New Phytologist*, **76**, 31–9.

Augspurger, C.K. (1983). Seed dispersal of the tropical tree, *Platypodium elegans* and the escape of its seedlings from fungal pathogens. *Journal of Ecology*, **71**, 759–71.

Augspurger, C.K. (1984a). Light requirements of neotropical tree seedlings: a comparative study of growth and survival. *Journal of Ecology*, **72**, 777–95.

Augspurger, C.K. (1984b). Seedling survival of tropical tree species: interactions of dispersal distance, light-gaps and pathogens. *Ecology*, **65**, 1705–12.

Augspurger, C.K. and Kelly, C.K. (1984). Pathogen mortality of tropical tree seedlings: experimental studies of the effects of dispersal distance, seedling density and light conditions. *Oecologia* (Berlin), **61**, 211–17.

Barclay, A.S. and Earle, F.R. (1974). Chemical analyses of seeds. III. Oil and protein content of 1253 species. *Economic Botany*, **28**, 178–236.

Barrera Torres, E. (1985–1986). Identificación de plántulas de algunas especies arbóreas del bosque de niebla. *Perez-Arbelaezia*, **1–2**, 39–95; 165–209.

Bazzaz, F.A. (1991). Regeneration of tropical forests: physiological responses of pioneer and secondary species. In Gómez-Pompa, A., Whitmore, T.C. and Hadley, M. (eds.) *Rain Forest Regeneration and Management*, pp. 91–118. UNESCO/Parthenon, Paris/Carnforth.

Bazzaz, F.A. and Pickett, S.T.A. (1980). Physiological ecology of tropical succession: a comparative review. *Annual Review of Ecology and Systematics*, **11**, 287–310.

Becker, P. and Castillo, A. (1990). Root architecture of shrubs and saplings in the understorey of a tropical moist forest in lowland Panama. *Biotropica*, **22**, 242–9.

Bokdam, J. (1977). Seedling morphology of some African Sapotaceae and its taxonomical significance. *Mededelingen Landbouwhogeschool Wageningen*, **77**, 1–84.

Bongers, F., Popma, J. and Iriarte-Vivar, S. (1988). Response of *Cordia megalantha* Blake seedlings to gap environments in tropical rain forest. *Functional Ecology*, **2**, 379–90.

Boot, R.G.A. (1996). The significance of seedling size and growth rate of tropical rain forest tree seedlings for regeneration in canopy openings. In Swaine, M.D. (ed.) *Ecology of Tropical Forest Tree Seedlings*, pp. 267–83. UNESCO/Parthenon, Paris/Carnforth.

Brokaw, N.V.L. (1985). Gap-phase regeneration in a tropical forest. *Ecology*, **66**, 682–7.

Brokaw, N.V.L. (1987). Gap-phase regeneration of three pioneer tree species in a tropical forest. *Journal of Ecology*, **75**, 9–19.

Brown, N.D. and Whitmore, T.C. (1992). Do dipterocarp seedlings really partition tropical rain forest gaps? *Philosophical Transactions of the Royal Society of London*, Series B, **335**, 369–78.

Burger Hzn., D. (1972). *Seedlings of Some Tropical Trees and Shrubs, Mainly of South East Asia*. Centre for Agricultural Publishing and Documentation (PUDOC): Wageningen.

Burghouts, T., Ernsting, G., Korthals, G. and De Vries, T. (1992). Litterfall, leaf litter decomposition and litter invertebrates in primary and selectively logged dipterocarp forest in Sabah, Malaysia. *Philosophical Transactions of the Royal Society of London*, Series B, **335**, 407–16.

Burslem, D.F.R.P. (1996). Differential responses to nutrients, shade and drought among tree seedlings of lowland tropical forest in Singapore. In Swaine, M.D. (ed.) *Ecology of Tropical Forest Tree Seedlings*, pp. 211–43. UNESCO/Parthenon, Paris /Carnforth.

Burtt, B.L. (1972). Plumular protection and some related aspects of seedling behaviour. *Transactions of the Botanical Society, Edinburgh*, **41**, 393–400.

Chase, M.W., Soltis, D.E., Olmstead, R.G., Morgan, D., Les, D.H., Mishler, B.D., Duvall, M.R., Price, R.A., Hills, H.G., Qiu, Yin-L., Kron, K.A., Rettig, J.H., Conti, E., Palmer, J.D., Manhart, J.R., Sytsma, K.J., Michaels, H.J., Kress, W.J., Karol, K.G., Clark, W.D., Hedrén, M., Gaut, B.S., Jansen, R.K., Kim, Ki-J., Wimpee, C.F., Smith, J.F., Furnier, G.R., Strauss, S.H., Xiang, Q., Plunkett, G.M., Soltis, P.S., Swensen, S.M., Williams, S.E., Gadek, P.A., Quinn, C.J., Eguiarte, L.E., Goldenberg, E., Learn, G.H., Jr., Graham, S.W., Barrett, S.C.H., Dayanandan, S. and Albert, V.A. (1993). Phylogenetics of seed plants: an analysis of nucleotide sequences from the plastid gene rbcL. *Annals of the Missouri Botanical Garden*, **80**, 528–80.

Clark, D.B. and Clark, D.A. (1989). The role of physical damage in the seedling mortality regime of a neotropical forest. *Oikos*, **55**, 225–30.

Clark, D.B. and Clark, D.A. (1991). The impact of physical damage on canopy tree regeneration in tropical rain forest. *Journal of Ecology*, **79**, 447–58.

Coombe, D.E. (1960). An analaysis of the growth of *Trema guineensis*. *Journal of Ecology*, **48**, 219–31.

Coombe, D.E. and Hadfield, W. (1962). An analysis of the growth *Musanga cecropioides*. *Journal of Ecology*, **50**, 221–34.

Coutinho, L.M. and Struffaldi, Y. (1971). Observações sôbre a germinação das sementes e o crescimento das plântulas de uma leguminosa da mata amazônica de igapó (*Parkia auriculata* Spruce Mss.). *Phyton*, **28**, 149–59.

Croat, T.B. (1978). *Flora of Barro Colorado Island*. Stanford University Press, Stanford.

Denslow, J.S. (1980). Notes on the seedling ecology of a large-seeded species of Bombacaceae. *Biotropica*, **12**, 220–2.

de Steven, D. and Putz, F.E. (1984). Impact of mammals on early recruitment of a tropical canopy tree, *Dipteryx panamensis*, in Panama. *Oikos*, **43**, 207–16.

Duke, J.A. (1965). Keys for the identification of seedlings of some prominent woody species in eight forest types in Puerto Rico. *Annals of the Missouri Botanical Garden*, **52**, 314–50.

Duke, J.A. (1969). On tropical tree seedlings. I. Seeds, seedlings, systems and systematics. *Annals of the Missouri Botanical Garden*, **56**, 125–61.

Duke, J.A. (1970). Post irradiation woody seedlings. In Odum, H. T. (ed.) *A Tropical Rain Forest*, pp. D189–D192. US Atomic Energy Commission, Oak Ridge.

Duke, J.A. and Polhill, R.M. (1981). Seedlings of Leguminosae. In Polhill, R.M. and Raven, R.M. (eds.) Proceedings of the International Legume Conference, Kew, 24–29 July, 1978, Vol. 2: *Advances in Legume Systematics*, Part 2, pp. 941–9. Royal Botanic Garden, Kew.

Everitt, B.S. (1977). *The Analysis of Contingency Tables*. Chapman and Hall, London.

Facelli, J.M. and Pickett, S.T.A. (1991). Plant litter: its dynamics and effects on plant community structure. *Botanical Review*, **57**, 1–32.

Farrant, J.M., Berjak, P. and Pammenter, N.W. (1987). Ecological significance of three-phase production of roots during germination and establishment of the recalcitrant propagules of *Avicennia marina*. *South African Journal of Science*, **83**, 236–7.

Fenner, M. (1986). A bioassay to determine the limiting minerals for seeds from nutrient-deprived *Senecio vulgaris* plants. *Journal of Ecology*, **74**, 497–505.

Fenner, M. (1987). Seedlings. *New Phytologist*, **106** (Supplement), 35–47.

Fetcher, N., Strain, B.R. and Oberbauer, S.F. (1983). Effects of light regime on the growth, leaf morphology and water relations of seedlings of two species of tropical tree. *Oecologia* (Berlin), **58**, 314–19.

Fetcher, N., Oberbauer, S.F., Rojas, G. and Strain, B.R. (1987). Efectos del regimen de luz sobre la fotosíntesis y el crecimiento en plántulas de arboles de un bosque lluvioso tropical de Costa Rica. *Revista de Biología Tropical* (San José), **35** (Suplemento 1), 97–110.

Flores, E.M. (1992). Fruta dorada – Wild nutmeg. *Arboles y semillas del Neotropico – Trees and Seeds from the Neotropics*, **1**, 45–64.

Flores, E.M. and Rivera, D.I. (1989). Criptocotilia en algunas dicotiledoneas tropicales. *Brenesia*, **32**, 19–26.

Forget, P.-M. (1990). Seed-dispersal of *Vouacapoua americana* (Caesalpiniaceae) by caviomorph rodents in French Guiana. *Journal of Tropical Ecology*, **6**, 459–68.

Forget, P.-M. (1991). Comparative recruitment patterns of two non-pioneer canopy tree species in French Guiana. *Oecologia* (Berlin), **85**, 434–9.

Forget, P.-M. and Milleron, T. (1991). Evidence for secondary seed dispersal by rodents in Panama. *Oecologia* (Berlin), **87**, 596–9.

Foster, S.A. (1986). On the adaptive value of large seeds for tropical moist forest trees: a review and synthesis. *Botanical Review*, **52**, 260–99.

Foster, S.A. and Janson, C.H. (1985). The relationship between seed size and establishment conditions in tropical woody plants. *Ecology*, **66**, 773–80.

Garwood, N.C. (1979). *Seed Germination in a Seasonal Tropical Forest in Panama*. Ph.D. thesis. University of Chicago.

Garwood, N.C. (1983). Seed germination in a seasonal tropical forest in Panama: a community study. *Ecological Monographs*, **53**, 159–81.

Garwood, N.C. (1985). The role of mucilage in the germination of cuipo, *Cavanillesia platanifolia* (H. & B.) H.B.K. (Bombacaceae), a tropical tree. *American Journal of Botany*, **72**, 895–905.

Garwood, N.C. (1986). Constraints on the timing of seed germination in a tropical forest. In Estrada, A. and Fleming, T.H. (eds.) *Frugivores and Seed Dispersal*, pp. 347–55. W. Junk Publishers, Dordrecht.

Garwood, N.C. (1989). Tropical soil seed banks: a review. In Leck, M.A., Parker, V.T. and Simpson, R.L. (eds.) *Ecology of Soil Seed Banks*, pp. 149–209. Academic Press, San Diego.

Garwood, N.C. (1994). Morphology and ecology of seedlings, fruit and seeds of Panama: Bixaceae and Cochlospermaceae. *Bulletin of the Natural History Museum, London (Botany)*, **24**, 161–71 .

Garwood, N.C. (1995). Studies in Annonaceae. XX. Morphology of seedlings, seeds and fruits of selected Panamanian species. *Botanische Jahrbücher für Systematik, Pflanzengeschichte und Pflazengeographie*, **117**, 1–152

Gómez-Pompa, A. and Vázquez-Yanes, C. (1974). Studies of the secondary succession of tropical lowlands: the life cycle of secondary species. In *Proceedings of the First International Congress of Ecology, The Hague, The Netherlands*, pp. 336–42.

Grubb, P.J. (1977). The maintenance of species-richness in plant communities: the importance of the regeneration niche. *Biological Review*, **52**, 107–45.

Gunatilleke, C.V.S., Perera, G.A.D., Ashton, P.M.S., Ashton, P.S. and Gunatilleke, I.A.U.N. (1996). Seedling growth of *Shorea* section *Doona* (Dipterocarpaceae) in soils from topographically different sites of sinharaja rain forest in Sri Lanka. In Swaine, M.D. (ed.) *Ecology of Tropical Forest Tree Seedlings*, pp. 245–65. UNESCO/Parthenon, Paris /Carnforth.

Guzmán-Grajales, S.M. and Walker, L.R. (1991). Differential seedling response to litter after hurricane Hugo in the Luquillo Experimental Forest, Puerto Rico. *Biotropica*, **23**, 407–13.

Hallé, N. (1962). Monographie des Hippocrateacées d'Afrique occidentale. *Mémoires de l'Institut Français d'Afrique Noire*, **64**, 1–215.

Hallwachs, W. (1986). Agoutis (*Dasyprocta punctata*): the inheritors of guapinol (*Hymenaea courbaril*: Leguminosae). In Estrada, A. and Fleming, T.H. (eds.) *Frugivores and Seed Dispersal*, pp. 285–304. W. Junk, Dordrecht.

Halvorson, J.J., Black, R.A., Smith, J.L. and Franz, E.H. (1991). Nitrogenase activity, growth and carbon and nitrogen allocation in wintergreen and deciduous lupin seedlings. *Functional Ecology*, **5**, 554–61.

Harper, J.L. (1977). *Population Biology of Plants*. Academic Press, London.

Harvey, P.H. and Pagel, M.D. (1991). *The Comparative Method in Evolutionary Biology*. Oxford University Press, New York.

Hladik, A. and Mitja, D. (1996). Seedlings, saplings and tree temperaments: potential for agroforestry in the African rain forest. In Swaine, M.D. (ed.) *Ecology of Tropical Forest Tree Seedlings*, pp. 173–91. UNESCO/Parthenon, Paris /Carnforth.

Hladik, A. and Miquel, S. (1990). Seedling types and plant establishment in an African rain forest. In Bawa, K.S. and Hadley, M. (eds.) *Reproductive Ecology of Tropical Forest Plants*, pp. 261–82. UNESCO/Parthenon, Paris /Carnforth.

Hogan, K.P. (1988). Photosynthesis in two neotropical palm species. *Functional Ecology*, **2**, 371–7.

Hopkins, M.S. and Graham, A.W. (1983). The species composition of soil seed banks beneath lowland tropical rainforests in North Queensland, Australia. *Biotropica*, **15**, 90–9.

Howe, H.F. (1990). Survival and growth of juvenile *Virola surinamensis* in Panama: effects of herbivory and canopy closure. *Journal of Tropical Ecology*, **6**, 259–80.

Howe, H.F. and Richter, W.M. (1982). Effects of seed size on seedling size in *Virola surinamensis*: a within and between tree analysis. *Oecologia* (Berlin), **53**, 347–52.

Howe, H.F., Schupp, E.W. and Westley, L.C. (1985). Early consequences of seed dispersal for a neotropical tree (*Virola surinamensis*). *Ecology*, **66**, 781–91.

Hubbell, S.P. and Foster, R.B. (1986). Canopy gaps and the dynamics of a neotropical forest. In Crawley, M.J. (ed.) *Plant Ecology*, pp. 77–96. Blackwell, Oxford.

Jackson, G. (1974). Cryptogeal germination and other seedling adaptations to the burning of savanas: the origin of the pyrophytic habit. *New Phytologist*, **73**, 771–80.

Janos, D.P. (1977). Vesicular-arbuscular mycorrhizae effect the growth of *Bactris gasipaes* HBK. *Principes*, **21**, 12–18.

Janos, D.P. (1980a). Mycorrhizae influence tropical succession. *Biotropica*, **12** (Supplement), 56–64.

Janos, D.P. (1980b). Vesicular-arbuscular mycorrhizae affect lowland tropical rain forest plant growth. *Ecology*, **61**, 151–62.

Janzen, D.H. (1969). Seed density versus seed size, number, toxicity and dispersal. *Evolution*, **23**, 1–27.

Jeník, J. (1978). Roots and root systems in tropical trees: morphologic and ecologic aspects. In Tomlinson, P.B. and Zimmermann, M.H. (eds.) *Tropical Trees as Living Systems*, pp. 323–49. Cambridge University Press, Cambridge.

Kelly, C.K. and Purvis, A. (1993). Seed size and establishment conditions in tropical trees: on the use of taxonomic relatedness in determining ecological patterns. *Oecologia* (Berlin), **94**, 356–60.

Kiew, R. (1982). Germination and seedling survival in kemenyan, *Styrax benzoin*. *Malaysian Forester*, **45**, 69–80.

King, D.A. (1990). Allometry of saplings and understorey trees of a Panamanian forest. *Functional Ecology*, **4**, 27–32.

King, D.A. (1991). Correlations between biomass allocation, relative growth rate and light environment in tropical forest saplings. *Functional Ecology*, **5**, 485–92.

Kitajima, K. (1992a). *The Importance of Cotyledon Functional Morphology and Patterns of Seed Reserve Utilization for the Physiological Ecology of Neotropical Tree Seedlings*. Ph.D. thesis, University of Illinois, Urbana-Champaign.

Kitajima, K. (1992b). Relationship between photosynthesis and thickness of cotyledons for tropical tree species. *Functional Ecology*, **6**, 582–9.

Kitajima, K. (1996). Cotyledon functional morphology and patterns of seed reserve utilization by neotropical tree seedlings. In Swaine, M.D. (ed.) *Ecology of Tropical Forest Tree Seedlings*, pp. 193–210. UNESCO/Parthenon, Paris /Carnforth.

Kitajima, K. and Augspurger, C.K. (1989). Seed and seedling ecology of a monocarpic tropical tree, *Tachigalia versicolor*. *Ecology*, **70**, 1102–14.

Kohyama, T. (1987). Significance of architecture and allometry in saplings. *Functional Ecology*, **1**, 399–404.

Kohyama, T. (1991). A functional model describing sapling growth under a tropical forest canopy. *Functional Ecology*, **5**, 83–90.

Kohyama, T. and Hotta, M. (1990). Significance of allometry in tropical saplings. *Functional Ecology*, **4**, 515–21.

Lack, A.J. (1991). Dead logs as a substrate for rain forest trees in Dominica. *Journal of Tropical Ecology*, **7**, 401–5.

Ladiges, P.Y. and Humphries, C.J. (1983). A cladistic study of *Arillastrum*, *Angophora* and *Eucalyptus* (Myrtaceae). *Botanical Journal of the Linnean Society*, **87**, 105–34.

Ladiges, P.Y., Humphries, C.J. and Brooker, M.I.H. (1983). Cladistic relationships and biogeographic patterns in the peppermint group of *Eucalyptus* (Informal subseries *Amygdalininae*, subgenus *Monocalyptus*) and the description of a new species, *E. willisii*. *Australian Journal of Botany*, **31**, 565–84.

113

Langenheim, J.H., Osmond, C.B., Brooks, A. and Ferrar, P.J. (1984). Photosynthetic responses to light in selected Amazonian and Australian rainforest tree species. *Oecologia* (Berlin), **63**, 215–24.

Larson, D. and Howe, H.F. (1987). Dispersal and destruction of *Virola surinamensis* seeds by agoutis: appearance and reality. *Journal of Mammalogy*, **68**, 859–60.

Léonard, J. (1957). Genera des Cynometreae des Amherstieae africaines. (Leguminosae Caesalpinioideae) Essai de blastogénie appliquée à la systématique. *Mémoires de l'Académie Royale de Belgique, Classe des Sciences* (8°, Sér. II), **30**, 1–312.

Levin, D.A. (1974). The oil content of seeds: an ecological perspective. *American Naturalist*, **108**, 193–206.

Lieberman D.D. (1996). Demography of tropical tree seedlings: a review. In Swaine, M.D. (ed.) *Ecology of Tropical Forest Tree Seedlings*, pp. 131–8. UNESCO/Parthenon, Paris/Carnforth.

Little, E.L., Jr. and Wadsworth, F.H. (1964). *Common Trees of Puerto Rico and the Virgin Islands*, Agricultural Handbook No. 249. United States Department of Agriculture, Washington, D.C.

Lovell, P.H. and Moore, K.G. (1970). A comparative study of cotyledons as assimilatory organs. *Journal of Experimental Botany*, **21**, 1017–30.

Lovell, P.H. and Moore, K.G. (1971). A comparative study of the role of the cotyledon in seedling development. *Journal of Experimental Botany*, **22**, 153–62.

Lubbock, J. (1892). *A Contributions to our Knowledge of Seedlings*. Kegan Paul, Trench and Trüber, London.

Marshall, P.E. and Kozlowski, T.T. (1974a). Photosynthetic activity of cotyledons and foliage leaves of young angiosperm seedlings. *Canadian Journal of Botany*, **52**, 2023–32.

Marshall, P.E. and Kozlowski, T.T. (1974b). The role of cotyledons in growth and development of woody angiosperms. *Canadian Journal of Botany*, **52**, 239–45.

Marshall, P.E. and Kozlowski, T.T. (1975). Changes in mineral contents of cotyledons and young seedlings of woody angiosperms. *Canadian Journal of Botany*, **53**, 2026–31.

Marshall, P.E. and Kozlowski, T.T. (1976a). Compositional changes in cotyledons of woody angiosperms. *Canadian Journal of Botany*, **54**, 2473–7.

Marshall, P.E. and Kozlowski, T.T. (1976b). Importance of photosynthetic cotyledons for early growth of woody angiosperms. *Physiologia Plantarum*, **37**, 336–40.

Marshall, P.E. and Kozlowski, T.T. (1977). Changes in structure and function of epigeous cotyledons of woody angiosperms during early seedling growth. *Canadian Journal of Botany*, **55**, 208–15.

Maury-Lechon, G. and Poncy, O. (1986). Dynamique forestière sur le 6 hectares de forêt dense humide de Guyane française, á partir de quelques espèces de forêt primaire et de cicatrisation. *Mémoires de Muséum National d'Histoire Naturelle, Paris, série A, Zoologie*, **132**, 211–42.

McHargue, L.A. and Hartshorn, G.S. (1983). Seed and seedling ecology of *Carapa guianensis*. *Turrialba*, **33**, 399–404.

Medina, E., Mooney, H.A. and Vázquez-Yanes, C. (eds.) (1984). *Physiological Ecology of Plants of the Wet Tropics*. W. Junk, The Hague.

de la Mensbruge, G. (1966). *La Germination et les Plantules des Essences Arborées de la Forêt Dense Humide de la Côte d'Ivoire*, Publication 26. Centre Technique Forestier Tropical: Nogent-sur-Marne, France.

Miquel, S. (1987). Morphologie fonctionnelle de plantules d'espèces forestières du Gabon. *Bulletin du Muséum National d'Histoire Naturelle*, 4e série, section B, Adansonia, **9**, 101–21.

Molofsky, J. and Augspurger, C.K. (1992). The effect of leaf litter on early seedling establishment in a tropical forest. *Ecology*, **73**, 68–77.

Ng, F.S.P. (1975). The fruits, seeds and seedlings of Malayan trees: I–XI. *Malaysian Forester*, **38**, 33–99.

Ng, F.S.P. (1976). The fruits, seeds and seedlings of Malayan trees. XII–XV. *Malaysian Forester*, **39**, 110–46.

Ng, F.S.P. (1978). Strategies of establishment in Malayan forest trees. In Tomlinson, P.B. and Zimmermann, M.H. (eds.) *Tropical Trees as Living Systems*, pp. 129–62. Cambridge University Press, Cambridge.

Ng, F.S.P. (1991–1992). *Manual of Forest Fruits, Seeds and Seedlings*. Volumes 1–2. Malayan Forest Record, No. 34. Forest Research Institute Malaysia: Kuala Lumpur, Malaysia.

Oberbauer, S.F. and Donnelly, M.A. (1986). Growth analysis and successional status of Costa Rican rain forest trees. *New Phytologist*, **104**, 517–21.

Oberbauer, S.F. and Strain, B.R. (1986). The effects of canopy position and irradiance on the leaf physiology and morphology of *Pentaclethra macroloba* (Mimosaceae). *American Journal of Botany*, **73**, 409–16.

Okali, D.U.U. (1971). Rates of dry-matter production in some tropical forest-tree seedlings. *Annals of Botany* New Series, **35**, 87–97.

Okali, D.U.U. (1972). Growth-rates of some West African forest-tree seedlings in shade. *Annals of Botany* New Series, **36**, 953–9.

Okali, D.U.U. and Onyeachusim, H.D. (1991). The ground flora and rain forest regeneration at Omo Forest Reserve, Nigeria. In Gómez-Pompa, A., Whitmore, T.C. and Hadley, M. (eds.) *Rain Forest Regeneration and Management*, pp. 273–83. UNESCO/Parthenon, Paris/Carnforth.

Oldeman, R.A.A. and van Dijk, J. (1991). Diagnosis of the temperament of tropical rain forest trees. In Gómez-Pompa, A., Whitmore, T.C. and Hadley, M. (eds.) *Rain Forest Regeneration and Management*, pp. 21–65. UNESCO/Parthenon, Paris/Carnforth.

Osunkoya, O.O., Ash, J.E., Graham, A.W. and Hopkins, M.S. (1993). Growth of tree seedlings in tropical rain forests of North Queensland, Australia. *Journal of Tropical Ecology*, **9**, 1–18.

Parker, G.G., Smith, A.P. and Hogan, K.P. (1992). Access to the upper forest canopy with a large tower crane. *BioScience*, **42**, 664–70.

Popma, J. and Bongers, F. (1988). The effect of canopy gaps on growth and morphology of seedlings of rain forest species. *Oecologia* (Berlin), **75**, 625–32.

Popma, J. and Bongers, F. (1991). Acclimation of seedlings of three Mexican tropical rain forest tree species to a change in light availability. *Journal of Tropical Ecology*, **7**, 85–97.

Poppendieck, H.-H. (1980). A monograph of the Cochlospermaceae. *Botanische Jahrbücher für Systematik, Pflanzengeschichte und Pflazengeographie*, **101**, 191–265.

Press, M.C., Brown, N.D., Barker, M.G. and Zipperlen, S.W. (1996). Photosynthetic responses to light in tropical rain forest tree seedlings. In Swaine, M.D. (ed.) *Ecology of Tropical Forest Tree Seedlings*, pp. 41–58. UNESCO/Parthenon, Paris /Carnforth.

Putz, F.E. (1983). Treefall pits and mounds, buried seeds and the importance of soil disturbance to pioneer trees on Barro Colorado Island, Panama. *Ecology*, **64**, 1069–74.

Putz, F.E. and Holbrook, N.M. (1989). Strangler fig rooting habits and nutrient relations in the llanos of Venezuela. *American Journal of Botany*, **76**, 781–8.

Ramos, J. and Grace, J. (1990). The effects of shade on the gas exchange of seedlings of four tropical trees from Mexico. *Functional Ecology*, **4**, 667–77.

Ricardi, M., Hernandez, C. and Torres, F. (1987). *Morfología de plántulas de árboles de los bosques del estado Mérida*. Talleres Graficos Universitarios, Mérida, Venezuela.

Riddoch, I., Grace, J., Fasehun, F.E., Riddoch, B. and Ladipo, D.O. (1991). Photosynthesis and successional status of seedlings in a tropical semi-deciduous rain forest in Nigeria. *Journal of Ecology*, **79**, 491–504.

Riera, B. (1985). Importance des buttes de déracinement dans la régénération forestière en Guyane française. *Revue d'Ecologie (La Terre et La Vie)*, **40**, 321–30.

Rizzini, C.T. (1965). Experimental studies on seedling development of cerrado woody plants. *Annals of the Missouri Botanical Garden*, **52**, 410–26.

Rousteau, A. (1983). *100 plantules d'arbes guadeloupéens. Aspects morphologique et écologiques*. 3ème cycle Thèses. Université Pierre & Marie Curie, Paris.

Rousteau, A. (1986). Les plantules d'arbres forestiers de Guadeloupe: adaptations structurales et dimensionnelles. *Mémoires du Muséum National d'Histoire Naturelle, Série A, Zoologie*, **132**, 185–91.

Sagers, C.L. (1996). Persistence in a tropical understorey: clonal growth in *Psychotria horizontalis*. In Swaine, M.D. (ed.) *Ecology of Tropical Forest Tree Seedlings*, pp. 163–72. UNESCO/Parthenon, Paris /Carnforth.

Sasaki, S. and Mori, T. (1981). Growth responses of dipterocarp seedlings to light. *Malaysian Forester*, **44**, 319–45.

Scarano, F.R. and Crawford, R.M.M. (1992). Ontogeny and the concept of anoxia-tolerance: the case of the Amazonian leguminous tree *Parkia pendula*. *Journal of Tropical Ecology*, **8**, 349–52.

Schupp, E.W. (1988). Predation on seeds and early seedlings in the forest understory and in treefall gaps. *Oikos*, **51**, 71–8.

Smythe, N. (1978). The natural history of the Central American agouti (*Dasyprocta punctata*). *Smithsonian Contributions to Zoology*, **257**, 1–52.

Sokal, R.R. and Rohlf, F.J. (1981). *Biometry*. W. H. Freeman and Company, San Francisco.

Sork, V.L. (1985). Germination responses in a large-seeded neotropical tree species, *Gustavia superba* (Lecythidaceae). *Biotropica*, **17**, 130–6.

Sork, V.L. (1987). Effects of predation and light on seedling establishment in *Gustavia superba*. *Ecology*, **68**, 1341–50.

Sousa, M.S. and Peña de Sousa, M. (1981). New World Lonchocarpinae. In Polhill, R.M. and Raven, P.H. (eds.) *Advances in Legume Systematics*, Part 1, pp. 261–81. Royal Botanic Gardens, Kew.

van Steenis, C.C.G.J. (1958). Rejuvenation as a factor for judging the status of vegetation types: the biological nomad theory. In *Study of Tropical Vegetation: Proceedings of the Kandy Symposium*, pp. 212–18. UNESCO, Paris.

Swaine, M.D. (1983). Stilt roots and ephermeral germination sites. *Biotropica*, **15**, 240.

Swaine, M.D. and Hall, J.B. (1983). Early succession on cleared forest land in Ghana. *Journal of Ecology*, **71**, 601–27.

Swaine, M.D. and Hall, J.B. (1986). Forest structure and dynamics. In Lawson, G.W. (ed.) *Plant Ecology in West Africa: Systems and Processes*, pp. 45–90. John Wiley, New York.

Swaine, M.D. and Whitmore, T.C. (1988). On the definition of ecological species groups in tropical rain forests. *Vegetatio*, **75**, 81–6.

Tomlinson, P.B. (1990). *The Structural Biology of Palms*. Clarendon Press, Oxford.

Troup, R.S. (1921). *The Silviculture of Indian Trees*. Volume I–III. Clarendon Press, Oxford.

Turner, I.M. (1990a). The seedling survivorship and growth of three *Shorea* species in a Malaysian tropical rain forest. *Journal of Tropical Ecology*, **6**, 469–78.

Turner, I.M. (1990b). Tree seedling growth and survival in a Malaysian rain forest. *Biotropica*, **22**, 146–54.

Vázquez-Yanes, C. and Orozco Segovia, A. (1984). Ecophysiology of seed germination in the tropical humid forests of the world: a review. In Medina, E., Mooney, H.A. and Vázquez-Yanes, C. (eds.) *Physiological Ecology of Plants in the Wet Tropics*, pp. 37–50. W. Junk, The Hague.

de Vogel, E.F. (1980). *Seedlings of Dicotyledons: Structure, Development, Types; Descriptions of 150 Woody Malesian Taxa*. Centre for Agricultural Publishing and Documentation (PUDOC), Wageningen.

Voorhoeve, A.G. (1965). Liberian High Forest Trees. *Belmontia*, **I**, 1–416. (Second impression, 1979, Centre for Agricultural Publishing and Documentation (PUDOC), Wageningen).

Webb, C.O. and Curran, L.M. (1992). *An Illustrated Key to the Dipterocarp Seedlings of the Gunung Palung Region (West Kalimantan, Indonesia)*. Report to the Indonesian Institute of Science (LIPI).

Weber, W.A. (1982). Mnemonic three letter acronyms for the families of vascular plants: a device for more effective herbarium curation. *Taxon*, **31**, 74–88.

Welden, W.C., Hewettt, S.W., Hubbell, S.P. and Foster, R.B. (1991). Sapling survival, growth and recruitment: relationship to canopy height in a neotropical forest. *Ecology*, **72**, 35–50.

Whitmore, T.C. (1996). A review of some aspects of tropical rain forest seedling ecology with suggestions for further enquiry. In Swaine, M.D. (ed.) *Ecology of Tropical Forest Tree Seedlings*, pp. 3–39. UNESCO/Parthenon, Paris /Carnforth.

Whitmore, T.C. and Bowen, M.R. (1983). Growth analyses of some *Agathis* species. *Malaysian Forester*, **46**, 186–96.

Whitmore, T.C. and Gong, W-K. (1983). Growth analysis of the seedlings of balsa, *Ochroma lagopus. New Phytologist*, **95**, 305–11.

Wilkinson, L. (1990). *SYSTAT: The System for Statistics*. Systat, Inc., Evanston, Illinois.

Wright, H. (1904). The genus *Diospyros* in Ceylon: its morphology, anatomy and taxonomy. Parts I and II. *Annals of the Royal Botanic Gardens, Peradeniya*, **2**, 1–106; 134–210.

Ye, N. (1983). Studies on the seedling types of dicotyledonous plants (Magnoliophyta, Magnoliopsida). *Phytologia*, **54**, 161–89.

APPENDICES

INTRODUCTION

In the following Appendices, I examine the association of seedling types and several ecological traits, including site, life form, dispersal mode and seed size, using published data from a number of sources. Comparisons are based on the number of species with each combination of traits. I have determined the significance of an association with a log-likelihood ratio test of independence, using the G-statistic (Sokal and Rohlf, 1981). In tests of association (also called tests of independence), the variation among classes can be partitioned into several orthogonal comparisons, in which the G-values and degrees of freedom sum to that of the original comparison. I use these contrasts to explore differences among sites. Differences among seedling types are explored using multiple non-orthogonal contrasts, in which the G-values and degrees of freedom do not sum to that of the original comparison. When testing many multiple comparisons, there is the danger that some will be significant by chance alone: for example, in twenty comparisons, about one significant result would have been expected by chance alone at $\alpha = 0.05$. As a more conservative measure, I have calculated the Bonferroni level of significance by dividing the critical probability ($\alpha = 0.05$) by the number of comparisons tested (Wilkinson, 1990).

I have usually analysed several ways of grouping the data into classes, primarily because different authors use different boundaries for their classes or different numbers of classes. Using fewer groups, by pooling classes with small sample sizes, may conceal differences among classes, but groups tested have larger sample sizes and the results are statistically trustworthy; using more groups highlights differences, but rarer groups may have low expected cell frequencies and yield suspect statistical results. Luckily, different groupings of the data usually yield similar results, suggesting that the results are robust. Whenever any cells had zero counts, one was added to all cells so that the sum of the G-statistics for the orthogonal contrasts would equal the value of the G-statistic of the overall comparison. In many statistical texts, an expected cell frequency of five is used as the cut-off point for valid statistical comparisons; but, others consider this approach too conservative and would include expected frequencies as low as one in some situations (see references in Everitt, 1977). My approach has been to present all of the results, but indicate which suffer from low expected frequencies. Whenever a particular contrast has more than one-fifth of the cells with expected cell frequencies less than five, I have annotated it with an 'L' (for low expected frequencies): this is almost always caused by too few species with CER type seedlings. In spite of large sample sizes (about 100–200 species), it was not possible to compare more than two factors simultaneously, as there would have been far too many small expected cell frequencies.

Appendix 3.1 Comparisons of the number of species with different seedling types at eight tropical sites. The abundance of all five seedling types (PEF, PER, PHR, CHR, and CER) could be determined for seven sites; for Guadeloupe, CHR and PHR seedling type could not be separately scored. When these five seedling types were not used in the original references, I scored types based on illustrations, descriptions, or other sources (see caption of Figure 3.2 for further discussion and additional references). Seedling types are described in the text

Appendix 3.1a Summary of site characteristics and number of species with each seedling type for eight sites

Site characteristics	Sites							
	Guadeloupe	Venezuela	Puerto Rico	Panama	Gabon	Nigeria	Malaysia	Indonesia
Continent	America	America	America	America	Africa	Africa	Asia	Asia
Forest altitude	<1500 m	Montane	Various	Lowland	Lowland	Lowland	Lowland	<1500 m
Forest type	Various	Various	Various	Semi-deciduous	Evergreen	Semi-evergreen	Various	Everwet/monsoon
Life forms	Trees	Mixed	Mixed	Mixed	Mixed	Trees	Trees	Mixed
Number of species								
Total	102	194	160	205	210	113	210	150
Seedling type								
PEF	52	109	77	88	82	39	73	49
PER	16	38	29	33	52	49	61	28
CHR	32 (+ PHR)	28	38	59	46	13	39	43
PHR	—	14	14	18	19	8	21	18
CER	2	5	2	7	11	4	16	12
Original reference	Rousteau (1983)	Ricardi et al. (1987)	Duke (1965)	Garwood (1979, 1983)	Miquel (1987)	Okali and Onyeachusim (1991)	Ng (1978)	de Vogel (1980)

Appendix 3.1b Tests of association between seedling types and sites and orthogonal contrasts between and among Old World and New World sites. Analyses are first presented using all five seedling types at seven sites, then using three seedling types (combining CHR, PHR and CER types) at eight sites; and finally using two seedlings types, 'epigeal' (PER + PEF types) and 'non-epigeal' (CHR + CER + PHR types). Data on other site-specific characteristics, such as altitude or forest type (Appendix 3.1a), were insufficient for further orthogonal contrasts; therefore, multiple comparisons between pairs of sites were made (Appendix 3.1c)

	G-statistic (degrees of freedom, probability) Sites × seedling types		
	7×5	8×3	8×2
Overall association	93.21 (24, < 0.001)	73.23 (14, < 0.001)	34.75 (7, < 0.001)
Orthogonal contrasts:			
New versus Old World	39.17 (4, < 0.001)	31.57 (2, < 0.001)	1.73 (1, 0.188)
Among New World	16.34 (8, 0.038)	13.27 (6, 0.039)	12.86 (3, 0.005)
Among Old World	37.69 (12, < 0.001)	28.39 (6, < 0.001)	20.16 (3, < 0.001)

Appendix 3.1c Tests of association between seedling type and site for each pair of sites. Statistical results above the diagonal compare all five seedling types in seven floras (df = 4); those below the diagonal compare three seedling types in all eight floras (df = 2). The Bonferroni level of significance for these non-orthogonal contrasts is ≈0.002 (above the diagonal: 0.05/21 = 0.0024; below the diagonal: 0.05/28 = 0.0018): significant contrasts ($p \leq 0.002$) are in bold (see introduction to Appendices for further information). n/a = not applicable

G-statistic (probability)

	Guadeloupe	Venezuela	Puerto Rico	Panama	Gabon	Nigeria	Malaysia	Indonesia
Guadeloupe	—	n/a	n/a	n/a	n/a	n/a	n/a	n/a
Venezuela	2.88 (0.238)	—	6.32 (0.176)	14.42 (0.006)	12.87 (0.012)	**26.15 (<0.001)**	**21.21 (<0.001)**	**25.91 (<0.001)**
Puerto Rico	0.32 (0.850)	3.96 (0.138)	—	3.46 (0.485)	8.38 (0.078)	**31.71 (<0.001)**	**18.78 (0.001)**	14.70 (0.005)
Panama	2.02 (0.364)	**12.89 (0.002)**	2.00 (0.367)	—	6.97 (0.137)	**41.06 (<0.001)**	**17.77 (0.001)**	6.96 (0.138)
Gabon	5.12 (0.077)	**12.28 (0.002)**	3.74 (0.154)	4.83 (0.089)	—	**20.21 (<0.001)**	2.85 (0.583)	5.84 (0.211)
Nigeria	**20.24 (<0.001)**	**21.07 (<0.001)**	**20.63 (<0.001)**	**29.26 (<0.001)**	**13.10 (0.001)**	—	9.51 (0.023)	**33.10 (<0.001)**
Malaysia	9.59 (0.008)	**18.32 (<0.001)**	8.40 (0.015)	9.99 (0.007)	1.13 (0.570)	9.20 (0.010)	—	8.24 (0.083)
Indonesia	8.75 (0.013)	**24.92 (<0.001)**	8.82 (0.012)	3.88 (0.143)	5.73 (0.057)	**26.27 (<0.001)**	7.35 (0.025)	—

Appendix 3.2 Association of seedling types with life form and dispersal mode. Original data: Gabon (Miquel, 1987: Appendix)

Appendix 3.2a Number of species in each category. *n*, total number of species in each comparison

Seedling type	*Life form (n = 172)*		*Dispersal mode (n = 159)*		
	Tree	*Liana*	*Animal*	*Wind*	*Autochorous*
PEF	58	16	53	12	1
PER	35	4	19	9	11
CHR	24	11	30	2	1
PHR	10	5	7	1	6
CER	9	0	7	0	0
Total	136	36	116	24	19

Appendix 3.2b Tests of association between seedling types and life form or dispersal mode. The Bonferroni level of significance for non-orthogonal contrasts is 0.0125 (= 0.05/4): significant non-orthogonal contrasts ($p \leq 0.0125$) are in bold (see Introduction to Appendices for further information). OTHER = CHR + PHR + CER types

	G-statistic (degrees of freedom, probability)	
	Life forms	*Dispersal mode*
Overall association:		
Five seedling types	7.59 (4, 0.108)	32.87 (8, < 0.001) L
Three seedling types	4.46 (2, 0.108)	26.57 (4, < 0.001)
Non-orthogonal contrasts:		
PEF vs. PER	2.44 (1, 0.119)	**19.87** (2, < 0.001)
PEF vs. OTHER	0.54 (1, 0.462)	**10.48** (2, 0.005) L
PER vs. OTHER	4.42 (1, 0.035)	**11.80** (2, 0.003)
Among OTHER	3.14 (2, 0.208) L	11.00 (4, 0.027) L

Appendix 3.3 Association of seedling type and regeneration strategy. Original data: Malaysia (Ng, 1978: Table 5.1). Ng did not separate the PEF and PER seedling types: but all species tabulated as PER types had fleshy rather than leafy cotyledons (Ng, 1991–1992)

Appendix 3.3a Number of species in each category. *n*, total number of species in the comparison

Seedling type	Regeneration strategy (n = 210)	
	Pioneer	*Non-pioneer*
PEF	18	55
PER	4	57
CHR	0	39
PHR	1	20
CER	0	16
Total	23	187

Appendix 3.3b Tests of association between seedling type and regeneration strategy. The Bonferroni level of significance for the non-orthogonal contrasts is 0.0125 (= 0.05/4): significant non-orthogonal contrasts ($p \le 0.0125$) are in bold (see introduction to Appendices for further information). OTHER = CHR + PHR + CER

	G-statistic (degrees of freedom, probability)
Overall association:	
Five seedling types	17.17 (4, 0.002) L
Three seedling types	23.39 (2, < 0.001)
Non-orthogonal contrasts:	
PEF vs. PER	**8.60** (1, 0.003)
PEF vs OTHER	**21.53** (1, < 0.001)
PER vs. OTHER	2.74 (1, 0.098) L
Among OTHER	1.25 (2, 0.536) L

124

Appendix 3.4 Association of seedling types and seed size classes. Original data: Malaysia (Ng, 1978: Table 5.1), Gabon (Miquel, 1987: Appendix). Ng did not separate the PEF and PER seedling types: see caption of Figure 3.2 for explanation of how these were scored. For Malaysia, data are tabulated for six seed size classes (Appendix 3.4a), combining the two largest seed size classes used by Ng; analyses are presented for two and four classes only (Appendix 3.4b), but results using either six or seven classes were generally similar except that the number of cells with low expected frequencies was greater. Note that the two or four Malaysian seed size classes are similar but not identical to those used in the Gabonese study

Appendix 3.4a Number of species in each category and percentage of species with PEF + PER and PEF type seedlings within each seed size class. *n*, total number of species in each comparison

| | Malaysian trees (n = 209) | | | | | | | Gabonese species (n = 170) | | | | |
| | Seed length (mm) | | | | | | | Seed length (mm) | | | | |
Number of seed size classes	<3	3–10	10–20	20–30	30–40	40–80	Total	1–5	5–20	20–40	>40	Total
4	a	a	b	c	d	d	—	a	b	c	d	—
2	a	a	b	b	b	b	—	a	b	b	b	—
Seedling type	Number of species [Number of pioneer species]							Number of species				
PEF	12 [7]	20 [11]	26	11	3	1	73	27	32	10	4	73
PER	1 [1]	11 [3]	22	12	6	9	61	1	15	10	8	34
CHR	0 [0]	5 [0]	11	12	2	8	38	5	19	8	6	38
PHR	0 [0]	3 [1]	10	5	1	2	21	0	7	5	3	15
CER	0 [0]	0 [0]	5	3	7	1	16	0	7	3	0	10
Total	13 [8]	39 [15]	74	43	19	21	209	33	80	36	21	170
	Percentage of species within each seed size class [Percentage of pioneer species within each seed size class]											
PEF + PER	100 [100]	79 [94]	65	53	47	48	64	85	59	56	57	63
PEF	92 [88]	51 [73]	35	26	16	5	35	82	40	28	19	43

Appendix 3.4b Tests of association between seed size class and seedling type and regeneration strategy. The Bonferroni level of significance for the non-orthogonal contrasts is 0.0125 (= 0.05/4): significant non-orthogonal contrasts ($p \leq 0.0125$) are in bold (see Introduction to Appendices for further information). OTHER = CHR + PHR + CER types

	Malaysian trees				Gabonese species	
	All species		*Non-pioneer species*		*All species*	
G-statistic (degrees of freedom, probability)						
Number of seed size classes	2	4	2	4	2	4
Overall association:						
Five seedling types	21.30 (4, <0.001)	36.42 (12, <0.001)	5.68 (4, 0.224)	20.15 (12, 0.064)	22.69 (4, <0.001)	31.45 (12, 0.002) L
Three seedling types	23.00 (2, 0.001)	33.86 (6, <0.001)	6.04 (2, 0.049)	16.90 (6, 0.010)	27.18 (2, <0.001)	9.50 (3, 0.023)
Non-orthogonal contrasts:						
PEF vs. PER	**9.07** (1, 0.003)	**16.55** (3, 0.001)	2.33 (1, 0.270)	9.82 (3, 0.020)	**17.79** (1, 0.001)	**23.29** (3, <0.001)
PEF vs OTHER	**21.71** (1, <0.001)	**31.10** (3, <0.001)	5.89 (1, 0.015)	**15.28** (3, 0.002)	**17.28** (1, <0.001)	**19.27** (3, <0.001)
PER vs OTHER	2.17 (1, 0.141)	2.93 (3, 0.403)	0.66 (1, 0.417)	1.42 (3, 0.701)	1.06 (1, 0.302)	1.06 (3, 0.302)
Among OTHER	1.56 (2, 0.458) L	6.25 (6, 0.396) L	1.22 (2, 0.544) L	5.93 (6, 0.431)	1.20 (2, 0.548) L	3.41 (6, 0.756) L
Regeneration strategy and seed size class	67.74 (1, <0.001)	59.15 (3, <0.001)	—	—	—	—

Appendix 3.5 Association of seedling type and germination time. Original data: Malaysia (Ng, 1978, Table 5.1), Gabon (Miquel, 1987, Appendix). Time until germination was divided into groups in two ways. Germination time (R–D), as described by Ng (1978): rapid (R), all seeds germinated before 12 weeks; delayed (D), all seeds germinated after >12 weeks; intermediate (I), first seed germinated before 12 weeks and last seed after 12 weeks; for analysis, the intermediate and delayed categories were combined because of the infrequency of species with delayed germination. Germination time (F–S), used to compare data of Ng (1978) and Miquel (1987): fast (F), first seed germinated before 6 weeks; slow (S), first seed germinated in or after 6 weeks. Ng (1978) did not separate the PEF and PER seedling types: see caption of Figure 3.2 for explanation of how these were scored

Appendix 3.5a Numbers of species in each category; numbers of pioneer species enclosed in brackets. *n*, total number of species in each comparison

	Number of species [number of pioneer species]						
	Malaysian trees (n = 180)					*Gabonese species (n = 105)*	
	Germination time (R–D)			*Germination time (F–S)*		*Germination time (F–S)*	
Seedling type	*Rapid*	*Intermediate*	*Delayed*	*Fast*	*Slow*	*Fast*	*Slow*
PEF	40 [13]	19 [3]	6 [1]	52 [16]	13 [1]	29	7
PER	45 [2]	7 [2]	0 [0]	51 [4]	1 [0]	19	4
CHR	12 [0]	15 [0]	4 [0]	15 [0]	16 [0]	11	15
PHR	13 [1]	5 [0]	1 [0]	16 [1]	3 [0]	6	8
CER	8 [0]	4 [0]	1 [0]	11 [0]	2 [0]	3	3
Total	118 [16]	50 [5]	12 [1]	145 [21]	35 [1]	68	37

127

Appendix 3.5b Tests of association between seedling type and germination time. The Bonferroni level of significance for non-orthogonal contrasts within each comparison is 0.0125 (= 0.05/4): significant non-orthogonal contrasts ($p \leq 0.0125$) are in bold (see introduction to Appendices for further information). There is also a significant association between germination time (F–S) and site, Malaysia and Gabon: $G = 8.56$, df = 1, $p = 0.003$. OTHER = CHR + PHR + CER types

	G-statistic (degrees of freedom, probability)					
	Malaysian trees				Gabonese species	
	All species		Non-pioneer species		All species	
Germination grouping	R–D	F–S	R–D	F–S	F–S	
Overall association:						
Five seedling types	21.71 (4, <0.001)	31.72 (4, <0.001)	25.96 (4, <0.001)	28.90 (4, <0.001)	16.68 (4, 0.002) L	
Three seedling types	16.92 (2, <0.001)	22.20 (2, <0.001)	21.69 (2, <0.001)	20.26 (2, <0.001)	16.56 (2, <0.001) L	
Non-orthogonal contrasts:						
PEF vs. PER	**9.59** (1, 0.002)	**10.77** (1, <0.001)	**14.28** (1, <0.001)	**12.43** (1, <0.001)	0.04 (1, 0.843) L	
PEF vs. OTHER	1.10 (1, 0.295)	2.93 (1, 0.087)	0.23 (1, 0.628)	0.70 (1, 0.404)	**12.08** (1, 0.001) L	
PER vs. OTHER	**16.20** (1, <0.001)	**22.18** (1, <0.001)	**19.64** (1, <0.001)	**19.57** (1, <0.001)	**10.24** (1, 0.001) L	
Among OTHER	4.79 (2, 0.091)	9.52 (2, 0.009)	4.27 (2, 0.118)	8.65 (2, 0.013)	0.12 (2, 0.942) L	

Appendix 3.6 Association of regeneration strategy and germination type. Original data: Malaysia (Ng, 1978, Table 5.1). See Appendix 3.5 for description of germination groups

	Number of species			
	Germination time: R–D		*Germination time: F–S*	
Regeneration strategy	*Rapid*	*Delayed and intermediate*	*Fast*	*Slow*
Pioneers	16	6	21	1
Non-pioneers	102	56	124	34
Total	118	62	145	35
	G-statistic (degrees of freedom, probability)			
Overall association	0.59 (1, 0.442)		4.64 (1, 0.031)	

Appendix 3.7 Association of seed size class and dispersal mode. Original data: Gabon (Miquel, 1987: Appendix)

Appendix 3.7a Numbers of species in each category. *n*, total number of species in comparison

	Dispersal mode ($n = 159$)		
Seed size class (*length*, mm)	*Animal* (Z)	*Wind* (W)	*Autochorous* (A)
A (≤ 5)	21	7	0
B (5–20)	56	13	12
C (20–40)	28	2	2
D (>40)	11	2	5

Appendix 3.7b Tests of association and orthogonal contrasts between dispersal mode and seed size classes

	G-statistic (degrees of freedom, probability)	
Number of seed size classes	*4 (A, B, C, D)*	*2 (A + B, C + D)*
Overall association	11.57 (6, 0.072) L	3.23 (2, 0.199)
Orthogonal contrasts:		
Z vs. W+A	4.81 (3, 0.186)	0.96 (1, 0.326)
W vs. A	6.76 (3, 0.080) L	2.27 (1, 0.132)

Revised manuscript received April 1994

CHAPTER 4

DEMOGRAPHY OF TROPICAL TREE SEEDLINGS: A REVIEW

Diana Lieberman

In his classic treatise on tropical rain forests, Richards (1952) considered studies of regeneration to be among the most urgent tasks confronting the rain forest ecologist. It is significant that his chapter on regeneration is among the shortest in the book and comes with the startling disclaimer (p. 41) that 'owing to the lack of data all the views expressed in this chapter must be considered tentative'. The literature on tropical seedlings has grown prodigiously in the ensuing forty years, yet our understanding of tropical regeneration processes remains fragmentary.

Forest species composition and diversity vary in broadly predictable ways in relation to environment and biogeography. However, we still know comparatively little about the population-level processes which produce these patterns. To what extent is the local abundance of a tropical tree species constrained by fecundity of parent trees, by availability of suitable germination sites, or by early survivorship in the face of seed predation, herbivory, pathogens, mechanical injury, presence of competitors and access to resources? To what extent is the geographical distribution of a tree species limited by dispersal of propagules and to what extent by barriers to establishment operating once seeds have arrived on a site? Are there generalities, or will the diversity of answers to these questions parallel the diversity of species and sites studied? As in any field of research, what we know reflects the sorts of questions that have been posed; and in this particular field, a very few seminal papers have been disproportionately influential.

Two disparate sets of objectives can be recognized in the literature of tropical seedling ecology in recent decades. First, studies with a population-level focus have sought to link the processes affecting juvenile stages with the demography and dynamics of the mature age classes of the species (Hartshorn 1975; Sarukhán, 1978; Augspurger, 1983; McHargue and Hartshorn, 1983; De Steven and Putz, 1984; Becker and Wong, 1985; Howe et al., 1985; Clark and Clark, 1987; De Steven, 1989; Kitajima and Augspurger, 1989; Howe, 1990; and many others). Although these studies address within-population questions, many have adopted a comparative frame of reference and consider large numbers of species together (Li, 1991; Li et al., 1996).

Population studies have shown that a variety of sources of juvenile mortality may be important, depending upon the species, the site and the time of the study. Experimental protection of seedlings from major sources of mortality can have a pronounced effect on establishment and survivorship; hence when particular risks are moderated, the survivors are not necessarily doomed by alternate sources of early mortality. The long-term effects of escape from early mortality have not been determined; we do not know whether bumper crops of successful seedlings lead to substantial changes in local abundance of adults.

Second, studies with an assemblage-level focus have evaluated juvenile-stage processes as determinants of adult species diversity and spatial pattern (Hubbell, 1979; Clark and Clark, 1984; Connell et al., 1984; Hubbell and Foster, 1986; Sterner et al., 1986; Hubbell et al., 1990; and many others). Much of this work has its intellectual underpinnings in the ideas of Janzen (1970) and Connell (1971), who hypothesized that high tropical diversity was maintained by compensatory processes involving density-dependence, distance-dependence, or frequency-dependence. The concept of the regeneration niche (Grubb, 1977) has also been highly influential in this area. Although these studies address assemblage-level questions, some have dealt with only one or two target species.

Rigorous, community-wide analyses reveal a general absence of compensatory mechanisms (Connell et al., 1984; Hubbell et al., 1990); a few species have been found to show density-dependence or frequency-dependence, but such appear to be the exceptions. If compensatory mechanisms are important in the maintenance of local diversity, it is assumed that these processes would be common throughout the assemblage. Studies of Janzen-Connell spacing have documented occasional instances of hyperdispersion or tendencies toward it, but large-scale tests indicate the process is not of general importance, and alternative explanantions can often be invoked (Hubbell, 1979; Condit et al., 1992; Lieberman and Lieberman, 1994).

Another group of studies, which spans the two foregoing categories, has considered the role of seedling processes in the development of species composition, particularly following canopy disturbance (Whitmore, 1974; Brandani et al., 1988; Bongers and Popma, 1988, Lieberman et al., 1990b, Raich and Gong, 1990).

Recent studies have shown that a wide range of forest species are capable of invading disturbed sites or treefall gaps, as long as distances from seed sources are not excessive (Lieberman et al., 1990b, Welden et al., 1991). This finding poses interesting challenges to conventional models of succession. Experimental studies of tropical tree seedlings indicate a marked capacity for morphological and physiological acclimatization to light conditions (Fetcher et al., 1983, 1994; Oberbauer and Strain, 1985; Bongers and Popma, 1988), suggesting that tropical tree seedling species may be broadly overlapping in their environmental tolerances (Lieberman et al., 1995). Patterns of floristic change following distur-bance may reflect proximity of potential seed sources, timing of fruit production and presence of advance regeneration at the time of the disturbance – all of which render explicit predictive modelling of floristic change especially diffi-cult.

Tropical forests are typically diverse and the species in them poorly known. In order to provide a quantitative framework in which to analyse and interpret species-level data, it is often useful to assess demography across the assemblage as a whole, sampling species in proportion to their abundance. In addition, tropical trees are very long-lived, and occasional or sporadic events may play an important role in recruitment and subsequent processes for the stand. Yet long-term studies of tropical rain forest regeneration have been few. The reproductive lifespan of even a single individual may be five to ten times longer than the longest ongoing study of seedling dynamics. Among the few extant long-term, assemblage-wide studies of tropical seedlings are those of J.H. Connell, M. Lowman and co-workers in Australia (begun 1963); S.P. Hubbell and R.B. Foster in Panama (begun 1982); M. Lieberman, D. Lieberman, R. Peralta and G.S. Hartshorn in Costa Rica (begun 1983); and R.B. Primack and P. Hall in Sarawak (begun in 1986, augmenting plots established in 1965 by P.S. Ashton). In addition, studies on representative species are in progress in Ghana by M.D. Swaine (1990) and in the Solomon Islands by the Forestry Department and T.C. Whitmore (1989), among others. Swaine (1994) reviews long-term permanent sample plot studies in tropical forests.

While the value of long-term, assemblage-wide studies of tropical seedling demography has been convincingly articulated elsewhere (Garwood, 1983; Clark and Clark, 1985; Schupp, 1990; Li, 1991), such studies have seldom been undertaken, and there are practical reasons why this is so. Identification of tropical seedlings is a formidable task, one which demands exceptional knowledge of the flora as well as a tremendous investment in time and effort. Seedlings are less well known than adult trees, and at early stages may appear quite unlike their parents. Because of high diversity, the majority of species are comparatively rare; large areas must therefore be sampled to ensure that a good number of species are represented by more than token numbers. The poor survivorship of young seedlings demands that large initial sample sizes be included in each species of interest, and that the timetable of censuses is rather frequent. As seedlings are extremely vulnerable, they must be handled with care, and study sites must be absolutely protected from trampling.

Certain features of seedling demography are now well supported by a growing body of evidence from these long-term studies. Early seedling mor-tality is often exceedingly high. Garwood (1982) recorded a loss of up to 67 per cent of newly germinated seedlings (species pooled) during the first 2 weeks of age in Panama. Li et al. (1996) found the mean mortality in the first year after germination to be 86 per cent in Costa Rica; the mean half-life of cohorts was approximately 2.5 months.

Dramatic year-to-year variation in recruitment appears characteristic of tropical tree seedlings. Such patterns are reported for forests in Australia (Connell et al., 1984), Costa Rica (Li, 1991; Li et al., 1996), Brazil (Sizer, 1992), Panama (Garwood, 1983, 1986; Schupp, 1990), and Ghana (Lieberman, 1979; Swaine et al., 1990; Lieberman and Li, 1992), and are well-known for western Malesian dipterocarps (T.C. Whitmore, personal communication). Basing his inferences on size-class distributions, Knight (1975) classified rain forest tree species according to frequency of reproduction. Variation in frequency of recruitment is indeed common in tropical forests; some species produce new cohorts of seedlings more or less continuously, others sporadically, and some at very long intervals. Viewed over the whole assemblage, however, these differences are probably best thought of as a continuum of reproductive timing, with Knight's two classes forming the end-points.

Sampled over long enough periods of time or large enough sample areas, most tropical forest tree populations exhibit a 'reverse-J' size-class distribution, with very large numbers of small individuals and few large individuals. Does this reflect a superabundance of juveniles? In dense, well-stocked, mixed-species forest stands, size categories (species pooled) show a log–log relationship between size-class and numbers per size-class, and this has been interpreted as evidence of preemption of space by larger size-classes (Lieberman, 1977; Lieberman and Lieberman, 1994). Trees are capable of remaining in the same size-class for lengthy periods until space to grow or other limiting resources become available; if the opportunities to enter the ranks of adult trees are exceptionally limited, how critical are processes at seed and seedling stages to the outcome? Longer periods of study are needed before this kind of question can be answered.

Rates of survivorship improve as seedlings become larger and older. Turner (1990) reports mortality of Malaysian rain forest seedlings to be ten times higher in the 10–20 cm height class than the 30–40 cm height class. Similarly, Sizer (1992) found that seedlings less than 10 cm tall face mortality rates ten times higher than those 11–20 cm tall in Amazonian rain forest. Established mixed-species, uneven-aged seedling cohorts typically survive at much higher rates than cohorts of newly-germinated seedlings, or even seedlings 5–6 years of age (Li et al., 1996). Survivorship among trees more than 10 cm dbh is far higher than that of seedlings and is often found to be independent of size; at what stage does the shift to a constant risk of mortality take place?

Huge differences are seen among species in survivorship rates. Connell et al. (1984) report great differences in mortality among species. Half-life values varied 100-fold among seventy-five species in a Costa Rican seedling assemblage (Li et al., 1996). These differences appear to be diminished among taxonomically related species. Palm seedlings, for example, share rather high rates of survivorship (Li et al., 1996). Established seedlings of a number of dipterocarps in Malaysia varied in annual mortality by a factor of only three (Still, 1996). Certain ecological groups of species also share demographic traits (Swaine and Whitmore, 1988; Swaine, 1990). Seedling abundance and survivorship levels vary dramatically between understorey, subcanopy, canopy and shade-intolerant species (Lieberman et al., 1990a). Attempts to develop and improve categorizations of species based on demographic patterns, seedling ecology, or other relevant traits should be pursued vigorously. More information is needed on the syndromes of traits that are associated with relative success of juveniles. What are the trade-offs between abundance of seed production, mortality rates, breadth of tolerance of site conditions (light, drainage and so on), growth rates and quality of timber? To what extent are demographic patterns associated with morphological and ecophysiological features of tree species?

Early survivorship has been shown to be a good indicator of subsequent survivorship for periods up to 6 years of age (Li et al., 1996). Although absolute survivorship rates may improve with age, the relative success among species appears to be maintained. It would seem that factors affecting early survivorship of a given species on a particular site do not shift greatly during the first few years of life. On a pragmatic level, this finding may enable experimental ecologists and silviculturists to apply rapid screening procedures to young seedlings to compare performance of species on a site.

Although the abundance and quality of information pertaining to the demography of tropical forest seedlings has grown enormously, a number of crucial questions clearly have yet to be resolved. In particular, a more synthetic understanding of forest regeneration processes is called for if we are to make use of our knowledge to confront the problems of forest conservation, management and restoration.

REFERENCES

Augspurger, C.K. (1983). Seed dispersal of the tropical tree, *Platypodium elegans* and the escape of its seedlings from fungal pathogens. *Journal of Ecology*, **71**, 759–71.

Becker, P. and Wong, M. (1985). Seed dispersal, seed predation and juvenile mortality of *Aglaia* sp. (Meliaceae) in lowland dipterocarp rain forest. *Biotropica*, **17**, 230–7.

Bongers, F. and Popma, J. (1988). *Trees and gaps in a Mexican tropical rain forest: species differentiation in relation to gap-associated environmental heterogeneity.* Ph.D. Thesis, Utrecht University, Utrecht, Netherlands.

Brandani, A., Hartshorn, G.S. and Orians, G.H. (1988). Internal heterogeneity of gaps and species richness in Costa Rican tropical wet forest. *Journal of Tropical Ecology*, **4**, 99–119.

Clark, D.A. and Clark, D.B. (1984). Spacing dynamics of a tropical rain forest tree: evaluation of the Janzen-Connell model. *American Naturalist*, **124**, 769–88.

Clark, D.A. and Clark, D.B. (1985). Seedling dynamics of a tropical tree; impacts of herbivory and meristem damage. *Ecology*, **66**, 1884–92.

Clark, D.B. and Clark, D.A. (1987). Population ecology and microhabitat distribution of *Dipteryx panamensis*, a neotropical rain forest emergent tree. *Biotropica*, **19**, 236–44.

Condit, R., Hubbell, S.P. and Foster, R.B. (1992). Recruitment near conspecific adults and the maintenance of tree and shrub diversity in a neotropical forest. *American Naturalist*, **140**, 261–8.

Connell, J.H. (1971). On the role of natural enemies in preventing competitive exclusion in some marine animals and in rain forest trees. In den Boer, P.J. and Gradwell, G.R. (eds.), *Dynamics of Populations*, pp. 298–310. Centre for Agricultural Publishing and Documentation, Wageningen.

Connell, J.H., Tracey, J.G. and Webb, L.J. (1984). Compensatory recruitment, growth and mortality as factors maintaining rain forest tree diversity. *Ecological Monographs*, **54**, 141–64.

De Steven, D. (1989). Light gaps and long term seedling performance of a neotropical canopy tree (*Dipteryx panamensis*, Leguminosae). *Journal of Tropical Ecology*, **4**, 407–11.

De Steven, D. and Putz, F.E. (1984). Impact of mammals on early recruitment of a tropical canopy tree, *Dipteryx panamensis*, in Panama. *Oikos*, **43**, 207–16.

Fetcher, N., Oberbauer, S.F. and Chazdon, R.L. (1994). Physiological ecology of plants. In McDade, L., Bawa, K.S., Hespenheide, H.A. and Hartshorn, G.S. (eds.), *La Selva: Ecology and Natural History of a Neotropical Rain Forest*, pp. 128–41. University of Chicago Press, Chicago.

Fetcher, N., Strain, B and Oberbauer, S.F. (1983). Effects of light regime on the growth, leaf morphology and water relations of seedlings of two species of tropical trees. *Oecologia*, **58**, 314–19.

Garwood, N.C. (1982). Seasonal rhythm of seed germination in a semideciduous tropical forest. In Leigh, E.G. Rand, A.T. and Windsor, D.M. (eds.) *The Ecology of a Tropical Forest, Seasonal Rhythms and Long-term Changes*, pp. 173–85. Smithsonian Institution Press, Washington, DC, USA.

Garwood, N.C. (1983). Seed germination in a seasonal tropical forest in Panama: a community study. *Ecological Monographs*, **53**, 159–81.

Garwood, N.C. (1986). Constraints on the timing of seed germination in a tropical forest. In Estrada, A. and Fleming, T.H. (eds.), *Frugivores and Seed Dispersal*, pp. 347–55. Junk, Dordrecht.

Grubb, P.J. (1977). The maintenance of species richness in plant communities: the importance of the regeneration niche. *Biological Reviews*, **52**, 107–45.

Hartshorn, G.S. (1975). A matrix model of tree population dynamics. In Golley, F.B. and Medina, E. (eds.), *Tropical Ecological Systems*, pp. 41–51. Springer-Verlag, New York, NY, USA.

Howe, H.F. (1990). Survival and growth of juvenile *Virola surinamensis* in Panama: effects of herbivory and canopy closure. *Journal of Tropical Ecology*, **6**, 259–80.

Howe, H.F., Schupp, E.W. and Westley, L.C. (1985). Early consequences of seed dispersal for a neotropical tree (*Virola surinamensis*). *Ecology*, **66**, 781–91.

Hubbell, S.P. (1979). Tree dispersion, abundance and diversity in a tropical dry forest. *Science*, **203**, 1299–309.

Hubbell, S.P., Condit, R. and Foster, R.B. (1990). Presence and absence of density dependence in a neotropical tree community. *Philosophical Transactions Royal Society London* B, **330**, 269–81.

Hubbell, S.P. and Foster, R.B. (1986). Biology, chance and history in the structure of tropical rain forest tree communities. In Diamond, J. and Case, T.J. (eds.), *Community Ecology*, pp. 314–29. Harper & Row, New York.

Janzen, D.H. (1970). Herbivores and the number of tree species in tropical forests. *American Naturalist*, **104**, 501–28.

Kitajima, K. and Augspurger, C.K. (1989). Seed and seedling ecology of a monocarpic tropical tree, *Tachigalia versicolor. Ecology*, **70**, 1102–14.

Knight, D.H. (1975). A phytosociological analysis of species-rich tropical forest on Barro Colorado Island, Panama. *Ecological Monographs*, **45**, 259–84.

Li, M. (1991). *The ecology of neotropical forest tree seedlings*. Ph.D. Dissertation, University of North Dakota, Grand Forks, ND, USA.

Li, M., Lieberman, M. and Lieberman, D. (1996). Seedling demography in undisturbed tropical wet forest in Costa Rica. In Swaine, M.D. (ed.) *Ecology of Tropical Forest Tree Seedlings*, pp. 285–314. UNESCO/Parthenon, Paris /Carnforth.

Lieberman, D. (1979). *Dynamics of forest and thicket vegetation on the Accra Plains, Ghana*. PhD thesis, University of Ghana.

Lieberman, D., Hartshorn, G.S., Lieberman, M. and Peralta, R. (1990a). Forest dynamics at La Selva Biological Station, 1969–1985. In Gentry, A. (ed.) *Four Neotropical Rainforests*, pp. 509–21. Yale University Press, New Haven, CT, USA.

Lieberman, D. and Li, M. (1992). Seedling recruitment patterns in a tropical dry forest in Ghana. *Journal of Vegetation Science*, **3**, 375–82.

Lieberman, D., Lieberman, M. and Peralta, R. (1990b). Forest succession in an abandoned pasture in Braulio Carrillo National Park, Costa Rica. *Bulletin of the Ecological Society of America*, **71** Supplement, 230.

Lieberman, M. (1977). A stochastic model based upon computer simulation using preemption to predict size distribution and species equitability. *Bulletin of Mathematical Biology*, **39**, 59–72.

Lieberman, M. and Lieberman, D. (1994). Patterns of density and dispersion of forest trees. In McDade, L., Bawa, K.S., Hespenheide, H.A. and Hartshorn, G.S. (eds.), *La Selva: Ecology and Natural History of a Neotropical Rain Forest*, pp. 106–19. University of Chicago Press, Chicago, IL, USA.

Lieberman, M., Leiberman, D., Peratta, R. and Hartshorn, G.S. (1995). Canopy closure and the distribution of tropical forest tree species at La Selva, Costa Rica. *Journal of Tropical Ecology*, **11**, 161–78.

McHargue, L. and Hartshorn, G.S. (1983). Seed and seedling ecology of *Carapa guianensis. Turrialba*, **33**, 399–404.

Oberbauer, S.F. and Strain, B.R. (1985). Effects of light on the growth and physiology of *Pentaclethra macroloba* (Mimosaceae) in Costa Rica. *Journal of Tropical Ecology*, **1**, 303–20.

Raich, J.W. and Gong, W-K. (1990). Effects of canopy openings on the seed germination in a Malaysian dipterocarp forest, *Journal of Tropical Ecology*, **6**, 203–17.

Richards, P.W. (l952). *The Tropical Rain Forest*. Cambridge University Press, London.

Sarukhán, J. (1978). Studies on the demography of tropical trees. In Tomlinson, P.B. and Zimmermann, M.H. (eds.), *Tropical Trees as Living Systems*, pp. 163–84. Cambridge University Press, Cambridge.

Schupp, E.W. (1990). Annual variation in seedfall, postdispersal predation and recruitment of a neotropical tree. *Ecology*, 71, 504–15.

Sizer, N. (1992). *The impact of edge formation on regeneration and litter fall in a tropical rain forest in Amazonia*. PhD Dissertation, University of Cambridge.

Sterner, R.W., Ribic, C.A. and Schatz, G.E. (1986). Testing for life historical changes in spatial patterns of four tropical tree species. *Journal of Ecology*, 74, 621–33.

Still, M. (1996). Rates of mortality and growth in three groups of dipterocarp seedlings in Sabah, Malaysia., In Swaine, M.D. (ed.) *Ecology of Tropical Forest Tree Seedlings*, pp. 315–32. UNESCO/Parthenon, Paris /Carnforth.

Swaine, M.D. (1990). Population dynamics of moist tropical forest at Kade, Ghana. In Maitre, H.F. and Puig, H. (eds.), *Actes de l'Atelier sur l'Amenagement de l'Ecosysteme Forestier Tropical Humide*, pp. 40–61. UNESCO/MAB, Paris.

Swaine, M.D. (1994). Long-term studies of tropical forest dynamics. In Leigh, R.A and Johnston, A.E. (eds.), *Long-term Experiments in Agricultural and Ecological Sciences*, pp. 305–19. CAB International, Oxford.

Swaine, M.D., Lieberman, D. and Hall, J.B. (1990). Structure and dynamics of a tropical dry forest in Ghana. *Vegetatio*, 88, 31–51.

Swaine, M.D. and Whitmore, T.C. (1988). On the definition of ecological species groups in tropical rain forests. *Vegetatio*, 75, 81–6.

Turner. I.M. (1990). Tree seedling growth and survival in a Malaysian rain forest. *Biotropica*, 22, 146–54.

Welden, C.W., Hewett, S.W., Hubbell, S.P. and Foster, R.B. (1991). Sapling survival, growth, and recruitment: relationship to canopy height in a neotropical forest. *Ecology*, 72, 35–50.

Whitmore, T.C. (1974). Changes with time and the role of cyclones in tropical rain forest on Kolombangara, Solomon Islands. *Commonwealth Forestry Institute Paper* **46**.

Whitmore, T.C. (1989b). Changes over 21 years in the Kolombangara rain forests. *Journal of Ecology*, 77, 469–83.

Revised manuscript received December 1994

CHAPTER 5

SEEDLING ECOLOGY AND TROPICAL FORESTRY

John B. Hall

INTRODUCTION

Seedling ecology has been no more than a minor part of tropical forestry. The need to consider seedlings in management was not generally recognized at first. Preoccupation was with the exploitation of forest resources well into the twentieth century and interest in seedlings arose only as management aspirations evolved. Concern was restricted to indigenous species of particular significance for timber. Among these, *Shorea* and *Tectona* in the more seasonal forests of India, *Tectona* in Burma and Indonesia, *Palaquium* and a few dipterocarp species in Malesia, *Milicia*, mahoganies and *Diospyros* in West Africa and *Ocotea*, *Swietenia* and *Cedrela* in tropical America, were noteworthy. For some decades, from around 1930, formal forest management prescriptions were applied to promote regeneration of such species after exploitation.

The tropical forest remained, however, an awkward subject for management. Several factors contributed. The diversity of response to management action among species in mixture was underestimated. Fruiting periodicity was often erratic and poorly understood. Constant change occurred in floristics on the local scale as a result of harvesting. In consequence, efforts to refine management techniques and acquire knowledge of timber species and their seedlings in the forest environment declined. Instead, interest grew in species more amenable to plantation forestry. Even where levels of forest management activity remained higher, notably in Malaya, market demands shifted from heavy to light hardwoods. These trends biased forest research activities towards naturally gregarious species of the drier parts of the tropical forest zone (e.g. *Shorea, Tectona*) or even from beyond it (e.g. some *Eucalyptus* spp., *Pinus caribaea* Morelet). Plantation forestry soon accounted for most of forestry's silvicultural activity. Interest in the seedling phase of plantation species largely replaced interest in the seedlings of non-plantation species.

During recent years, forest services have undertaken additional responsibilities. Involvement with forest ecosystems has been revived, not simply for timber production but through tropical forestry action plans and national conservation strategies. As the process gains momentum seedling ecology will receive attention in this wider context. While forestry's past efforts to promote regeneration focused sharply on timber production, information about seedlings was generated. The account offered here summarizes this information with respect to species and management.

THE SPECIES CONTEXT

The total number of tropical forest tree species which are, or have been, of importance in economic timber terms is of the order of several hundreds. Only a few, however, have received considered management attention and have been the subject of published accounts of their biology and ecology. The present review is concerned with twenty-nine species, representing the American, African and Asian tropics, falling into this category. An annotated listing is appended, including references to relevant literature and full names: in the text generic names only are used where there is no ambiguity. All the major broadleaved plantation species native to the rain forest communities of the lowland tropics are included. In the annotations, changes over time in the attention these species have been given are noted. The persisting emphasis on artificial regeneration which developed in most of the tropics in the 1960s and the restriction of an appreciable number of species to particular regions are also apparent. Ignorance of seedling ecology, or its refractory nature, is partly responsible.

The American species

Only four of the species listed are American in origin. Despite several centuries of timber trading, the extent of the resource has survived increasing exploitation. Only since about 1980 (FAO, 1993) has there been serious pressure to apply management actions and amass information to support these. Reflecting firmly established reputations, *Cedrela* and *Swietenia* were species which attracted early interest as exotics. The reputation of *Cordia* did not arise from trade. In its natural range this species has long enjoyed popularity for its timber. Individuals regenerating spontaneously are retained in indigenous land management. When the identification of potential plantation species became a priority the combination of desirable timber quality and pioneer regeneration behaviour attracted wide forestry attention. *Ocotea* remains a species procured from the natural forest – one of localized distribution (almost confined to Guyana). Experience of its seedling ecology is limited.

Forestry attention has often been attracted by timber quality. Involvement in well-established trade is, however, no indication of the amenability of a species in management terms within or outside the natural range. Both *Cedrela* and *Swietenia* proved problematical because of *Hypsipyla* (Lepidoptera) attacks on seedlings, poles and young trees in the natural range. While, around parents, seedlings may be densely concentrated, mortality is high and stands do not develop. This detracts from potential as a plantation species. With *Cedrela*, other factors, notably narrow amplitude of tolerance of soil moisture conditions and requirements of high fertility, are known to exacerbate the situation. Because it is adapted for growth in full light, suitable sites away from the range of *Hypsipyla grandella* Zell. have proved exceptionally productive for pure stands. The disadvantages of naturally short periods of seed viability are countered by regular fruiting and the development of appropriate seed storage procedures. *Cordia* is less susceptible to pest and disease attack and is able to develop as stands where light is adequate. Seeds are readily available and, as storage methods have been devised, there is increasing interest in its use as an exotic species.

The African species

Thirteen species of African origin are listed. Most have not become routinely used plantation trees and have received, at best, limited attention alongside efforts dedicated to major plantation species. As current emphasis is on good form and fast growth rather than on wood quality, formal silvicultural interest in the specialized ornamental and cabinet woods, and even the West African mahoganies, has diminished. Slow growth has been one contributory element. Another has been general failure to establish stands because inadequate seed technology limited germination success – notably with *Diospyros* – especially when combined with other adverse features. In the case of the mahoganies (*Entandrophragma* and *Khaya*), losses at the seedling stage, due to the depredations of *Hypsipyla robusta* Moore, have been the primary impediment. In addition, recorded individual growth rates have rarely reached the values sought today. *Lovoa*, the solitary listed meliaceous species free of *Hypsipyla* attacks, is also slow-growing compared with today's preferred plantation species. For all the Meliaceae listed, progress has been made in extending seed viability. Nevertheless, ensuring this and using nurse crops to provide the shade needed at the seedling stage (and essential to reduce *Entandrophragma* and *Khaya* exposure to *Hypsipyla* attack) are management complications. *Milicia*, the remaining neglected member of the listed African species, has a high light requirement. This is a species ill-suited to growth in high-density stands because of a serious pest – the gall bug *Phytolyma*. The plasticity of open-grown form associated with Troll's architectural model (Hallé et al., 1978) is a problematical feature. Seed viability is short and there are attendant problems of storage, but fruiting is sufficiently frequent to allow use of fresh seed as required.

The African species enjoying continuing forestry interest, with the sole exception of *Maesopsis*, have been used routinely only within the continent. Although *Maesopsis* has somewhat extended seed viability, simplifying transfer beyond Africa, for none of these species is seed amenable to storage in ambient conditions. All six species are considered to need high light intensity as seedlings. *Aucoumea* and *Maesopsis* are gregarious and stocking of *Terminalia superba* and *Triplochiton* reaches high values towards the drier, more seasonal, forest limit. Greater acceptability where they are most familiar has been translated into robust local markets. These have been supplied until now with logs harvested from natural forests. Markets have not developed elsewhere because of a combination of biological, management and utilization disadvantages. *Triplochiton* yields seed so infrequently that long-term planting targets could not be set until recent successes with the mass production of vegetatively propagated stock (Verhaegen et al., 1992). The performance of *Aucoumea* has been disappointing west of Cameroon, suggesting that it has poor tolerance of more seasonal climates. For architectural reasons, *Terminalia* (Aubréville's model) requires such wide spacing in pure production stands that the attraction of acknowledged fast growth is offset by a reduced number of trees per unit area. *Maesopsis* has suffered pest problems as an exotic and in Malaysia, where good growth has been demonstrated, evident suitability as a pulping wood is questioned as sufficient justification for its use. *Nauclea* displays very rapid early height growth on suitable (highly fertile) sites but much reduced increment beyond the pole stage (Kio, 1976) – indicating unrealistically long rotations for saw-timber.

The Asian/Pacific species

The Asian/Pacific species illustrate patterns similar to the African ones. Formal interest in *Palaquium* lapsed with the collapse of the *gutta-percha* market but it is evident, from early experience summarized by Barnard (1954), that natural regeneration interventions to raise production levels were not worthwhile. The more effective plantation approach is not well-reported in the Malaysia forestry literature, although it is clear that the area involved was no more than a few hundred hectares by 1912 (Barnard, 1954). More information relates to activities in Indonesia – abstracts are included by Goor and Kartasubrata (1982). *Neobalanocarpus* and *Shorea curtisii*, have not proved amenable to plantation action. For *Dryobalanops* and *Shorea leprosula*, artificial regeneration prospects are better. The last two species, in addition, have been regenerated quite successfully with the Malayan Uniform System and the Selective Management System (Salleh Mohd Nor, 1988). However, the success of these systems derives from the overall prominence of economic species, especially light hardwoods, in the regeneration and does not depend only on the abundance of *Dryobalanops* and *Shorea leprosula*. A greater level of natural regeneration has been achieved in Malaysia than in the African mahogany-producing forests where the scarcity of seedlings of any economic species has long caused concern.

Among the listed Asian/Pacific species are several of current significance as exotic plantation species. As for Africa, some have only (*Shorea robusta*), or principally (*Neolamarckia, Paraserianthes*), regional resource value. Thus, in India, previously acceptable natural regeneration systems for drier forests rich in *Shorea robusta* have fallen into disuse. They have been replaced by planting programmes. Growth rates, form and the working properties of the timber are, however, not good enough to invite adoption outside the natural range of the species. *Neolamarckia* and *Paraserianthes* are pioneer species with extended seed viability and forestry appeal for their fast-growth (particularly *Paraserianthes*, reputed to be the fastest-growing of all trees). Only limited areas of the moist tropics are potentially suitable for these species. Their disadvantages are that they have no major forestry role other than pulpwood production and require climates with little or no dry season. *Neolamarckia* is very site sensitive. *Eucalyptus* has much in common with *Neolamarckia* and *Paraserianthes* in terms of forestry interest: fast growth, gregariousness and colonizing behaviour. Disadvantages are also shared: primary potential use is for pulp and it requires a climate without a pronounced dry season particularly in the case of *E. deglupta*. The speed of adoption beyond the natural range is attributable to the established reputation of *Eucalyptus* as a genus. It is relatively free of pests, form is excellent and growth is fast. As exotics, *Gmelina* and *Tectona*, the remaining species, are the most firmly established of all. *Gmelina* and *Tectona* owe much of their acceptance and success at the present time to their long silvicultural history. Silvicultural routines have been devised by trial and error and extensive research activity, securing their status as resources. Relatively precise characterization of environmental requirements engenders more confidence in choosing appropriate planting sites. Available tables and equations allow prediction of yields and, especially for *Tectona*, provenances can be matched to the site conditions envisaged. Utilization motivation is strong, based on exceptional quality as a plantation grown wood (*Tectona*) or predictability of pulp yield on predetermined short rotations (*Gmelina*). Nevertheless, to attain this situation with *Gmelina* and *Tectona* it has been necessary to ensure a regular supply of planting stock by complex seed pretreatment procedures (*Tectona*) and to evade pests by moving away from the natural range (*Gmelina*). It is doubtful if such perseverence would be forthcoming for any species attracting silvicultural attention for the first time today.

SEEDLINGS IN FOREST CONDITIONS

For about half the species listed in the Appendix, plantation initiatives have succeeded. Nursery routines for these guarantee planting stock as required and reliance is on artificial regeneration. For most of the remaining species artificial regeneration is still of little or no importance and any measures to sustain

143

supplies are by management to promote regeneration in the forest. Ecological studies of these species provide guidance for refining management interventions to improve establishment and growth. A review of natural regeneration field experience has been given by Baur (1968), although in his account all natural regeneration work is combined and seedlings are not considered separately. Relevant natural regeneration work has mainly been in West Africa, Uganda and Malaysia and the paucity of reports from the neotropics is noteworthy.

Primary forestry concern was to decide how much of a management unit was stocked with regeneration. Simple routines were employed for this, the main concession to quantification being adoption of a standard recording unit of 0.0004 ha (0.001 acre). However, these were aggregated into transects 1 km or more in length and only about 2 m wide, and not compact areas. Procedure was to score only the regenerating individual considered most likely to be a tree for future exploitation (namely, 'leading desirable'). Plants smaller and/or of species inferior in the quality ranking of the time were disregarded. Individuals were not monitored and only the crudest indication of seedling distribution through the forest emerged.

The environmental factor most often given attention has been light. A limitation of forestry's natural regeneration research has been that little account was taken of change in light conditions over time. Also, most studies were done when assessment could only be in subjective or relative terms. Even in more closely controlled experimental work on seedling growth in different light regimes, values were expressed as percentage of full exposure rather than as levels of irradiance (e.g. Nicholson, 1960; Wadsworth and Lawton, 1968).

Within the different countries, more specific studies have been carried out but the data sets assembled have often been extremely limited where species noteworthy in forestry are concerned. Surprisingly few seedling studies relating to typical forest conditions are reported by foresters in major research journals. Most ecological comments in general accounts of particular species of interest (e.g. Symington, 1943; Taylor, 1960) originate in observations of natural regeneration in the field (e.g. Wyatt-Smith, 1958 – *Shorea leprosula*; Wyatt-Smith, 1960 – *Neobalanocarpus, Shorea leprosula*). Studies by biologists tend to focus on species selected because they were thought to contrast in character or were convenient or intriguing to study (e.g. Njoku, 1964). Occasionally, species listed in the Appendix were involved, but rarely in a context relevant to natural regeneration initiatives.

Reports from the neotropics refer to *Ocotea* and *Swietenia* in forest conditions. Where stocking is highest, *Ocotea* contributes over 40 per cent of individuals >40 cm diameter at breast height and seedling populations of 5,000 ha^{-1} and 20,000 ha^{-1} have been estimated (Clarke, 1956; Steege, 1990). Few of these seedlings persist. Further development may be arrested by exposed conditions or in gaps where more vigorous regrowth suppresses the slow-growing *Ocotea* seedlings. At the other extreme seedlings do not survive in heavy shade, perhaps combined with competition for other resources, beneath parent trees. At an early stage a high proportion of seedlings may be attacked by phytophagous insects – Steege (1990) gives a figure of 40 per cent. Seedling growth is slow (Fanshawe, 1947).

Lamb (1966) reviews information on *Swietenia* and describes the species as a pioneer. In heavy shade survival is for only a few months. Gaps are not essential for germination, however, and in moderate shade seedlings persist, retaining the capacity to recover from suppression if overhead light increases sufficiently. Young seedlings are sensitive to extended droughts and at risk from the shoot-borer (*Hypsipyla grandella*). Lamb notes an ability to recover from fire damage.

None of several reviews of management initiatives including natural regeneration in African forest (Lawton, 1978; Okali, 1979; Wadsworth, 1987; FAO 1989) offers ecological insight at the species level, where the seedling phase is concerned. There have been, however, studies involving the Meliaceae and *Milicia*.

Khaya ivorensis, Lovoa and *Milicia* have all been evaluated for line planting as seedlings in forest (Cooper, 1961): the two Meliaceae survived and grew in 'light to somewhat heavy' shade but *Milicia* performed poorly in these conditions. Similar findings resulted from most other studies. Natural regeneration and line planting work in Uganda has been reviewed by Synnott (1975) who also conducted a series of experiments on *Entandrophragma utile*. Seedling mortality and growth, in relation to watering and shade were monitored. It was concluded that *E. utile* could grow in some shade but responded to increased light with accelerated increment. However, mortality among seedlings was higher with more exposure. More seedlings became established where litter was present.

In experimental monitoring, seedling growth of *Khaya* (Wadsworth and Lawton, 1968; Okali and Dodoo, 1973) has been quantified, in accordance with the concepts of net assimilation rate, relative growth rate and leaf area ratio. Okali and Dodoo (1973) found the leaf anatomy and specific leaf area of *Khaya ivorensis* indicative of adaptation to shaded conditions. For another member of the genus, *Khaya grandifoliola*, the ability to grow at low light intensities was indicated (Wadsworth and Lawton, 1968). Jackson (1973) tallied seedlings of the same species in a forest outlier in Nigeria. None of 237 seedlings (stocking $1,900 \, ha^{-1}$) survived for ten years in plots undisturbed apart from a single climber cutting. In contrast with Wadsworth and Lawton, Jackson concluded that despite slow growth the species was a pioneer.

There has been study of the response of *Milicia* seedlings to a range of day lengths (Longman, 1966, 1978) but as these depart from natural conditions few inferences of ecological value result. Other work (Okali, 1971, 1972) reveals *Milicia* is less tolerant than *Khaya* of low light, underlining its lack of appeal as a management subject within the forest as well as its problematical character for artificial regeneration mentioned above. *Milicia* has recently received attention from Riddoch et al. (1991) using more sophisticated techniques and instruments. Leaf chamber studies of photosynthetic parameters were made on seedlings in Nigerian forest and related to diurnal variations in ambient conditions. The CO_2 concentrations were $350–420 \, \mu mol \, mol^{-1}$ and photon flux densities ranging from $< 50 \, \mu mol \, m^{-2} \, s^{-1}$ to $800 \, \mu mol \, m^{-2} \, s^{-1}$. Mesophyll conductance $(0.019 \, mol \, m^{-2} \, s^{-1})$, apparent quantum efficiency $(0.036 \, mol \, CO_2 \, photon^{-1})$ and dark respiration rate $(1.1 \, \mu mol \, m^{-2} \, s^{-1})$ were all considered high values typifying the photosynthetic characteristics of a pioneer species *sensu* Swaine and Whitmore (1988).

In Malaysia, past experience has engendered more confidence in natural forest management than in Africa. Interest has been maintained in the regeneration of species in the forest environment alongside increasing plantation activity. Most emphasis has been on *Shorea leprosula*. Wyatt-Smith (1958) drew attention to the persistence in shade of seedlings of *S. leprosula* but recorded more establishment and persistence where operations to increase overhead light had been conducted (Wyatt-Smith, 1960). Nicholson (1960) raised more robust *S. leprosula* plants at 50 per cent full daylight than at 75 per cent, 87.5 per cent or 100 per cent. Fox (1973) assessed *S. leprosula* seedling growth rates in forest conditions. Liew and Wong (1973) assessed density, recruitment, mortality and growth rates in virgin and logged-over forest. Chan (1980) carried out a more detailed examination of seedling populations, finding no consistent patterns and concluding that for *S. leprosula* there was no reason to accept the idea of density-dependent predation determining distribution and survival. Several studies consider the vulnerability of *S. leprosula* seedlings to damage. Daljeet-Singh (1975) found low incidence of borer attacks of line-planted individuals 0.3–2 years old. Becker's (1981) confirmation of the presence of phenolics and proanthocyanidin in seedling foliage may be a contributory factor. Becker (1985), however, reported catastrophic wild boar damage. Association of *S. leprosula* with mycorrhizae has also been confirmed (Becker, 1983). On 3.5-year-old seedlings ectomycorrhizae were not a constant feature but 70 per cent of individuals were infected. Incidence of infection was higher in more open parts of a site at Pasoh than under a closed canopy.

Field observations have been made on *S. curtisii* as part of an appraisal of the autecology of the species (Burgess, 1969) and in relation to measures to suppress *Eugeissona tristis* Griffith (Arecaceae), an associated species (Chong, 1970). When the palm was suppressed, the establishment of *Shorea curtisii* seedlings was enhanced and their growth accelerated. Turner (1989) grew *S. curtisii* seedlings in shade provided by a natural canopy and under screens incorporating a filter to simulate the red:far red ratio (R:FR) below a natural canopy. The fastest growth over six months was at the lightest shading

(70 μmol m^{-2} s^{-1}, R:FR ≈ 0.7) as it was with *S. macroptera* Dyer, included for comparison. However, in heavier shade (25 μmol m^{-2} s^{-1}, R:FR ≈ 0.4) growth was significantly faster in *S. curtisii* than in *S. macroptera*. Turner inferred from this that the former was better adapted than the latter to gap edge/small gap conditions. Wyatt-Smith (1960) reported that the growth of *Neobalanocarpus* seedlings was slow. Mori et al. (1990) grew this species experimentally to represent the response of a slow-growing forest tree to a range of temperatures and light intensities. At light intensity equivalent to an open situation (>400 μmol m^{-2} s^{-1}) net photosynthesis was highest (3.8 μmol m^{-2} s^{-1}) at 27°C. With leaf temperature maintained at 28°C net photosynthesis was highest (3–8 μmol CO_2 m^{-2} s^{-1}) at a photon flux density of 200–300 μmol m^{-2} s^{-1}. Net photosynthesis in *Neobalanocarpus* declined sharply as temperature rose above 27°C or light intensity increased to more than 400 μmol m^{-2} s^{-1}. *Dryobalanops*, included in the same study, displayed a similar peak rate of net photosynthesis but at a higher temperature (29.5°C) and maintained it under photon flux densities as high as 600 μmol m^{-2} s^{-1}. Mori et al. (1990) interpreted their results as evidence that *Neobalanocarpus* was adapted for a stable, sheltered forest environment.

SEEDLINGS AND ARTIFICIAL REGENERATION

In artificial regeneration, only a small number of tropical plantation species are widely used and there have been calls to diversify the resource base. This pressure reflects current concerns over the environment and biodiversity. Nevertheless, the management attractions of confining action to the species currently in use are obvious. They can be handled with near-identical procedures. The training of staff is simplified and, ostensibly, more cost-effective and efficient plantation programmes operate. With allowance for dry season interruption where appropriate, continual fast growth typifies forestry's favoured species, minimizing rotation length. Most of them are relatively free of pests, given suitable growing conditions. The rest are pest-free when used outside their natural ranges. Fast growth and freedom from pests are attributes associated with aggressive secondary species. These are naturally species of forest edges or rather unstable riverine situations, where disturbances constantly open new sites for colonization. All the favoured species are, at least at the seedling/sapling stages, gregarious and most live for decades rather than centuries.

The environment of a nursery-raised seedling and that for seedlings arising spontaneously within the forest contrast sharply. Light and temperature conditions are provided in the nursery which approach the optimum as far as facilities permit. Competition between neighbouring seedlings is eliminated. Potting mixtures routinely ensure good aeration and moisture retention and a balanced nutrient content, and are made weakly acid to inhibit fungal pests.

These contrasts have led to two lines of research with plantation species, although their relevance to seedling ecology within forest ecosystems is limited. The studies are conventional experiments with conditions of light, temperature, moisture and nutrition prescribed, or held within narrow limits. Both lines acknowledge the light-demanding nature of the species by including exposure to high light among the treatments. One involves monitoring growth under conditions known to be favourable and assessing sensitivity to departure from these. For example, Ladipo et al. (1984) measured photosynthetic parameters of *Triplochiton* seedlings in relation to irradiance and Kwesiga and Grace (1986) evaluated the response of *Terminalia ivorensis* to differences in R:FR ratio. The second line has been to manipulate growing conditions other than the light regime to enhance gowth. Thus Fasehun (1979) compared seedling growth in *Gmelina* at different soil matric potentials and Aluko and Aduayi (1983) applied different fertilizer treatments to *Terminalia ivorensis* seedlings.

DISCUSSION

Tropical forestry has seen interest switch from an exclusively trade-driven assemblage of high quality hardwood species (e.g. Meliaceae, *Tectona*) to fast-growing species amenable to uncomplicated silviculture. This change was essentially synchronous with the era when many tropical forest countries became independent and redefined forest policies. The priority became accelerated volume production, uniform in quality, in anticipation of internal need surpassing export trade in importance. Only the most firmly established of the traditionally sought species, such as *Cedrela, Gmelina, Swietenia* and *Tectona*, survived this transition. Forestry is presently preoccupied with light-demanding species which qualify as 'pioneers' (*sensu* Swaine and Whitmore, 1988), *Tectona* being the exception.

Most forest-based work on seeds, seedlings and regeneration was effectively suspended before any research or monitoring protocols were generally adopted. Emphasis on simplicity has drastically restricted forestry's contribution to today's knowledge of seedling ecology. The renewed interest in forest ecosystems has been in a wider context. Forestry has extended interest to 'lesser known species', to the wider implementation of polycyclic silvicultural systems and to environmentally sound harvesting. Biodiversity conservation and sustainable management principles are taken into account. Collectively (sustainable forest management) and on a species-by-species basis (biodiversity conservation), the responses of seedlings to management action require evaluation. Comparative studies within a specific framework of ecological information on forest tree seedlings – an aspect of the standardized data sought by Oldeman and van Dijk (1991) – would contribute to this.

A three-part framework is suggested. Within each part a range of aspects arise:

(1) Biological characteristics of the species,
   Aspects of seed biology: periodicity of availability, dispersal, dormancy, viability, germination period,
   Aspects of seedling growth:
   germination type, seedling architecture, rate of development, growth periodicity,

(2) Environmental factors affecting the individual,
   Atmospheric factors:
   light regime, humidity, temperature,
   Soil factors:
   moisture, fertility, reaction,
   Influence of other individuals and organisms:
   allelopathy, symbiosis, competition, pests and diseases, browsing, presence of litter,
   Unpredictable catastrophic events:
   fire, drought/flood, erosion/deposition, cyclones, and

(3) Population dynamics,
   Establishment rates,
   Survival,
   Density.

Existing information for the species relevant to this review is scattered and fragmentary. Unified accounts of different species are mostly brief and inconsistent in content. Even in longer accounts the treatment of seedlings and their ecology is superficial. Only for *Shorea robusta* (Joshi, 1980) is there extensive coverage of seedling biology and ecology in relation to forestry and interest in this species is limited.

Seed biology information can be retrieved from conventional descriptions of species and seed laboratory records but, surprisingly, is often unsatisfactory. Weights reported may refer to propagules rather than seed in the strict sense. Sometimes figures denote the estimated number viable per unit weight of bulk seed material. Estimates of time to germination also lack a consistent basis. There has been little standardization of conditions prevailing for assessment. Nor have there been assessments of success in natural conditions. There is obvious scope for allocating all the species to classes within schemes such as that of Ng (1978) who defined size and germination rate categories (see also Garwood, 1996). Seed size is concentrated in the smaller categories (seed length <2 cm) among the 'favoured' species of this review. With these species, germination is mostly rapid (most seed that germinates does so in <12 weeks from sowing).

Aspects of seedling growth are poorly documented except with respect to germination type and seedling height growth. Germination type is consistently epigeal among currently favoured species. More elaborate classifications (Ng, 1978, 1991; Hladik and Miquel, 1990) which have revealed correlations of germination type with seed size, dispersal and ability to become established under definable conditions, now invite foresters' attention. Reports of seedling height growth, however, lack a consistent basis. Rates refer to periods which vary widely with species and locality and relate to forest nurseries or plants initially raised there. Seedling architecture and growth periodicity appear to have received negligible attention in forestry.

Awareness of relationships with environmental factors mainly results from incidental observations. Comment is frequent on the adverse effect of excessive or extended shading on the favoured species. Most of the species receiving less attention than formerly are described as shade-demanding or are (especially the dipterocarps) well known for the occurrence in shade of healthy advance growth which responds to increased light. For most species, including *Nauclea* and *Neolamarckia*, species typical of sites in low toposequence positions, healthy growth requires good drainage. Only *Aucoumea* has been associated with waterlogging. This species grows more rapidly where drainage is better (Becking, 1960). It is, however, rarely clear if comments refer to site relations applicable to mature trees or to regeneration or both.

Understanding of how the species considered here relate to other organisms in the community is rudimentary. No reports of allelopathy were located. Only for two species (*Eucalyptus deglupta* and *Shorea leprosula*) was any association of the seedlings with mycorrhizae noted. Close relationships with ants are reported for *Cordia*. On reaching a height of about 30 cm, domatia develop which in the natural range become colonized by ants. Some ant species, such as *Azteca longiceps*, are obligate tenants but the relationship is not considered symbiotic (Greaves and McCarter, 1990). Competition from other plants has been cited as a management problem for several species. This has usually been in the context of artificial regeneration activities when vigorous grass growth overwhelms the trees – particularly if their development is checked by fire. For *Cordia, Gmelina, Maesopsis, Nauclea, Neolamarckia, Paraserianthes* and *Terminalia superba*, litter fall from conspecific or other individuals has been regarded as an obstacle to establishment. New stands of these species, like those of many other pioneers, typically develop on exposed soil surfaces.

Once transferred from the nursery to the field, attacks from many pests can no longer be prevented. This has been a major determinant of the species used and where they are planted. Specialized pests and diseases noted on seedlings in nurseries and newly established plantations are often mentioned in silvicultural profiles or data sheets. It is not clear, however, how experience with artificial regeneration relates to their incidence on natural regeneration. Browsing animals are more strongly polyphagous than many insect pests and most tree species in the field are at risk if accessible to game or stock. *Eucalyptus* and other aromatic species are relatively immune and *Cedrela* and *Tectona* also suffer little browsing.

The consequences of catastrophic events on seedling dispersal, establishment and survival for the forestry species are a further gap in knowledge. Sensitivity to fire at the seedling stage can be assumed for most of the favoured species, There are noteworthy exceptions. Young *Tectona*, while the aerial organs may be lost repeatedly, ultimately produce a perennial, fire-tolerant shoot (Troup, 1921). A degree of fire tolerance in *Swietenia* seedlings has been mentioned above. *Shorea robusta* behaves similarly to *Tectona* (Joshi, 1980).

Seedling population dynamics at the species level are very superficially treated in the most accessible forestry literature. Archival records, however, are likely to be much more comprehensive. Published comments are essentially subjective but highlight the abundance of regeneration for the favoured species generally. Mostly this regeneration occurs around parents but sometimes elsewhere. With *Neolamarckia*, which germinates most successfully in disturbed, exposed soil, concentrations of seedlings occur around spar trees in logging areas. For the African Meliaceae, heavy pre-germination predation of dispersed seed drastically reduces seedling populations. This is one of the features of these species which forestry has found discouraging. Post-establishment losses have been mentioned as features of several species, in some cases with suggested explanations (*Cedrela* and *Swietenia* – poor survival in forest; *Nauclea* due to shade and insects). Evident need remains for more systematic analysis of causes of mortality and more quantitative appraisals. Estimates of seedling density per hectare of a species vary enormously – figures from fewer than fifty to tens of thousands are often reported. Differences between species can be expected and within a species the number of seed sources per unit area may vary. Much variation, however, can be explained by inconsistent methodology, particularly sample timing relative to dispersal events and the definition of 'seedling' used. There is also variation between studies in area sampled and how this is subdivided and distributed.

A gulf remains between the forester and the ecologist. Ideas and techniques already accepted by the ecologist have been neglected or little applied for species favoured by forestry. A generation of foresters has developed which largely lacks experience beyond artificial regeneration. Professional preparation has been for a future geared to rapid wood production by simple, prescribed routines applied to only a handful of species. More is expected of their successors as resource interest diversifies in terms of both forest products and forest functions. To understand ecological processes and interactions in the natural environment at both tree and stand level will become essential. Some relevant information will come from experience with key plantation species and the re-introduction of seed/seedling studies in the forest. More significant, however, will be integration and refinement of foresters and ecologists knowledge and its application in the resource context. The ecology of forest tree seedlings needs elucidation through defined research frameworks rather than opportunistically. Encouragingly, the first signs that this need is acknowledged are already emerging (e.g. Anderson, 1990; Ng, 1991).

REFERENCES

Aluko, A.P. and Aduayi, E.A. (1983). Response of forest tree seedlings *(Terminalia ivorensis)* to varying levels of nitrogen and phosphorus fertilizers. *Journal of Plant Nutrition*, **6**, 219–38.

Anderson, A.B. (1990). *Alternatives to Deforestation: Steps toward Sustainable Use of the Amazon Rain Forest.* Columbia University Press, New York.

Barnard, R.C. (1954). A manual of Malayan silviculture for inland lowland forests. *Forest Research Institute Pamphlet*, **14**, 1–199.

Baur, G.N. (1968). *The Ecological Basis of Rainforest Management.* Forestry Commission of New South Wales, Sydney.

Becker, P. (1981). Potential physical and chemical defenses of *Shorea* seedling leaves against insects. *Malaysian Forester*, **44**, 346–56.

Becker, P. (1983). Ectomycorrhizae on *Shorea* (Dipterocarpaceae) seedlings in a lowland Malaysian rainforest. *Malaysian Forester*, **46**, 146–70.

Becker, P. (l985). Catastrophic mortality of *Shorea leprosula* juveniles in a small gap. *Malaysian Forester*, **48**, 263–5.

Becking, R.W. (1960). A summary of information on *Aucoumea klaineana. Forestry Abstracts*, **21**, 1–6; 163–72.

Burgess, P.F. (1969). Preliminary observations on the autecology of *Shorea curtisii* Dyer ex King in the Malay Peninsula. *Malaysian Forester*, **32**, 438.

Chan, H.T. (1980). Reproductive biology of some Malaysian dipterocarps. II. Fruiting biology and seedling studies. *Malaysian Forester*, **43**, 438–51.

Chong, P.W. (1970). The effect of bertam control on regeneration of *Shorea curtisii* Dyer. *Malaysian Forester*, **33**, 166–82.

Clarke, E.G. (1956). The regeneration of worked-out greenheart *(Ocotea rodiaei)* forest in British Guiana. *Empire Forestry Review*, **35**, 173–83.

Cooper, L.G. (1961). Line planting. *Nigeria Federal Department of Forest Research Technical Note*, **9**, 1–15.

Daljeet-Singh, K. (1975). A preliminary survey of insect attack on seedlings and saplings in Bukit Belata Forest Reserve. *Malaysian Forester*, **38**, 14–16.

Eggeling, W.J. and Harris, C.M. (1939). *Fifteen Uganda Timbers.* Clarendon Press, Oxford.

Fanshawe, D.B. (1947). Studies of the trees of British Guiana. II. Greenheart *(Ocotea rodiaei). Tropical Woods*, **92**, 25–40.

FAO (1981). Eucalypts for planting. *FAO Forestry Series*, **11**, 1–677.

FAO (1986). Databook on endangered tree and shrub species and provenances. *FAO Forestry Paper*, **77**, 1–524.

FAO (1989). Review of forest management systems of tropical Asia. *FAO Forestry Paper*, **89**, 1–228.

FAO (1993). Management and conservation of closed forests in tropical America. *FAO Forestry Paper*, **101**, 1–141.

Fasehun, F.E. (1979). Effects of soil matric potential on leaf water potential, diffusive resistance, growth and development of *Gmelina arborea* L. seedlings. *Biologia Plantarum*, **21**, 100–4.

Fox, J.E.D. (1973). Dipterocarp seedling behaviour in Sabah. *Malaysian Forester*, **36**, 205–14.

Garwood, N.C. (1996). Functional morphology of tropical tree seedlings. In Swaine, M.D. (ed.) *Ecology of Tropical Forest Tree Seedlings*, pp. 59–138. UNESCO/ Parthenon, Paris/Carnforth.

Goor, C.P. van and Kartasubrata, J. (1982). *Indonesian forestry abstracts: Dutch literature until about 1960.* Centre for Agricultural Publishing and Documentation, Wageningen.

Greaves, A. (1981). *Gmelina arborea. Forestry Abstracts*, **42**, 237–58.

Greaves, A. and McCarter, P.S. (1990). *Cordia alliodora*: promising tree for tropical agroforestry, *Tropical Forestry Papers*, **22**, 1–37.

Groulez, J. and Wood, P.J. (1985). *Terminalia superba:* a monograph. Centre Technique Forestier Tropical/Commonwealth Forestry Institute, Nogent-sur-Marne/ Oxford.

Hallé, F., Oldemann, R.A.A. and Tomlinson, P.B. (1978). *Tropical Trees and Forests: an Architectural Analysis.* Springer, Berlin.

Hladik, A. and Miquel, S. (1990). Seedling types and plant establishment in an African rain forest. In Bawa, K.S. and Hadley, M. (eds.) *Reproductive Ecology of Tropical Forest Plants*, pp. 261–82. UNESCO/Parthenon, Paris/Carnforth.

Irozuru, G.N. (1986). *Nauclea diderrichii*: a monograph and appraisal. M.Sc. thesis, UCNW, Bangor.

Jackson, J.K. (1973). Regeneration of *Khaya grandifoliala* in a forest outlier in northern Nigeria. *Nigeria Federal Department of Forest Research, Research Paper (Savanna Series)*, **27**, 1–6.

Jones, E.W. (1957). *Report on* Chlorophora. Her Majesty's Stationery Office, London.

Joshi, H.B. (1980). *The Silviculture of Indian Trees, Vol. II, Dipterocarpaceae*, 2nd edn. Government of India Controller of Publications, Delhi.

Kio, P.R.O. (1976). What future for natural regeneration of tropical high forest? An appraisal with examples from Nigeria and Uganda. *Commonwealth Forestry Review*, **55**, 309–18.

Kwesiga, F. and Grace, J. (1986). The role of the red/far-red ratio in the response of tropical tree seedlings to shade. *Annals of Botany*, **57**, 283–90.

Ladipo, D.O., Grace, J., Sandford, A.P. and Leakey, R.R.B. (1984). Clonal variation in photosynthetic and respiration rates and diffusive resistances in the tropical hardwood *Triplochiton scleroxylon* K. Schum. *Photosynthetica*, **18**, 20–7.

Lamb, A.F.A. (1968a). Gmelina arborea, *Fast Growing Timber Trees of the Lowland Tropics*, **1**, 1–31.

Lamb, A.F.A. (1968b). Cedrela odorata. *Fast Growing Timber Trees of the Lowland Tropics*, **2**, 1–46.

Lamb, A.F.A. and Ntima, O.O. (1971). Terminalia ivorensis. *Fast Growing Timber Trees of the Lowland Tropics*, **5**, 1–72.

Lamb, F.B. (1966). *Mahogany of Tropical America*. University of Michigan Press, Ann Arbor.

Lawton, R.M. (1978). The management and regeneration of some Nigerian high forest ecosystems. *UNESCO Natural Resources Research*, **14**, 580–8.

Liew, T.C. and Wong, F.O. (1973). Density, recruitment, mortality and growth of dipterocarp seedlings in virgin and logged-over forests in Sabah. *Malaysian Forester*, **36**, 3–15.

Longman, K.A. (1966). Effects of the length of the day on growth of West African trees. *Journal of the West African Science Association*, **11**, 3–10.

Longman, K.A. (1978). Control of shoot extension and dormancy: external and internal factors. In Tomlinson, P.B. and Zimmermann, M. H. (eds.) *Tropical Trees as Living Systems*, pp. 465–95. Cambridge University Press, Cambridge.

MacGregor, W.D. (1934). Silviculture of the mixed deciduous forests of Nigeria. *Oxford Forestry Memoirs*, **18**, 1–108.

Mondal, X.I. (1986). Maesopsis eminii *and its potential for plantation forestry in Bangladesh*. M.Sc. thesis, UCNW, Bangor.

Mori, T., Nakashizuka, T. and Sumizono, T. (1990). Growth and photosynthetic responses to temperature in several Malaysian tree species. *Journal of Tropical Forest Science*, **3**, 44–57.

Ng, F.S.P. (1978). Strategies of establishment in Malayan forest trees. In Tomlinson, F.B. and Zimmermann, M.H. (eds.) *Tropical Trees as Living Systems*, pp. 129–62. Cambridge University Press, Cambridge.

Ng, F.S.P. (1991). Manual of forest fruits, seeds and seedlings, Volume 1. *Malayan Forest Record*, **34**, 1–400.

Nicholson, D.I. (1960). Light requirements of seedlings of 5 species of Dipterocarpaceae. *Malayan Forester*, **23**, 344–56.

Njoku, E. (1964). Seasonal periodicity in the growth and development of some forest trees in Nigeria. II. Observations on seedlings. *Journal of Ecology*, **52**, 19–26.

Okali, D.U.U. (1971). Rates of dry matter production in some tropical forest tree seedlings. *Annals of Botany*, **35**, 87–97.

Okali, D.U.U. (1972). Growth rates of some West African forest tree seedlings in shade. *Annals of Botany*, **36**, 953–9.

Okali, D.U.U. (1979). *The Nigerian Rainforest Ecosystem*. Federal Ministry of Science and Technology/MAB, Ibadan.

Okali, D.U.U. and Dodoo, G. (1973). Seedling growth and transpiration of two West African mahogany species in relation to water stress in the root medium. *Journal of Ecology*, **61**, 421–38.

Oldeman, R.A.A. and van Dijk, J. (1991). Diagnosis of the temperament of tropical rain forest trees. In Gomez-Pompa, A., Whitmore, T.C. and Hadley, M. (eds.), *Rain Forest Regeneration and Management*, pp. 21–65. UNESCO/Parthenon, Paris/Carnforth.

Riddoch, I., Grace, J., Fasehun, F. E., Riddoch, B. and Ladipo, D.O. (1991). Photosynthesis and successional status of seedlings in a tropical semi-deciduous rain forest in Nigeria. *Journal of Ecology*, **79**, 491–503.

Salleh Mohd Nor (1988). Forest management. In Earl of Cranbrook (ed.) *Malaysia*, pp. 126–37. Pergamon, Oxford.

Soerianegara, I. and Lemmens, R.H.M.J. (1993), Timber trees: major commercial timbers. *Plant Resources of South East Asia*, **5**. Pudoc, Wageningen.

Steege, H. ter (1990). *A monograph of wallaba, mora and greenheart*. Tropenbos, Ede.

Swaine, M.D. and Whitmore, T.C. (1988). On the definition of ecological groups in tropical rain forest. *Vegetatio*, **75**, 31–86.

Symington, C.F. (1943). Foresters' manual of dipterocarps. *Malayan Forest Record*, **16**, 1–244.

Synnott, T.J. (1975). *Factors affecting the regeneration and growth of seedlings of* Entandrophragma utile *(Dawe & Sprague) Sprague*. Ph.D. thesis, Makerere University.

Taylor, C.J. (1960). *Synecology and Silviculture in Ghana*. Nelson, Edinburgh.

Troup, A.S. (1921). *The Silviculture of Indian Trees*. Clarendon Press, Oxford.

Turner, I.M. (1989). A shading experiment on some tropical rain forest tree seedlings. *Journal of Tropical Forest Science*, **1**, 383–9.

Verhaegen, D., Kadio, A., Boutin, B., Delaunay, J and Legaré, D. (1992). Le Samba: selection phénotypique d'arbres ''+'' et production industrielle de boutures en Côte d'Ivoire. *Bois et Forêts des Tropiques*, **234**, 13–28.

Wadsworth, F.H. (1987). Applicability of Asian and African silviculture systems to naturally regenerated forests of the neotropics, In Mergen, F. and Vincent, J.R. (eds.) *Natural Management of Tropical Moist Forests: Silvicultural and Management Prospects of Sustained Utilization*, pp. 93–111. Yale University School of Forestry and Environmental Studies, New Haven.

Wadsworth, R.M. and Lawton, J.R.S. (1968). The effect of light intensity on the growth of seedlings of some tropical tree species. *Journal of the West African Science Association*, **13**, 211–14.

White, K.J. (1991). *Teak: some aspects of research and development*. FAO Regional Office for Asia and the Pacific, Bangkok.

Wyatt-Smith, J. (1958). Seedling/sapling survival of *Shorea leprosula, Shorea parvifolia Koompassia malaccensis. Malayan Forester*, **21**, 185–93 .

Wyatt-Smith, J. (1960). Diagnostic linear sampling of regeneration. *Malayan Forester*, **23**, 191–208.

APPENDIX

TROPICAL TREE SPECIES COMMANDING MOST FOREST MANAGEMENT INTEREST

(favoured species are asterisked)

Aucoumea klaineana Pierre   BURSERACEAE

Equatorial Africa; prominent in forestry activities from about 1900, particularly in natural regeneration and some enrichment action until about 1960; subsequently more often as a plantation species in the natural range (Becking, 1960).

Cedrela odorata Linn.   MELIACEAE
   South and Central America and the Caribbean; subject of research in relation to natural regeneration from the 1920s; most early plantation initiatives outside the natural range date from the same period; since 1960
   interest has been principally in plantation use in the humid tropics outside
   the natural range (Lamb, 1968b; FAO, 1986).

Cordia alliodora (Ruiz and Pavon) Oken   BORAGINACEAE
   South and Central America and the Caribbean; attracting forestry interest
   since the 1920s but to only a very limited extent until the 1960s since when
   it has been increasingly used as a plantation tree both within and outside
   the natural range (Greaves and McCarter, 1990).

Diospyros mespiliformis Hochst.   EBENACEAE
   Drier rain forests of West Africa (in riverain and outlying forest patches
   elsewhere on the continent); reflecting several decades as a major export
   timber, given limited attention in the 1920s and 1930s with regard mainly
   to natural regeneration; interest declined later (MacGregor, 1934).

Dryobalanops sumatrensis (J.F. Gmel.) Kosterm. DIPTEROCARPACEAE
   (Syn. *D. aromatica)*. Malesia; given attention in natural regeneration context from the 1920s (Soerianegara and Lemmens, 1993).

Entandrophragma cylindricum (Sprague) Sprague   MELIACEAE
   West and equatorial Africa; given attention in natural regeneration context
   from the 1920s (Eggeling and Harris, 1939; Taylor, 1960).

E. utile (Dawe and Sprague) Sprague   MELIACEAE
   West and equatorial Africa; given attention in natural regeneration context
   from 1930s (Eggeling and Harris, 1939; Taylor, 1960; Synnott, 1975).

Eucalyptus deglupta Blume   MYRTACEAE
   Malesia; given serious forestry attention from the 1940s, principally as a
   plantation species inside and beyond its natural range (FAO, 1981, 1986).

E. torelliana F. Muell.   MYRTACEAE
   Humid tropical Queensland; given serious forestry attention from the
   1960s, principally as an exotic plantation species in the humid tropics outside its natural range (FAO, 1981).

Gmelina arborea Linn.   VERBENACEAE
   Asian tropics; first used in forestry as a plantation species well before 1900
   but the early efforts, which were within its natural range, were not entirely
   successful; more rewarding results have been achieved with plantations
   established increasingly since the 1930s outside its natural range (Lamb,
   1968a; Greaves, 1981).

Khaya grandifoliola C. DC.   MELIACEAE
   Tropical Africa; serious forestry interest originated in the 1930s in attempts
   to raise the species in plantations (increasingly, associated with a nurse
   crop) but such interest – always limited – has been declining and reliance

has reverted to natural regeneration (MacGregor, 1934; Eggeling and Harris, 1939).

K. ivorensis A. Chev.   MELIACEAE

Tropical Africa; serious forestry interest originated in the 1920s which quickly developed into use associated with *Nauclea diderrichii* as a nurse crop but, as raising the latter pure has proved profitable, interest in *K. ivorensis* has reverted to the natural regeneration aspect (Taylor, 1960).

Lovoa trichilioides Harms   MELIACEAE

Tropical Africa; serious forestry interest originated in the 1920s with emphasis on natural regeneration – despite some subsequent success in establishing plantations within the natural range, the growth is slow compared with alternative species and natural regeneration remains the focus of forestry interest (Eggeling and Harris, 1939; Taylor, 1960).

*Maesopsis eminii Engl.   RHAMNACEAE

Tropical Africa; serious forestry interest originated in the 1930s and some plantations were established then in the eastern part of its range (where the mature trees are larger than further west – a clinal effect); from the 1950s the species was used in plantations elsewhere in the humid tropics – mainly the Far East – but this interest is declining (Mondal, 1986).

Milicia excelsa (Welw.) C.C. Berg   MORACEAE

(Syn. *Chlorophora excelsa)* Tropical Africa; serious forestry attention was given to this species before the First World War in attempts to promote natural regeneration; subsequent efforts to develop plantation techniques both within and beyond its natural range have had too little success to make this approach superior to reliance on natural regeneration (MacGregor, 1934; Eggeling and Harris, 1939; Jones, 1957; FAO, 1986).

*Nauclea diderrichii (De Wild. and Th. Dur.) Merr.   RUBIACEAE

Tropical Africa; serious forestry attention was first given to this species just before 1920 with plantation initiatives which have steadily expanded since; there have been some attempts to raise plantations in the tropics beyond Africa but these have not been significant and the main use remains for plantations in the western part of its natural range (Irozuru, 1986).

Neobalanocarpus heimii (King) Ashton   DIPTEROCARPACEAE

Malesia; given attention in natural regeneration context from the first decade of this century (Soerianegara and Lemmens, 1993).

*Neolamarckia cadamba (Roxb.) Bosser   RUBIACEAE

(Syn. *Anthocephalus chinensis*), Asian region; became prominent in forestry activities in the 1940s; adopted, mainly in its natural range, as a plantation species (Soerianegara and Lemmens, 1993).

Ocotea rodiaei Mez   LAURACEAE

Guyana; a renowned economic timber exploited for well over a century but not subjected to serious forestry attention until the 1950s, in relation to natural regeneration which remains the area of forestry interest (Fanshawe, 1947; Steege, 1990).

Palaquium gutta (Hooker f.) Baillon   SAPOTACEAE
Malesia; plantations were established within its natural range in the first decade of the century (primarily for *gutta-percha* latex, timber being a secondary consideration); since the Second World War synthetic alternatives have undermined the *gutta-percha* markets and interest has declined. Initiatives proposed some thirty years ago concerning natural regeneration have not been developed to any extent (Soerianegara and Lemmens, 1993).

*Paraserianthes falcataria (Linn.) Fosberg   LEG: PAPILIONOIDEAE
(Syn. *Albizia falcataria*). Malesia; initial commercial interest primarily as a shade tree and as such was spread far beyond its original range in association with tree and shrub crops from 1870 onwards; formal forestry interest developed in Hawaii in 1917 but accelerated sharply in the 1950s when knowledge of the wood quality indicated potential as a pulp source, prompting wide use as a plantation tree – mainly in Asia and the Pacific (Soerianegara and Lemmens, 1993).

Shorea curtisii King   DIPTEROCARPACEAE
South-East Asia; in connection with natural regeneration activities serious forestry interest originated in about 1920 but intensified in the period after the Second World War (Symington, 1943; Barnard, 1954; Baur, 1968).

S. leprosula Miq   DIPTEROCARPACAEAE
South-East Asia; serious forestry interest originated in the 1930s, involving both the natural regeneration and plantation aspects, although activities have remained within the natural range; artificial regeneration was pursued locally through *taungya* in the 1970s but has declined due to the appeal of faster-growing species now at the disposal of the forest services (Symington, 1943; FAO, 1989).

*S. robusta Gaertn. f.   DIPTEROCARPACEAE
South Asia at the drier extreme of tropical forest, particularly north-east India, the range extending north of the Tropic of Cancer; serious forestry interest originated about 1910 and the earliest plantations were established sixty years before; still only within its natural range, both artificial and natural regeneration continue to receive considerable attention although *S. robusta* is gradually being ousted by alternative species – particularly *Eucalyptus* and *Tectona* (Joshi, 1980; FAO, 1989).

*Swietenia macrophylla King   MELIACEAE
South and Central America; serious forestry interest extends back over a century to introductions to localities well outside the natural range and the initiation of continuing plantation programmes as an exotic species particularly in Sri Lanka (since 1897) and Fiji (since 1927) and natural regeneration initiatives seem to have been neglected – even within its natural range

emphasis has been on formal planting (Lamb, 1966; Soerianegara and Lemmens, 1993).

Tectona grandis Linn. f.   VERBENACEAE

South and South-East Asia; serious forestry attention turned to this species well before the end of the last century and has never waned; for over a century considerable effort has been devoted to natural regeneration in India and Myanmar and there are vigorous programmes of artificial regeneration throughout the tropics (Troup, 1921; White, 1991; Soerianegara and Lemmens, 1993).

Terminalia ivorensis A. Chev.   COMBRETACEAE

West tropical Africa; serious forestry attention originated around 1930 with use in artificial regeneration within the natural range, later (post-1950) being tried as an exotic species in other parts of the tropics; natural regeneration has received attention since the 1940s (Lamb and Ntima, 1971).

*T. superba Engl. and Diels   COMBRETACEAE

West tropical and equatorial Africa; serious forestry attention originated in the 1930s with artificial regeneration initiatives within its natural range, later (post-1950) being tried as an exotic plantation species in other parts of the tropics; natural regeneration has received attention since the 1940s (Groulez and Wood, 1985).

Triplochiton scleroxylon K. Schum.   STERCULIACEAE

West and equatorial tropical Africa; serious forestry interest originates from artificial regeneration in the 1920s; artificial regeneration activities remain restricted to its natural range but despite development of vegetative propagation techniques to overcome unpredictable seed availability the aggregate plantation area remains small and is not growing rapidly; natural regeneration activities originated in the 1940s (Taylor, 1960; Baur, 1968).

Revised manuscript received September 1994

Section 2

Research papers

CHAPTER 6

PERSISTENCE IN A TROPICAL UNDERSTOREY: CLONAL GROWTH IN PSYCHOTRIA HORIZONTALIS

Cynthia L. Sagers

INTRODUCTION

Most plant species bolster reproductive output by interspersing regular bouts of sexual reproduction with occasional vegetative efforts. Vegetative establishment by stems or leaves, stump sprouts, or root suckers, was once thought to be most common in grasslands, disturbed areas and high latitude, high elevation sites (Bell, 1982; Silander, 1985). Although many tropical species are known to reproduce vegetatively (Peñalosa, 1984; Gartner, 1989; Putz and Brokaw, 1989; Kinsman, 1990; Greig, 1991; Guariguata, 1992), studies of plant reproduction in the tropics have focused on sexual reproduction (Schemske, 1980; Horovitz and Schemske, 1988; Garwood, 1987; Augspurger and Franson, 1988; Schupp, 1990), or apomixis (Kaur et al., 1978; Ha et al., 1988).

In this article I suggest that vegetative reproduction is common in neotropical shrubs, that individuals vary in their ability to reproduce vegetatively and that selection during recruitment favours sexual propagules. I sampled common plants to determine which species can reproduce vegetatively. In one of these, *Psychotria horizontalis* Sw. (Rubiaceae), I investigated the establishment success of vegetative propagules and some mechanisms of propagule survival and establishment. The success of asexual propagules of *P. horizontalis* may be linked to properties such as tannin concentration, nitrogen content and photosynthesis. Finally, I use a demographic argument to evaluate the relative success of vegetative recruits into an adult, sexual population.

NATURAL HISTORY OF *PSYCHOTRIA HORIZONTALIS*

The genus *Psychotria* comprises approximately 1,650 species world-wide (Hamilton, 1989). *Psychotria horizontalis* is distributed throughout Central and South America and is abundant in the tropical moist forest on Barro Colorado Island, Panama (see Leigh et al. (1982) for a detailed site description). During the wet season (April–May), *P. horizontalis* produces heterostylous, self-sterile flowers that are visited by an array of hymenopteran and lepidopteran pollinators (Hamilton, 1989). Seeds have a dry season dormancy requirement with a mean latency to germination of 186 days (Garwood, 1979). The fleshy, red berries are often dispersed by understorey frugivorous birds, such as the red-capped manikin, though monkeys eat them as well (B. Mitchell, personal communication). Leaves are flushed early in the wet season (April–May), survive approximately 1 year and are abscised after leaf flush of the next wet season. Abscised leaves or leaf fragments may produce roots from the petiole or major veins and establish new plantlets (N. Garwood, personal communication). New ramets may be formed from broken stems, fallen leaves, or by root suckering.

METHODS

Vegetative propagation in common species

I assessed the capacity for vegetative propagation of thirteen species of understorey sub-canopy and canopy trees (Table 6.1). These species, representing eleven genera from nine plant families, are listed by Croat (1978) among the most common plants on Barro Colorado Island. In January 1990, I cut one shoot from ten individuals of each species, removed the leaves from each stem and kept both stems and leaves on damp sand in deep shade in a growing house. After three months I recorded leaf and stem survivorship.

Leaf fragments as propagules

Psychotria horizontalis readily produces new plants from leaf fragments and leaves may be an important source of recruits. Young plants produced vegetatively are easily recognized by a welt of callus tissue between the root and shoot (Sagers, 1993). To determine the frequency of vegetative propagules among young plants, small individuals of *P. horizontalis* were collected from six 2 m × 30 m transects in the understorey of a forested area thought to be undisturbed for about 300 years (Foster and Brokaw, 1982). Plants with woody growth were excluded to limit the sample to young plants. Collected plants were identified as either seedlings (absence of callus) or plantlets (presence of callus).

To evaluate the establishment success of leaf fragments, 100 fallen green leaves were found in the understorey and were marked nearby with plastic stakes. These leaves were censused at 20–40-day intervals from 10 December 1989 to 13 May 1991 (18 months). At each census, all 'missing' plantlets were presumed to have died.

Leaf properties

Many leaf characters are altered throughout the lifetime of a leaf. Characters such as nitrogen concentration, tannin content and photosynthetic rate, are

Table 6.1 Rooting success of stems and leaves for thiteen species of common understorey shrubs and sub-canopy trees. For each species, $n = 10$ for stems and leaves. Growth habit: t = tree, t/s = sub-canopy tree, s = shrub (classification by Croat, 1978)

	Stems	*Leaves*	*Habit*
Sorocea affinis Hemsl. (Moraceae)	0	0	t
Swartzia simplex Sw. (Caesalpinoideae)	0	0	t
Quassia amara L. (Simaroubaceae)	0	0	t/s
Ouratea lucens Engler (Ochnaceae)	0	0	t/s
Capparis frondosa Jacq. (Capparidaceae)	0	0	t/s
Rinorea sylvatica Seem. (Violaceae)	0	0	t/s
Hybanthus prunifolius Schult. (Violaceae)	6	0	t/s
Mouriri myrtilloides Sw. (Melastomataceae)	0	0	s
Acalypha diversifolia Jacq. (Euphorbiaceae)	4	3	s
Piper cordulatum C. DC. (Piperaceae)	4	9	s
Psychotria limonensis Krause (Rubiaceae)	2	2	s
Psychotria horizontalis Sw. (Rubiaceae)	*8*	*6*	*s*
Psychotria marginata Sw. (Rubiacieae)	*9*	*7*	*s*

likely to be important in successful plantlet establishment, but may be adversely affected in senescence. Most plants reclaim 50–90 per cent of leaf nitrogen during senescence (Fries, 1952; Williams, 1955; Guha and Mitchell, 1966). I compared nitrogen concentrations of abscising leaves with mature, attached leaves. Twenty plants were shaken. A fallen leaf and a remaining, fully expanded leaf were collected for comparison. Nitrogen concentration was measured using a micro-Kjeldahl procedure (Allen, 1974).

Leaves of *P. horizontalis* remain green on the forest floor long after abscission (M.A. Kobler, personal communication). To determine whether abscised leaves are capable of carbon gain, the carbon assimilation rate was measured on eight naturally-abscised, rooting leaves with a Li-Cor 6200 photosynthesis system at two light intensities; 0 and 800 μmol m^{-2} s^{-1} (dark respiration and saturating light levels, respectively; T. Kursar, personal communication). CO_2 concentration was maintained at 350 ppm. I subtracted dark respiration from net photosynthesis to obtain gross photosynthesis, a better estimate of photosynthetic capacity. Similar measures are reported for mature, attached leaves (J. Wright, unpublished data).

Total tannin concentration was measured as the amount of protein precipitated by a crude leaf extract (Hagerman, 1987). Condensed tannin was assessed with a procyanin reaction, a colorimetric procedure that measures the amount of condensed tannin precursor in solution (Mole and Waterman, 1987). I collected seventy naturally-abscised leaves from *P. horizontalis* plants growing in the understorey. A portion of each leaf was removed for tannin analysis and the remaining leaf fragment, which included the petiole, were tied to plastic markers and staked out in the forest understorey. Survivorship, establishment and shoot production were monitored monthly. After 12 months I harvested all survivors.

Variation in success among clones

To assess individual variation in the ability to propagate vegetatively, twelve stem cuttings were taken from each of eighty-eight plants growing in the understorey. Each stem was treated with a fungicide and rooting hormone (Rootone™), placed in a shaded, moist sand bench and left to root. Position within the growing house was assigned randomly. Survivorship within each clone was recorded after 6 weeks when all living stems had produced roots.

Patterns of polymorphism

The spatial distribution of genetic polymorphisms may reveal patterns of selection on vegetative recruits. *Psychotria horizontalis* flowers are dimorphic with a simple mode of inheritance (Hamilton, 1989), which makes style type a simple genetic marker. Further, *P. horizontalis* is self-sterile. Within a cluster of individuals, plants of different style type are necessarily progeny of different parents. In the absence of selection, clonal spread should generate a clumped distribution of morphs and seedling establishment should produce a more random pattern. Style morph was mapped for all flowering individuals of *P. horizontalis* on nine hectares of forest on Barro Colorado Island (R. Foster and S. Hubbell, unpublished data). An analysis of spatial autocorrelation was run to determine whether individuals with likestyle types have a clumped, non-random distribution.

RESULTS

Most understorey shrubs are able to root and initiate a shoot from above-ground vegetative structures. Three *Psychotria* species and two species from different genera (*Acalypha diversifolia* and *Piper cordulatum*) produced roots from cut stems or leaves, *Hybanthus prunifolius* produced roots from cut stems but not from leaves and the majority of trees and subcanopy trees did not root from either structure (Table 6.1).

Vegetative propagules of *P. horizontalis* establish and persist in the understorey. Of sixty-three small plants collected, fifty-eight (92 per cent) had a callus, wound tissue that distinguishes vegetative propagules, while the remaining plants lacked a callus and are presumed to have established as seedlings. Further, in the census of the naturally-abscised and rooting leaves 19 per cent (19/100) were surviving after 18 months.

Senescence clearly affects properties important for vegetative establishment (Table 6.2). Total tannin, condensed tannin and nitrogen concentration were

Table 6.2 Characteristics of abscised and attached, mature leaves of *Psychotria horizontalis*

	Abscised		*Attached*	*(n)*
Total tannin (mg/g FW)	27.4	***	37.4	(70)
Condensed tannin (mg/g FW)	10.8	***	13.7	(70)
Photosynthesis, 800 µmol/m^{-2} s^{-1}	2.5	ns	3.5	(8)
Nitrogen (mg/g DW)	18.4	**	19.9	(20

Table 6.3 Comparison of characters between *Psychotria horizontalis* leaves that survived to produce a plantlet and those that did not. Tannin concentrations are reported as in Table 6.2

	Surviving *(n = 34)*		*Dead* *(n = 36)*
Total tannin (mg/g FW)	26.1	ns	29.4
Condensedtannin (mg/g FW)	10.9	*	9.5
Leaf area (cm^2)	12.1	ns	11.9

Significance levels (Mann–Whitney U): ns $p > 0.05$, * $p < 0.01$

significantly reduced in the abscised leaves relative to mature, attached leaves. Despite this reduction, tannins in green fallen leaves appear to promote propagation. Condensed tannin concentrations were significantly higher in leaves that survived and established plantlets than in those that died (Table 6.3). Further, although nitrogen concentration in abscised leaves was reduced, assimilation rates at saturating light levels (800 µmol m^{-2} s^{-1}) did not differ. Leaf area did not differ significantly between the two groups (Table 6.3), but once established, larger leaves produced taller plantlets ($r^2 = 0.41$, $p = 0.001$, df = 24).

Parent individuals differed in their ability to establish vegetatively. In the growing house study, the proportion of cuttings that survived through the rooting phase varied among genotypes ($\chi^2 = 212.2$, $p < 0.001$, df = 87).

Spatial analysis demonstrates that though the species has a clumped distribution, individual stems are not clustered by style type (Moran's I = 0.005, $p = 0.10$) (Figure 6.1). These results are difficult to interpret, but suggest that vegetative propagules are no more successful than seedlings in recruiting into the adult stage.

DISCUSSION

Vegetative propagation is an important means of reproduction in *P. horizontalis*. Most newly established plants (92 per cent in this study) are products of leaf or stem rooting. The near absence of sexual propagules underscores the importance of vegetative reproduction for recruitment in this species. Fallen leaves had a 19 per cent probability of surviving 18 months, comparable to a 1-year survivorship

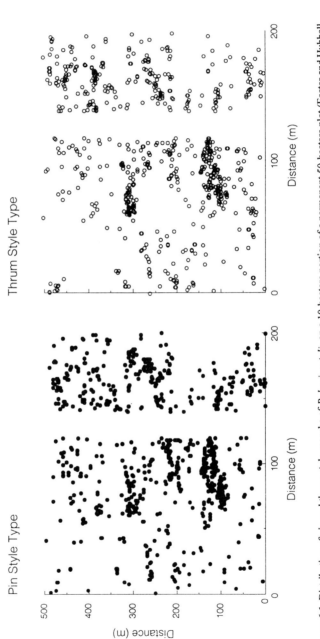

Figure 6.1 Distribution of pin and thrum style morphs of *P. horizontalis* on a 10-hectare portion of a permanent 50-hectare plot (Foster and Hubbell, unpublished data). No data were collected from the column at 120 m. (Note the scale change along the two axes)

of 20 per cent found for seedlings of *P. horizontalis* on Barro Colorado Island (N. Garwood, personal communication). This is not an isolated instance of a peculiar species. In the wet forest understorey at La Selva Biological Station, Costa Rica, Gartner (1989) found fifteen of sixteen species of *Piper* could root from stems. In a neotropical montane forest, Kinsman (1990) reported successful establishment from cut stems for twelve shrub species representing three plant families. Tropical shrubs reproduce vegetatively and at a rate that approaches the rate of successful seedling establishment.

Several characteristics of abscised leaves of *P. horizontalis* may promote successful vegetative establishment: retention of nitrogen, positive photosynthesis and elevated tannin concentrations. Although most plants recover 50–90 per cent of leaf nitrogen before senescence (Chapin, 1980), *P. horizontalis* removes only 7 per cent. This represents a substantial cost to the parent plant, one that may ultimately limit investment in vegetative growth. This may be an underestimate the actual assimilation rate for abscised leaves because CO_2 concentrations near the forest floor may reach 450 ppm (Bazzaz and Williams, 1991). The relatively high total tannin concentrations of *P. horizontalis* leaves may ward off fungal attack on the humid forest floor (Zucker, 1983). I suggest that retaining such unusually large nitrogen and perhaps carbon pools in abscised leaves may be an adaptation to enhance plantlet survival.

The genetic composition of plant populations is shaped by differential selection on vegetative and sexual propagules. Vegetative propagation will reduce the genotypic heterogeneity of the understorey community. In addition, if there is genetic variability in the capacity to reproduce asexually, some individuals will clone at higher rates than others, further reducing the heterogeneity of a population. In this study, stems of *P. horizontalis* cut from different individuals differed in their ability to root. It is possible, then, that some genotypes are better represented in the understorey than expected. The genetic diversity of *P. horizontalis* on Barro Colorado Island may therefore be very low. Conversely, large, monotypic stands of stems may be at a tremendous selective disadvantage. Monotypic stands provide concentrated resources that promote feeding and increase residence time by herbivores (Root, 1973) and may serve as reservoirs for genotype-specific pathogens (Augspurger, 1984). In addition, sexual recombination produces novel genotypes, presumably with unique combinations of defences. This novelty is itself a form of defence (Jones and Firn, 1991) that allows a further advantage to sexual propagules. Further preferential feeding within clones would increase the genotypic heterogeneity of the population by limiting the size of the existing clones or by restricting clonal establishment. Selection may be working to limit the size of clones, as evidenced by the low density of adults relative to juveniles, and the absence of clustering among common style morphs.

This report summarizes data on vegetative propagation in tropical understorey shrubs and in *P. horizontalis*, in particular. Little is known of the reproductive modes of canopy plants. The low rooting success of the sub-canopy and canopy trees (Table 6.1) suggests that vegetative propagation may be relatively unimportant for them. Further, vegetative reproduction by stems and leaves may be more common in tropical woody species than in temperate zones. Under an insulating layer of leaf litter, a *P. horizontalis* leaf or stem may survive a 3-month dry season while temperate winters may prohibit survival of plant fragments. Disturbance may also influence the relative importance of asexual reproduction. In fragmented forests, pollinators and dispersers may be limiting and vegetative establishment may become relatively more frequent. The ecological and evolutionary implications of asexual reproduction in woody plants deserve further attention.

ACKNOWLEDGMENTS

I thank Nimiadina de Gomez, José Lasso and Steve Travers for their diligence in the laboratory and field. Phyllis Coley and Tom Kursar introduced me to the wonders of Li-Cor 6200. I thank Phyllis Coley, Egbert G. Leigh, Jr. and two anonymous reviewers for their comments; Nancy Garwood, Robin Foster and Joseph Wright for allowing me to use unpublished data and Michael Swaine for inviting me to participate in this symposium. I am grateful to the Republic of Panama and the Smithsonian Tropical Research Institute for their co-operation and support. This work was funded by Sigma Xi, Fulbright and Smithsonian predoctoral fellowships and NSF doctoral dissertation improvement grant BSR 9001329.

REFERENCES

Allen, S.E. (1974). *Chemical Analysis of Ecological Materials*. Blackwell Scientific Publications, Oxford.

Augspurger, C.K. (1984). Seedling survival of tropical tree species: interactions of dispersal distance, light-gaps and pathogens. *Ecology*, **65**, 1705–12.

Augspurger, C.K. and Franson, S.E. (1988). Input of wind-dispersed seeds into light gaps and forest sites in a neotropical forest. *Journal of Tropical Ecology*, **4**, 239–52.

Bazzaz, F.A. and Williams, W.E. (1991). Atmospheric CO_2 concentrations within a mixed forest: implications for seedling growth. *Ecology*, **72**, 12–16.

Bell, G. (1982). *The Masterpiece of Nature*. University of California Press, Los Angeles.

Chapin, F.S., III. (1980). The mineral nutrition of wild plants. *Annual Review of Ecology and Systematics*, **11**, 233–60.

Croat, T.B. (1978). *Flora of Barro Colorado Island*. Stanford University Press, Stanford.

Foster, R.B. and Brokaw, N.V.L. (1982). Structure and history of the vegetation of Barro Colorado Island. In Leigh, E.G. Jr., Rand, A.S. and Windsor, D.M. (eds.), *The Ecology of a Tropical Forest*. pp. 67–81. Smithsonian Institution Press, Washington, D.C.

Fries, N. (1952). Variations in the content of phosphorus, nucleic acids and adenine in the leaves of some deciduous trees during the autumn. *Plant and Soil*, **4**, 29–42.

Gartner, B.L. (1989). Breakage and regrowth of *Piper* species in rain forest understorey. *Biotropica*, **21**, 303–7.

Garwood, N. (1979). *Seed Germination in a Seasonal Tropical Forest in Panama*. Ph.D. dissertation, University of Chicago, Chicago.

Garwood, N.C. (1987). Seed bank dynamics in a tropical forest. *American Journal of Botany*, **74**, 635.

Greig, N. (1991). *Ecology of Co-occuring Species of Neotropical* Piper: *Distribution, Reproductive Biology and Seed Predation*. Ph.D. dissertation, University of Texas, Austin.

Guariguata, M.R. (1992). Observations on the vegetative behavior in juveniles of the canopy tree, *Alseis blackiana*, in lowland Panama. *Biotropica*, **24**, 575–6.

Guha, M. and Mitchell, R. (1966). The trace and major element composition of the leaves of some deciduous trees. II. Seasonal changes. *Plant and Soil*, **24**, 90–112.

Ha, C.O., Sands, V.E., Soepadmo, E. and Jong, K. (1988). Reproductive patterns of selected understorey trees in the Malaysian rain forest: the apomictic species. *Botanical Journal of the Linnean Society*, **97**, 317–31.

Hagerman, A.E. (1987). Radial diffusion method for determining tannin in plant extracts. *Journal of Chemical Ecology*, **13**, 437–49.

Hamilton, C.W. (1989). Variations on a distylous theme in Mesoamerican *Psychotria* subgenus *Psychotria* (Rubiaceae). *Memoirs of the New York Botanical Garden*, **55**, 62–75.

Horovitz, C.C. and Schemske, D.W (1988). Demographic cost of reproduction in a neotropical herb: an experimental study. *Ecology*, **69**, 1741–5.

Jones, C.G. and Firn, R. (1991). On the evolution of plant secondary chemical diversity. *Philosophical Transactions of the Royal Society of London*, Series B, **333**, 273–80.

Kaur, A., Ha, C.O., Jong, K., Sands, V.E., Chan, H.T., Soepadmo, E. and Ashton, P.S. (1978). Apomixis may be widespread among trees of the climax rain forest. *Nature*, **271**, 440–2.

Kinsman, S. (1990). Regeneration by fragmentation in tropical montane forest shrubs. *American Journal of Botany*, **77**, 1626–33.

Leigh, E.G., Jr., Rand, A.S. and Windsor, D.M. (1982). *The Ecology of a Tropical Forest*. Smithsonian Institution Press, Washington, D.C.

Mole, S. and Waterman, P.G. (1987). A critical analysis of techniques for measuring tannins in ecological studies. I. Techniques for chemically defining tannins. *Oecologia*, **72**, 137–47.

Peñalosa, J. (1984). Basal branching and vegetative spread in two tropical rainforest lianas. *Biotropica*, **16**, 1–9.

Putz, F.E. and Brokaw, N.V.L. (1989). Sprouting of broken trees on Barro Colorado Island, Panama. *Ecology*, **70**, 508–12.

Root, R.B. (1973). Organization of a plant–arthropod association in simple and diverse habitats: the fauna of collards (*Brassica oleracea*). *Ecological Monographs*, **43**, 95–124.

Sagers, C.L. (1993). *Variation in Secondary Metabolites and some Effects on Plant Fitness*. Ph.D. Dissertation. University of Utah.

Schemske, D.W. (1980). Evolution of floral display in the orchid *Brassavola nodosa*. *Evolution*, **34**, 489–93.

Schupp, E.W. (1990). Annual variation in seedfall, postdispersal predation and recruitment of a neotropical tree. *Ecology*, **71**, 504–15.

Silander, J.A., Jr. (1985). Microevolution in clonal plants. In Jackson, J.B.C., Buss, L.W. and Cook, R.E. (eds.) *Population Biology and Evolution of Clonal Organisms*. Yale University Press, New Haven.

Williams, R. (1955). Redistribution of mineral elements during development. *Annual Review of Plant Physiology*, **6**, 25–42.

Zucker, W.V. (1983). Tannins: does structure determine function? An ecological perspective. *American Naturalist*, **121**, 335–65.

Revised manuscript received March 1994

CHAPTER 7

SEEDLINGS, SAPLINGS AND TREE TEMPERAMENTS: POTENTIAL FOR AGROFORESTRY IN THE AFRICAN RAIN FOREST

Annette Hladik and Danielle Mitja

INTRODUCTION

Recent results from experimental treefall gaps in tropical forest have demonstrated that gap size has less influence than expected on tree density and floristic composition following gap opening (Uhl et al., 1988; Brown and Whitmore, 1992; Kennedy and Swaine, 1992). Rather than the occurrence of new species from the seed bank, what appears to be the most important change is the rate of vegetative growth of the various trees in place, either as seedlings, or juveniles, or mature individuals. By contrast, after slash and burn cultivation, vegetation changes are a result of both seedlings from the seed bank in soil, and sproutings from individual plants surviving after fire. The balance between these two processes depends on the history of the site, on the previous cultural practices and on the species cultivated (Mitja and Hladik, 1989; see review in de Rouw, 1993).

The germination of tropical tree seeds is generally immediate and their viability is very short (Ng, 1978; Miquel, 1987). Seed dormancy is a characteristic of few tropical species (Vázquez-Yanes and Orozco-Segovia, 1990). However, tree seedlings and saplings of many species can survive in the undergrowth of a tropical forest for several years and wait for favourable light conditions to start growing (Hallé et al., 1978; Whitmore, 1990).

In this context, the adaptive strategies of seedlings of trees and lianas of the Gabon rain forest were related to seedling morphology (Miquel, 1987). The resulting plant establishment in plots was analysed in terms of proportions of the various seedling types from which trees and lianas originated (Hladik and Miquel, 1990). The success of sapling establishment (Hladik and Blanc, 1987) as well as lifetime performances of tree species were studied by measuring survival and growth rates in permanent plots (Hladik, 1982).

All biological and ecological characteristics of forest species, which define a species' temperament (*sensu* Oldeman and van Dijk, 1991), are essential for understanding forest dynamics. Data presented here may provide useful information for future tropical agroforestry systems.

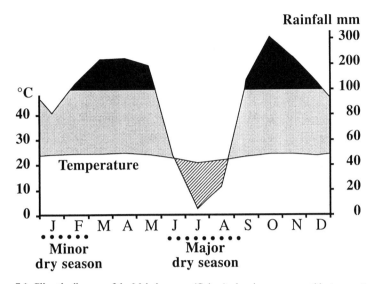

Figure 7.1 Climatic diagram of the Makokou area (Gabon), showing mean monthly temperatures (1953–1975) and mean monthly rainfall (1951–1975)

THE STUDY AREA

The station where the observations of seedlings and saplings were carried out is located in Gabon, near Makokou (0° 31′ North 12° 48′ East, at about 500 m altitude), inside the biosphere reserve of UNESCO. This permanent field station allows long-term studies to be sustained in the African rain forest, and data have been collected in this area since the early 1960s (Anon., 1987).

The Makokou forest has an annual rainfall of 1,700 mm and a mean temperature of 24 °C. The major dry season (Figure 7.1), is accompanied by low temperatures because of a persistent cloud cover allowing a wet evergreen forest to be maintained in spite of limited annual rainfall. Some deciduous tree species are present in Makokou (Hladik, 1978); but there is no species such as *Triplochiton scleroxylon* (Sterculiaceae), *Ceiba pentandra* (Bombacaceae), or *Terminalia* spp. (Combretaceae) characterizing semi-deciduous forests. Tree species diversity is lower than that of Asia, but is as high as that of most American rain forests (e.g. forty to fifty species per hectare for trees over 30 cm diameter, Hladik, 1986), including several leguminous tree species, especially Caesalpiniaceae (35 per cent of the total basal area).

Two five-year-old fallows where the observations of plant regrowth were carried out are also located near Makokou, but outside the biosphere reserve. In this area, shifting cultivation is practised after burning forest plots or old fallows of about a quarter of one hectare per family. Mixed fields of manioc, including plantains, yams and maize, are used for two or three years without weeding. Since population density is low, the period of fallow may last for more than twenty years, during which tree species participate in vegetation recovery.

SEEDLING TYPES AND SEED DISPERSAL

Faced with the large number of morphological and functional adaptations of seedlings of the various tropical trees, several authors have proposed a classification according to the role of the cotyledons. Duke (1965) was the first to introduce two contrasting terms for tropical seedlings: phanerocotylar, applied to seedlings with exposed cotyledons; and cryptocotylar, applied to seedlings with cotyledons hidden in the seed coat. Duke discussed the occurrence of these two categories according to environmental conditions, especially light intensity and humidity. The seedling types that were previously described, mostly from observations in temperate zones, referred exclusively to the hypocotyl: epigeal and hypogeal, respectively with a hypocotyl and without (or with a very reduced) hypocotyl. Ng (1978) combined these two classifications, making four seedling types.

After Garwood (1983) had emphasized the important difference between green foliaceous, photosynthetic cotyledons versus fleshy cotyledons, which are rich storage organs, Miquel (1987) recognized – among 210 species in the Makokou forest – the five distinctive seedling types illustrated in Figure 7.2. These five types, adopted in this paper, are defined as follows:

(1) Exposed leafy cotyledons above ground level (epigeal), with photosynthetic capacity and no reserve;
(2) Exposed fleshy cotyledons above ground level (epigeal);
(3) Exposed fleshy cotyledons at ground level (semi-hypogeal);
(4) Cryptic cotyledons at ground level or below ground (hypogeal); and
(5) Cryptic cotyledons above ground level (epigeal).

A comparison of various tropical forests, using this seedling classification, revealed that the frequencies of the five types are very similar on different continents (Miquel, 1987; Hladik and Miquel, 1990). The most abundant seedling type among the tropical rain forest species is the first one – with foliaceous photosynthetic cotyledons – accounting for about 40 per cent of the species (whereas, in the temperate zone, this type occurs in 95 per cent). Seedling type 2 (25 per cent) and seedling type 4 (22 per cent) are also abundant. Seedling type 3 is less frequent (9 per cent), but the rarest (5 per cent), is type 5. Although described as 'suicidal', because the plants die when the cotyledons remain locked inside the seed coat if raised in the dry conditions of a nursery, this last type is present in all tropical forests. It is quite successful, since most species of this type are abundant.

In the heterogeneous structure of a rain forest, each of these five seedling types have to live with various potentially limiting factors – light intensity,

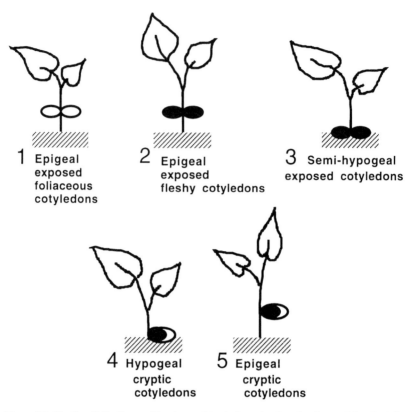

1 Epigeal
exposed
foliaceous
cotyledons

2 Epigeal
exposed
fleshy cotyledons

3 Semi-hypogeal
exposed cotyledons

4 Hypogeal
cryptic
cotyledons

5 Epigeal
cryptic
cotyledons

Figure 7.2 The five distinctive seedling types of tropical species, based on hypocotyl and cotyledon morphology (source: Miquel, 1987)

light spectral composition, carbon dioxide level, temperature and humidity – according to their photosynthetic capacity, potential resting stages with storage organs, and the resulting growth rate for above and below ground parts. However, it might be difficult to distinguish the limit between type 1, with green photosynthetic foliaceous cotyledons, and type 2 with fleshy storage cotyledons which are sometimes green. The study of Kitajima (1992), based on measurements of the thickness and photosynthetic efficiency of cotyledons of ten species from Barro Colorado Island (Panama), demonstrated that there is a continuum between these two types.

The spatial distribution of different seedling types mostly depends on the behaviour of animal populations, since many tropical plants bear fruits with the 'animal syndrome' of seed dispersal. These relationships have been generally studied according to the fruit and seed type and to the specific animal characteristics – body weight, oral cavity and digestive tract, home range activity in time and space – (see review in Estrada and Fleming, 1986; Fleming and Estrada, 1993). The seedling type, which is particularly important for the success of plant establishment, was more recently taken into consideration in seed dispersal systems (Hladik and Miquel, 1990).

Seed size is the first parameter to be considered in relation to animal dispersal and seedling establishment. All seedlings from small seeds (below 5 mm as measured along the largest axis, excluding wing) have the foliaceous cotyledons of seedling type 1. Species with seeds of medium and large size may have seedlings of any of the five types. For instance, very large leaf-like cotyledons can emerge from large seeds of the forest species such as *Picralima nitida* (Apocynaceae), *Panda oleosa* (Pandaceae), and many species of the Sapotaceae family. However, there is no seedling type 5 among species with very large seeds, and one can wonder whether these seeds are too heavy to be supported by a hypocotyl.

Among plant species actually dispersed by vertebrates in the Makokou rain forest (Gautier-Hion et al., 1985), those with seedling type 1 are dispersed by the largest array of animals: the elephant, six primate species, seven large birds, seven ruminants, nine squirrels, eight small rodents and two large rodents. Seeds from these plant species take advantage of being dispersed over long distances, thus increasing their chance to reach a place with enough light in the forest mosaic for the immediate photosynthetic requirements.

As shown in Figure 7.3, species with seedling types 2 to 5 are dispersed by a more limited number of animals than those with seedling type 1. There are few species with seedling type 3 (only 9 per cent out of the 210 species studied at Makokou) and they are rarely dispersed by animals, being mostly autochorous (with fruits falling directly on the ground). Some seedling types, within specific seed size categories, are dispersed by particular animals; for instance, dispersal of plants with seedling type 4 (e.g. liana species of the Apocynaceae and Dichapetalaceae families) depends on monkeys, whereas plants with seedling types 1 and 2, with the largest seeds, depend exclusively on the elephant.

SAPLING GROWTH AND FOREST DYNAMICS

Established seedlings, after about 1 year, are usually called saplings. Sapling growth has been monitored on permanent plots in the Makokou rain forest during a 64-month study (about 5 years). Plant survival and growth rate were measured on two 50 m transects, one in undisturbed forest and the other in a recent single treefall gap (Hladik and Blanc, 1987). These data are discussed here in relation to seedling types.

The two transects were selected to show the effect of light availability on the growth of different species. Cumulative total incident light has been measured in 1980 and 1985, and expressed as the relative incident light. These measurements were made in ten locations and include the variation between days as well as

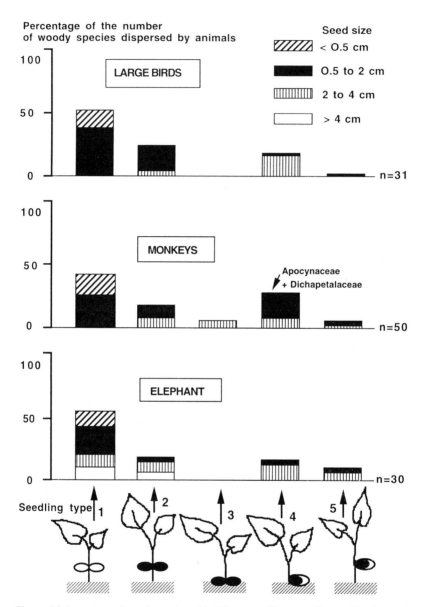

Figure 7.3 Percentage of woody species with different seedling types dispersed by three major animal groups of the Makokou forest, in relation to seed size (source: Hladik and Miquel, 1990)

diurnal sunfleck variation. As far-red and infra-red were included in the total light measurement, the minimum observed in one site was 2 per cent of incident light, whereas 1 per cent is the mean value generally obtained with a standard quantum sensor in the undergrowth of a rain forest. The mean relative light intensity varied from 8.5 to 3.4 per cent in the tree gap and from 3.0 per cent to 4.3 per cent in the undisturbed forest between 1980 and 1985, as a result of the changes in the forest structure: a progressive closing of the treefall gap and a slight opening of the undergrowth, where large branches had fallen.

Plants measuring 20 cm to 3 m tall were marked with aluminium tags in ten plots (4 × 4 m) adjacent to the light measurement sites, including at least fifty shrubs and saplings of trees and lianas. Identification of these 500 plants was made in the field, without taking herbarium samples to avoid trauma to the plants. Accordingly, some individuals that died before July 1982 remained unidentified. Liana species showed the highest rate of mortality: 57 per cent and 72 per cent respectively in the undisturbed forest and in the treefall gap. For tree species, the mortality was respectively 38 per cent and 50 per cent, and for the shrub species, adapted to life in the undergrowth of the forest, 25 per cent and 51 per cent. The lianas showed the highest growth rate in the tree gap (a mean of 141 per cent of the initial size, whereas tree growth was 96 per cent and shrub growth 65 per cent, over the five years). But, at the community level, however, the handicap of a slower rate for the trees is offset by the higher mortality rate of lianas (see details in Hladik and Blanc, 1987).

The percentage height increment of each species of the tree saplings (for surviving saplings) of these two transects (116 individuals) is presented in Table 7.1, in which the forty-four tree species have been grouped according to seedling types. Due to the higher light availability in the treefall gap, the total growth increment of tree saplings is more than double that in the undisturbed forest (103 per cent versus 40 per cent). The only exceptions are species with seedling type 5, because these plants died in the dry conditions of the treefall gap.

Intraspecific comparisons can be made for ten species present in both transects. Among species with seedling type 1, *Heisteria parvifolia* displayed its best performance in the treefall gap, although it survived in the undergrowth.

The best mean growth rate was found among tree species with seedling type 2. This performance was also found in experimental cultivations (see Discussion). One of the most common species of the Makokou forest, *Scorodophloeus zenkeri*, had a similar increment in the undergrowth and in treefall gap. The maximum growth rate (400 per cent) appeared during the first three years of observation, in a young *Milletia mannii*, although this pioneer tree was almost dead in 1985, the tree gap being initially too small and slowly closing.

The general trend that appears in comparing the proportions of species with various seedling types among these observed saplings, with the initial number

Table 7.1 Height increment of tree saplings in undisturbed forest and in a treefall gap within the Makokou forest, over a 5-year period. Species are grouped according to seedling types (source: Hladik and Blanc, 1987 and unpublished data)

	Undisturbed forest			Treefall gap		
	Initial number of individuals	Final number of living trees	Percentage height increment of surviving saplings	Initial number of individuals	Final number of living trees	Percentage height increment of surviving saplings
Species with seedling type 1						
Heisteria parvifolia	3	3	30	2	1	150
Gambeya boukokoensis	1	1	67	1	1	125
Grewia coriacea	2	0	0	1	0	0
Strombosia grandifolia	2	2	30	0		
Drypetes sp. (AH 4667)	2	2	30	0		
Drypetes sp. (AH 4670)	2	2	25	0		
Baphia pubescens	1	1	34	0		
Drypetes sp. (dead)	1	0	0	0		
Gambeya africana	0			1	1	33
Pausinystalia macroceras	0			1	1	113
Xyopia sp. (dead)	0			1	0	0
Petersianthus macrocarpus (dead)	0			2	0	0
Species with seedling type 2						
Scorodophloeus zenkeri	4	2	53	7	4	74
Piptadeniastrum africanum	1	1	68	0		
Dialium pachyphyllum	4	4	45	0		
Dacryodes klaineana	3	3	30	0		
Trichilia sp. (AH 4736)	2	2	6	0		
Miletia sp. (AH 4735)	1	1	34	0		
Milletia mannii	0			1	1	400
Dacryodes butneri	0			1	1	78
Santiria sp. I (AH 2986)	0			1	1	12
Santiria sp. II (AH 2941)	0			2	2	125

Species	1	2	3	4	5	Mean height increment
Trichilia sp. (AH 4709)	0	5	5	2	2	123
Trichilia sp. (dead)	0	1	3	2	0	0
Species with seedling type 3						
Pentaclethra eetveldeana	15			8	2	40
Cola rostrata	1			1	1	80
Species with seedling type 4						
Pancovia pedicellaris	3	0	0	4	3	85
Garcinia sp. (AH 4669)	2	2	27	1	1	21
Laccodiscus sp.	1	1	25	0		
Carapa procera	1	1	38	0		
Eriocoelum macrocarpum	0			1	1	180
Pycnanthus angolensis (dead)	0			1	0	0
Staudtia gabonensis (dead)	0			1	0	0
Lophira alata (dead)	0			1	0	0
Parinari excelsa (dead)	0			1	0	0
Beilschmedia sp. (dead)	0			1	0	0
Species with seedling type 5						
Polyalthia suaveolens	2	2	34	2	0	0
Plagiostyles africana	1	1	70	1	0	0
Coula edulis	2	2	95	0		
Afrostyrax lepidophyllus	7	1	33	0		
Anonidium mannii (dead)	1	0	0	0		
Species with seedling type unknown						
Diospyros piscatoria	1	1	25	0		
Sorindeia nitidula	0			1	1	50
Anacardiaceae (AH 4679)	0			1	1	30
Total	66	41	40	50	25	
Mean height increment						103

181

of species with seeds dispersed in the same area, is a reduction of type 1 (from 39 per cent to 27 per cent of the observed species), and an increase of type 5 (from 5 to 11 per cent). This trend appears to be accentuated if we consider the present mature forest composition, with only 20 per cent of the tree species (over 5 cm dbh) originated from seedling type 1, and the same proportion from seedling type 5.

TEMPERAMENTS OF TREE SPECIES

In their search for the most accurate description of the growing capacities of tree species, foresters and botanists have proposed several classifications, generally in relation to species' responses to light availability. Swaine and Whitmore (1988) provided a clear definition, based on seed and seedling ecology, of the two qualitatively distinct groups of tree species, respectively known as the 'pioneers' and the 'climax' (or non-pioneer) species. They also follow the concept of a continuum within each of these groups, although the attempted subdivisions previously proposed are arbitrary segments of this continuum. A comparison of the growth patterns of various tree species in the mature phase forest may help clarify these distinctions.

Tree growth, mortality and recruitment in the Makokou forest have been monitored during 7 years (1972–79), on two permanent plots of 4,000 m^2 (400 m × 10 m) and of 9,000 m^2 (1,800 m × 5 m), including respectively 397 trees with dbh > 5 cm belonging to ninety-two species and ninety-three trees with dbh > 30 cm belonging to forty-one species. The overall mortality was 10 per cent compensated by growth and recruitment (see details in Hladik, 1982). The major data concerning pioneer and non-pioneer species are presented in Table 7.2 according to species seedling types.

There are few pioneer trees in the forest mosaic (including treefall gaps, mature phase forest, and all the intermediate phases). In the study plots, which did not include any recent treefall gaps, the first four species in Table 7.2, for which the maximum growth increment during the study period was 48 per cent of the initial basal area, were represented by scarce individuals. Nevertheless, these species, which all have seedling type 1, account for 9 per cent of the total basal area. The next twelve species presented in Table 7.2 account for 50 per cent of the total basal area and reveal various growth patterns. For most of these species, the number of individuals in the forest was sufficient to show significant differences ($p < 0.05$; t-test).

Species with seedling type 1 are also included among those abundant species, for instance *Panda oleosa*, a medium-sized tree abundant in the Makokou forest (20 per cent of the total basal area of the plot) only had an increment of 4 per cent of the initial basal area over the 7-year study. In contrast, *Heisteria parvifolia*, a common small tree, may grow fast when enough light is available, as already shown above for its saplings.

Table 7.2 Basal area increment of tree species in undisturbed forests at Makokou, over a 7-year period. Species are grouped according to seedling types (source: Hladik, 1982 and unpublished data)

	Initial number of individuals	Final number of living trees	Recruitment	Basal area (m²) 1972	Basal area (m²) 1979	Basal area increment (%)
Pioneer species						
Species with seedling type 1						
Macaranga barteri	4	2	0	0.21	0.31	47.0
Ficus macrosperma	1	1	0	0.81	1.21	48.0
Croton oligandrus	1	1	0	0.12	0.26	40.0
Alstonia boonei	3	2	0	0.57	0.64	13.0
Non-pioneer species						
Panda oleosa	18	18	0	8.03	8.35	4.0
Petersianthus macrocarpus	8	7	1	0.83	0.88	6.7
Heisteria parvifolia	13	12	1	0.39	0.47	19.2
Species with seedling type 2						
Scorodophloeus zenkeri	35	31	4	3.16	3.37	6.5
Santiria sp. II	21	24	4	1.20	1.37	14.5
Species with seedling type 3						
Pentaclethra eetveldeana	9	9	0	1.78	1.88	5.4
Cola rostrata	8	8	1	0.23	0.27	7.0
Species with seedling type 4						
Pycnanthus angolensis	1	1	0	0.31	0.46	40.0
Species with seedling type 5						
Polyalthia suaveolens	27	27	0	0.97	1.08	11.5
Plagiostyles africana	21	20	1	1.05	1.12	6.0
Anonidium mannii	11	11	0	0.56	0.61	9.6
Coula edulis	8	8	1	0.89	1.00	11.5

Species with seedling type 2 also have characteristic growth patterns. For instance, the most common species in the plot, *Scorodophloeus zenkeri*, had a slow growth rate (6.5 per cent), whereas the best performance in this category was for *Santiria* sp. II (14.5 per cent).

Among species with seedling type 3, *Pentaclethra eetveldeana*, which has a high mortality rate among saplings, shows, in mature phase forest, a low growth rate (5.4 per cent), as does *Cola rostrata* (7.0 per cent).

Only one species with seedling type 4, *Pycnanthus angolensis*, is presented in Table 7.2. Although present in the mature phasae of the forest mosaic, this species' high growth rate (40 per cent of the initial basal area) would place it, in the continuum of non-pioneer species, very close to the pioneers.

Species with seedling type 5 are typically shade-tolerant, and thus non-pioneers, but among them, species such as *Polyalthia suaveolens*, and *Coula edulis*, both abundant in the Makokou forest, have increments higher than 11 per cent. In contrast, the increment was only 6 per cent for *Plagiostyles africana*.

These differences in growth potential during the mature phase of various species are thus complementing the adaptations of seedlings and saplings to grow in various environmental conditions. Altogether, these differences, which characterize the species' temperament, are of great significance to population dynamics.

PLANT REGROWTH IN FALLOWS: SEEDLINGS *VERSUS* RESPROUTS

Species' temperaments are particularly obvious after shifting cultivation, when the vegetation is reconstructed in the recent fallows such as those described by Mitja and Hladik (1989). For this study, the demographic composition of the annual herbs and perennial woody plants were determined along narrow transects (1 m wide), including 14,000 plant individuals, and covering a total area of 300 m² in two 5-year-old fallows.

The seedlings, saplings and 'adult' plants were counted, the adult stage being defined according to size, but not necessarily corresponding to the reproductive stage. For an approach to population dynamics, since repeated surveys were not feasible, the observed cumulative changes over 5 years of fallow growth were used to forecast future changes.

Four demographic groups, based on relative proportions of seedlings, saplings and adults were defined for the tree species as follows:

(I)   Group I: short-lived species, exclusively herbaceous plants and shrubs, with many senescent adults in the plots.

(II) Group II: adult tree species with few seedlings in the plots. Most species of this group have been described as pioneers.

184

(III) Group III: small, rapidly maturing trees and the seedlings germinated from their seeds.

(IV) Group IV: tree species with no adult and few seedlings in the plots. Trees of this group are known as the long-lived species of the forest.

Data on the tree species (860 individuals belonging to at least thirty-seven species), are presented in Table 7.3, to show the demographic groups (when a sufficient number of individuals was found) in relation to seedling types. Most of these plants (twenty-six species, accounting for 75 per cent of the total number of individuals and for three-quarters of the basal area) originated from the seedling type 1 with foliaceous cotyledons. This high proportion of plants with seedling type 1, much higher than that found inside the forest, is a characteristic of the open areas (Hladik and Miquel, 1990). These twenty-six species are distributed amongst the three demographic groups (II, III, IV). The measurement of the sprouting capacities, together with the demographic analysis, provided additional data about species' temperament.

Among species belonging to demographic group II, *Musanga cecropioides*, *Trema guineensis*, *Harungana madagascariensis* and *Pauridiantha callicarpoides* regenerated from seedlings. Others species such as *Macaranga monandra* and *Rauvolfia vomitoria*, regenerated partly from seedlings and partly from sprouting (20–30 per cent). Moreover, some species, such as *Caloncoba welwitschii*, regenerated exclusively by sprouting.

Sprouting capacity is not limited to tree species with the seedling type 1. *Myrianthus arboreus*, with seedling type 4, and *Albizia adianthifolia* with seedling type 2, also regenerate by sprouting. This capacity, revealed after severe treatment such as trunk cutting or fire, can be rarely observed within the rain forest. Several species of the genus *Albizia* that grow at the interface between forest and savannah, are well known to be fire-resistant.

Human activities such as frequent clearing, cutting and burning encourage some particular species to dominate either by sprouting or from seedlings. These species are generally described as pioneer although the definition related to seed and seedling ecology (Swaine and Whitmore, 1988), does not apply to all of them.

The degree of species dominance in regrowth vegetation, either from resprouts, or from seedlings, reflects the cultural process to which the cultivated plot was submitted (Mitja and Hladik, 1989). For example in Gabon, after the initial forest clearing, *Musanga cecropioides* dominates in fallows, whereas in the area submitted to a limited number of successive cycles of cultivation, *Trema guineensis* dominates; both species regenerate from seedlings. In contrast, in areas where shifting cultivation has been practised for many years (with many successive field–fallow cycles), *Trema guineensis* tends to decrease in density and the number of individuals of the species which can resprout increases.

185

Table 7.3 Comparison of the numbers of seedlings, saplings and 'adults' in the populations of trees species in five-year-old fallows of the Makokou area. The resulting demographic groups (see text) and the sprouting capacities are presented in relation to species' seedling types (source: Mitja and Hladik, 1989 and unpublished data)

	Basal area (cm²) for trees >2 m	Number of seedlings	Number of saplings	Number of 'adults'	Total number of individuals	Demographic group	Percentage of sprouting for trees >2 m
Species with seedling type 1							
Trema guineesis	523	0	25	16	41	II	0
Harungana madagascariensis	134	0	0	11	11	II	0
Pauridiantha callicarpioides	69	0	18	4	22	II	0
Musanga cecropioides	58	10	0	1	11	II	0
Macaranga monandra	49	0	7	1	8	II	20 (5)
Rauvolfia vomitoria	29	0	14	14	28	II	25 (8)
Psidium guajava	41	1	4	10	15	II	0
Macaranga spinosa	42	3	10	8	21	II	0
Ficus exasperata	10	3	15	3	21	II	0
Caloncoba welwitchii	7	0	7	6	13	II	100 (3)
Leea guineesis	3	45	54	17	116	III	
Vernonia cf. conferta	53	165	5	7	177	III	
Ficus sur	42	0	0	1	1		33 (2)
Anthocleista schweinfurthii	—	0	1	3	4		
Sapium cornutum	—	0	1	1	2		
Distemonanthus benthamianus	62	9	30	0	39	IV	80 (5)
Petersianthus macrocarpus	31	1	7	0	8	IV	50 (4)
Markhamia sessilis	9	1	14	0	15	IV	0

Bridelia atroviridis	8	26	37	0	63	IV	0
Bridelia cf. micrantha	—	1	16	0	17	IV	0
Fagara sp.	26	0	2	1	3		
Tricalysia sp.	18	0	1	1	2		
Gambeya boukokoensis	4	0	0	2	2		
Duboscia macrocarpa	—	0	0	2	2		
Xylopia hypolampra	—	0	1	0	1		
Lindacheria dentata	—	0	1	0	1		
Species with seedling type 2							
Milletia mannii	195	87	63	18	168	III	0
Albizia adianthifolia	122	1	1	8	10	II	100 (8)
Piptadeniastrum africanum	—	1	2	0	3		
Dialium sp.	—	0	1	0	1		
Species with seedling type 3							
Pentaclethra eetveldeana	133	0	1	11	12	IV	75 (11)
Pterocarpus soyauxii	—	0	1	0	1		
Species with seedling type 4							
Myrianthus arboreus	88	2	1	5	8	II	100 (4)
Anthonotha macrophylla	13	0	0	4	4		
Pycnanthus angolensis	23	0	0	1	1		
Species with seedling type 5							
Anonidium mannii	—	0	6	1	7		
Plagiostyles africana	—	0	1	0	1		
Species with seedling type unknown (three species)	35	0	5	6	11		
Total	1808	356	347	157	860		

187

DISCUSSION: WHAT ARE THE BEST SEEDLING TYPES AND SAPLING RESPONSES FOR AGROFORESTRY SYSTEMS?

The different species can be characterized by the growth potential of seedlings, saplings and adults, although individual plant behaviour varies during these different phases (Oldeman, 1990). These aspects of species temperament were observed in forest populations where dispersal and seedling establishment are key phases in species' population dynamics, as was emphasized by Schupp et al. (1989) in terms of arrival and survival.

The data presented in this paper focus on the gradual change of sapling and young tree populations. In the artificial environments of fallows, home gardens or agroforestry systems, the growing capacity of these species can be utilized. The introduction of agroforestry systems in Africa, which might partly replicate the efficient systems developed in Asia (Hladik and Hladik, 1984; Foresta and Michon, 1993), necessitates a thorough knowledge of seedling type responses and growth pattern changes throughout the life-cycle of a large number of potentially useful tree species. Since the link between seedling type and tree temperament is evident only for species with seedling type 1, it is important to know both characters for managing tree species.

Most observations about responses of trees introduced in African manmade forests concern species easy to handle in the nursery. They can grow rapidly in the open, and thus have seedling type 1, such as *Trema guineensis*, (Scheepers et al., 1968), *Terminalia* spp., *Aucoumea klaineana*, and most recently tested, *Nauclea diderrichii* (Maldague et al., 1986). In the agroforestry experiments conducted in the Makokou area (Miquel and Hladik, 1984) we tested species with various seedling types, selected for multi-purpose production, particularly fruit production, as well as timber and firewood. Species with seedling types 2 and 3 were efficient in terms of survival and growth. They could be planted either in association with other species, or directly inside fallows and home gardens.

Some examples (Figure 7.4) illustrate this discussion. Among the fruit trees with seedling type 2, *Dacryodes edulis*, the African plum tree (Figure 7.4A), and *Irvingia gabonensis*, the 'wild mango tree' (Figure 7.4C) can rapidly reach the height of surrounding plants, most of these having seedlings of type 1. The leguminous tree with seedling type 3, *Pentaclethra macrophylla*, (Figure 7.4B) performed even better than the 'plum tree' after 18 months, probably in response to mycorrhizal association. Among the few species with seedling type 4, *Lophira alata* (Figure 7.4D) can grow rapidly in open places like all other pioneers.

Accordingly, the best choice for agroforestry is not necessarily one species selected for its high performance. As emphasized by Huston (1979), competition is low in a complex environment and the 'best player' when light availability is maximum cannot necessarily express its full potential in an agroforestry system. By grouping plants according to potential growth, an

188

Figure 7.4 Saplings and young trees with seedling types typical of rain forest undergrowth, raised in experimental fields in the Makokou area. A, 18-month-old *Dacryodes edulis*, the African plum tree (seedling type 2); B, 18-month-old *Pentaclethra macrophylla*, a leguminous tree (seedling type 3); C, 4-year-old *Irvingia gabonensis*, the 'wild mango tree' (seedling type 2); and D, 4-year-old *Lophira alata*, known as a 'pioneer' of large stature (seedling type 4)

189

agroforestry system, even though it cannot be as complex as a rain forest, may allow efficient development of several tree species for the benefit of mankind.

ACKNOWLEDGEMENTS

We are indebted to the Gabonese government, which made possible the work of scientists at the Makokou Field Station, and to the Smithsonian Institution, which permitted us to start botanical studies in 1971 (postdoctoral fellowship awarded to A. Hladik). Funds available from the CNRS during several years and an additional grant from the MAB Programme of UNESCO supported our long-term studies. We both are grateful to M. Hadley and to M. Swaine for editing our manuscript. We would like to also thank all our colleagues working at the Makokou Field Station, especially H. Cooper who initiated the light measurements; S. Miquel who did a tremendous job on the seedlings survey; P. Blanc who permitted a better understanding of sapling growth; and C.M. Hladik for his help throughout our research work.

REFERENCES

Anonymous (1987). *Makokou, Gabon; a Research Station in Tropical Forest Ecology. Overview and Publications (1962–1986)*. UNESCO, Paris.

Brown, N.D. and Whitmore, T.C. (1992). Do dipterocarp seedlings really partition tropical rain forest gaps? *Philosophical Transactions of the Royal Society of London*, series B, **335**, 369–78.

Duke, J.A. (1965). Keys of the identification of seedlings of some prominent woody species in eight forest types in Puerto Rico. *Annals of the Missouri Botanical Garden*, **52**, 314–59.

Estrada, A. and Fleming, T.H. (eds.) (1986). *Frugivores and Seed Dispersal*. W. Junk, Dordrecht.

Fleming, T.H. and Estrada, A. (eds.) (1993). *Frugivory and Seed Dispersal: Ecological and Evolutionary Aspects*. Kluwer, Brussels.

Foresta, H. de and Michon, G. (1993). Creation and management of rural agroforests in Indonesia: potential applications in Africa. In Hladik, C.M., Hladik, A., Linares, O.F., Pagezy, H., Semple, A. and Hadley, M. (eds.) *Tropical, Forests, People and Food: Biocultural Interactions and Applications to Development*, Man and the Biosphere Series, **13**, pp. 709–24. UNESCO/Parthenon, Paris/Carnforth.

Garwood, N.C. (1983). Seed germination in a seasonal tropical moist forest in Panama. A community study. *Ecological Monographs*, **53**, 159–65.

Gautier-Hion, A., Duplantier, J.-M., Quris, R., Feer, F., Sourd, C., Decoux, J.-P., Dubost, G., Emmons, L., Erard, C., Hecketsweiler, P., Moungazi, A., Roussilhon, C. and Thiollay, J.-M. (1985). Fruit characters as a basis of fruit choice and seed dispersal in a tropical forest vertebrate community. *Oecologia*, **65**, 324–37.

Hallé, F., Oldeman, R.A.A. and Tomlinson, P.B. (1978). *Tropical Trees and Forests; an Architectural Analysis*. Springer-Verlag, Berlin.

Hladik, A. (1978). Phenology of leaf production in rain forest of Gabon: distribution and composition of food for folivores. In Montgomery, G.G. (ed.) *The Ecology of Arboreal Folivores*, pp. 51–71. Smithsonian Institution Press, Washington.

Hladik, A. (1982). Dynamique d'une forêt équatoriale africaine: mesures en temps réel et comparaison du potentiel de croissance des différentes espèces. *Acta Oecologica, Oecologia generalis*, **3**, 373–92.

Hladik, A. (1986). Données comparatives sur la richesse spécifique et les structures des peuplements des forêts tropicales d'Afrique et d'Amérique. *Mémoires du Muséum National d'Histoire Naturelle*, sér. A, **132**, 9–17.

Hladik, A. and Blanc, P. (1987). Croissance des plantes en sous-bois de forêt dense humide. *Revue d'Ecologie (Terre et Vie)*, **42**, 209–34.

Hladik, A. and Miquel, S. (1990). Seedling types and plant establishment in the African rain forest. In Bawa, K.S. and Hadley, M. (eds.), *Reproductive Ecology of Tropical Forest Plants*, pp. 261–82. UNESCO/Parthenon, Paris/Carnforth.

Hladik, C.M. and Hladik, A. (1984). L'Agroforesterie: science et technique d'avenir en Afrique noire. *Le Courrier du CNRS*, **58**, 40–3.

Huston, M. (1979). A general hypothesis of species diversity. *The American Naturalist*, **113**, 81–101.

Kennedy, D.N. and Swaine, M.D. (1992). Germination and growth of colonizing species in artificial gaps of different sizes in dipterocarp rain forest. *Philosophical Transactions of the Royal Society of London*, series B., **335**, 357–66.

Kitajima, K. (1992). Relationships between photosynthesis and thickness of cotyledons for tropical tree species. *Functional Ecology*, **6**, 582–9.

Maldague, M., Hladik, A. and Posso, P. (1986). *Agroforesterie en Zones Forestières Humides d'Afrique. Rapport du Séminaire Sous-régional, 1–8 juillet 1985, Makokou, Gabon.* UNESCO, Paris.

Miquel, S. (1987). Morphologie fonctionnelle de plantules d'espèces forestières du Gabon. *Bulletin du Muséum d'Histoire Naturelle, Paris, 4ème série, section B, Adansonia*, **9**, 101–21.

Miquel, S. and Hladik, A. (1984). Sur le concept d'Agroforesterie: exemple d'expériences en cours dans la région de Makokou, Gabon. *Bulletin d'Ecologie*, **15**, 163–73.

Mitja, D. and Hladik, A. (1989). Aspects de la reconstitution de la végétation dans deux jachères en zone forestière africaine humide (Makokou, Gabon). *Acta Oecologica, Oecologia generalis*, **10**, 75–94.

Ng, F.S.P. (1978). Strategies of establishment in Malayan forest trees. In Tomlinson, P.B. and Zimmermann, H.M. (eds.), *Tropical Trees as Living Systems*, pp. 129–62. Cambridge University Press, Cambridge.

Oldeman, R.A.A. (1990). *Forests: Elements of Silvology*. Springer, Heidelberg.

Oldeman, R.A.A. and van Dijk, J. (1991). Diagnosis of the temperament of tropical rain forest trees. In Gómez-Pompa, A., Whitmore, T.C. and Hadley, M. (eds.), *Rain Forest Regeneration and Management*, pp. 21–65. UNESCO/Parthenon, Paris/Carnforth.

Rouw, A. de (1993). Regeneration by sprouting in slash and burn rice cultivation, Taï rain forest, Côte d'Ivoire. *Journal of Tropical Ecology*, **9**, 387–408.

Scheepers, J.C., Van der Schijff, H.P. and Keet, J.D.M. (1968). Ecological account of the *Trema* plantation of Westfalia estate. *Natuurwetenskappe*, **8**, 105–20.

Schupp, E. W., Howe, H. F., Auspurger, C. K. and Levey, D. J. (1989). Arrival and survival in tropical treefall gaps. *Ecology*, **70**, 562–4.

Swaine, M.D. and Whitmore, T.C. (1988). On the definition of ecological species groups in tropical rain forests. *Vegetatio*, **75**, 81–6.

Uhl, C., Clark, K., Dezzeo, N. and Maquiro, P. (1988). Vegetation dynamics in Amazonian treefall gaps. *Ecology*, **69**, 751–63.

Vázquez-Yánes, C. and Orozco-Segovia, A. (1990). Seed dormancy in the tropical rain forest. In Bawa, K.S. and Hadley, M. (eds.), *Reproductive Ecology of Tropical Forest Plants*, pp. 247–59. UNESCO/Parthenon, Paris/Carnforth.

Whitmore, T.C. (1990). *An Introduction to Tropical Rain Forests.* Clarendon Press, Oxford.

Revised manuscript received September 1994

CHAPTER 8

COTYLEDON FUNCTIONAL MORPHOLOGY, PATTERNS OF SEED RESERVE UTILIZATION AND REGENERATION NICHES OF TROPICAL TREE SEEDLINGS

Kaoru Kitajima

INTRODUCTION

There is a wide and continuous gradient of shade tolerance at the early seedling stage from pioneer species that germinate or survive only in large gaps to shade-tolerant, climax species that regenerate *in situ* by establishing seedlings under the closed forest canopy (Augspurger, 1984a; Brokaw, 1985; Whitmore, 1989). This niche differentiation of seedling establishment sites may be a key for understanding the maintenance of tree species' diversity in tropical forest communities. What suites of seed and seedling traits have evolved with the regeneration niche specialization of tree species? Two syndromes of seed and seedling characteristics have been recognized by contrasting the ends of the continuum from 'pioneers' to shade-tolerant 'climax' species (Foster and Janson, 1985; Swaine and Whitmore, 1988; Brokaw and Scheiner, 1989). Pioneers typically have copious, small, well-dispersed seeds and grow rapidly in the abundance of light, while climax species often produce fewer, larger seeds and grow slowly. Apparently, high seedling survivorship in shade is associated with seed size, but is traded-off with the maximum growth rate (Kitajima, 1992a, 1994; Grime and Jeffrey, 1965 for temperate trees). For ecophysiological understanding of this trade-off relationship between shade tolerance and growth rate, it is essential to examine the associations and interactions among multiple seed and seedling traits, including seed size, seed reserve types, duration of seed reserve dependency, initial size and morphology of seedlings, and seedling growth rates. Such knowledge also provides clues about the constraints during the evolution of regeneration niche specialization.

Below, I first present an overview of the known relationships among morphological, physiological and ecological traits at seed and early seedling stages of tropical tree species. Second, I summarize some results from my comparative studies that examined interspecific correlation among specific seed and seedling traits of tropical tree species.

OVERVIEW

Functional morphology of cotyledons

The high diversity in pollination and seed dispersal syndromes represented by variation in flower and fruit morphologies is considered to be important in niche diversification among tropical tree species (Bawa and Hadley, 1991). Likewise, the high diversity of young seedling morphologies in tropical forests (Duke, 1965; Burger Hzn., 1972; Bokdam, 1977; Ng, 1978, 1992; de Vogel, 1980) must be an important aspect of reproductive ecology differentiating species with regard to regeneration niches. The young seedling morphologies have been classified based on cotyledon position (epigeal for those raised above ground, hypogeal for those that stay at or below ground level), degree of cotyledon enclosure by seed coat after germination (phanerocotylar for those that become free of seed coat, cryptocotylar for those remaining enveloped at least partially by the seed coat), and cotyledon morphology (papyraceous for thin leaf-like, coriaceous for flat and somewhat thick, and globoid for thick ball-like). Stylized pictures of the common combinations of these morphological traits are illustrated in Figure 8.1. Some hypogeal species have cotyledons that become partially or completely free from the seed coat and attain a deep green colour. With rare exceptions ('Durian type' of Ng, 1978), most cryptocotylar species are hypogeal.

Garwood (1983) distinguished three functional morphologies of cotyledons based on their apparent physiological functions. In the first type, cotyledons emerge from the seed coat completely and expand into leaf-like photosynthetic organs which remain attached to the seedling for a long time. In the second type, the cotyledons emerge completely from the seed coat, develop a green colour but do not expand in area, and are dropped in a relatively short time (i.e. within two months after germination, Augspurger, 1984b; Kitajima, 1992a). Very few studies have quantified the degree of photosynthetic function relative to storage function for this second group of tropical tree species (Olofinboba, 1975; Kitajima, 1992b). Studies on temperate herbaceous species suggest that their major function is to export stored food reserves into the developing seedling axis (Lovell and Moore, 1971; Harris et al., 1986). In the third type, cotyledons stay inside the seed coat and serve as storage organs to export seed reserves into the developing seedling axis. The majority of the species in this group finish absorbing endosperm before seed maturation, but, in rare cases, cotyledons are membranous organs embedded in abundant endosperm (haustorial cotyledons).

Importance of seed size *versus* cotyledon functional morphology

Foster and Janson (1985) assembled published data on seed mass for forty tropical tree species and their degrees of dependence on light gaps. They

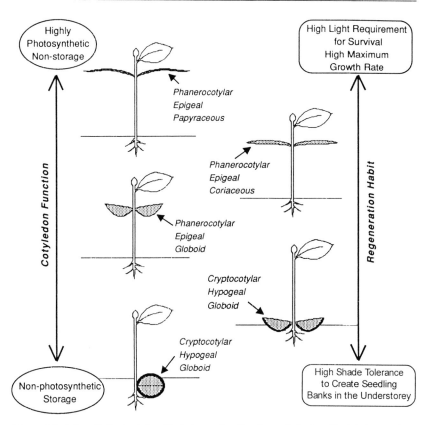

Figure 8.1 A hypothetical relationship between functional morphologies of cotyledons and regeneration habit of tropical tree species. Each stylized picture indicates a seedling with a pair of cotyledons (shaded area, shown in vertical section) and the first true leaf. From top to bottom, the degree of photosynthetic differentiation of cotyledons decreases with increase in thickness, lowering in position and decrease in exposure. Thick lines partially or completely encircling cotyledons in the bottom two pictures represent seed coat

concluded that mean seed mass is significantly greater for the species with little or no light gap requirement. The primary evolutionary advantage of increase in seed size appears to be enhancement of seedling survival in shade, although evolution of seed size is also influenced by the ecological interactions with dispersers and predators of seeds (Howe, 1984; Augspurger, 1986; Sork, 1987; Schupp, 1988) and by the trade-off between number and size of seeds (Smith and Fretwell, 1974). Several hypotheses attempt to explain how a larger seed reserve leads to a survival advantage in shade. One view is that a large seed provides a longer period of support of carbon to the seedlings (Thompson, 1987). This hypothesis assumes that seedlings in the shade generally have a negative net carbon budget (i.e. total seedling biomass continues to decline from seed biomass), although this assumption has not been evaluated

195

quantitatively. A contrasting view is that a large seed creates a large seedling and thus an important initial size advantage (Fenner, 1987; Westoby et al., 1992). This hypothesis is favoured by the findings that a large initial seedling size promotes emergence though leaf litter (Molofsky and Augspurger, 1992) and probably provides resistance to physical disturbance (Aide, 1987). However, it does not provide an explanation for why the initial size advantage is especially important in shade, resulting in stronger selection for large seed size in shade than in light gaps.

Alternatively, the relationship between seed size and seedling survivorship may be indirect via the correlation between seed mass and functional morphology of cotyledons as suggested by Miquel (1987) and Hladik and Miquel (1990). Their hypothesis is based on the observation of an association between cotyledon functional morphologies and seed size (length) classes in a wet forest in Gabon. The species with leaf-like photosynthetic cotyledons are represented more in smaller seed size classes, while the other two types with cotyledons that are primarily storage organs are represented more in larger size classes. In their study site, species with photosynthetic cotyledons constitute 62 per cent of twenty-nine species colonizing clearings, but only 42 per cent of fifty-one species whose established seedlings were found in the forest understorey. Thus, they suggested that cotyledon functional morphology is important in determining the habitat preference of a species for seedling establishment. This hypothesis is schematically shown in Figure 8.1. It is easy to imagine that a species with photosynthetic cotyledons can respond to the high light availability in gaps immediately after germination, while those with storage cotyledons probably have to wait until leaf development. However, no quantitative study has examined the ecophysiological consequences of having photosynthetic versus storage cotyledons.

Size, quality and utilization patterns of seed reserves

The earliest seedling stage is a physiologically dynamic phase as a seedling undergoes a major transition from complete heterotrophy (= dependence on seed reserves) to complete autotrophy. Seed mass, concentration of individual resources in seed, and cotyledon functional morphology should be examined as three key traits that determine the patterns of development and growth at the earliest seedling stage. An overview of the expected relationships among these three traits, as well as related traits of ecological importance is illustrated in Figure 8.2. Traits are organized by developmental stages. Seed size (seed mass) and resource concentration (concentration of energy, nitrogen and mineral reserves in seeds) together determine the total amount of resources initially available for seedling growth and development. There may be an evolutionary trade-off between seed mass and resource concentration such that strong selection for small seeds may be compensated by higher lipid content.

196

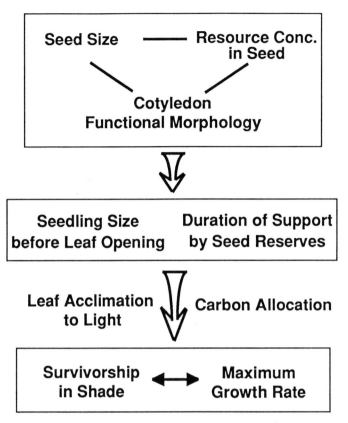

Figure 8.2 A diagram showing the relationships among seed and seedling traits that are likely to affect survival and growth of seedlings. Seed size and resource concentrations in the seed determine the total amount of resources available in a seed. Cotyledon functional morphology is considered to be a key trait that influences the utilization pattern of resources in a seed. The seedling traits at the bottom are ecological traits that are traded-off according to the regeneration niche of the species along the light gradient in the forest. See text for further explanation

Cotyledon functional morphology determines how this total amount of resource available for the seedling is allocated, whether utilized *in situ* for the immediate development of cotyledons into photosynthetic organs or exported to the rest of the seedlings. Cotyledon functional morphology is known to be associated with seed size as discussed in the previous section (Miquel, 1987). However, it is not known whether there is a relationship between cotyledon functional morphology and resource concentration in seeds. Such a relationship might exist if early development of photosynthetic cotyledons requires high nitrogen for construction of photosynthetic enzymes. The total seed reserve size and the mode of its utilization influence the initial seedling size and duration of support by seed reserves. Either the advantage of large initial seedling size or long duration of support by seed reserves may be correlated with high survivorship in shade, although the consequence may be modified significantly by later physiological traits during and after the development of the first true leaf. For example, photosynthetic acclimation potential of leaves to the light environment, as well as carbon allocation patterns during leaf development (e.g. root:shoot ratio and leaf area ratio), may be important in determining a species' ability to survive in shade.

COMPARATIVE STUDIES OF WOODY SPECIES OF PANAMA

The following summary of my comparative studies focuses on seed and early seedling traits before leaf development when the growth and development depend heavily on seed reserves. There are two reasons for this emphasis. First, much less is known about the interspecific variation in traits at this pre-leaf stage than post-leaf stage. Second, this stage is demographically one of the most vulnerable stages in the life of a tropical tree after germination. All studies were carried out on Barro Colorado Island, Panama, using the species native to its primary forest community. Barro Colorado Island is particularly suited for the study because of its well-preserved natural community, its well-known flora, climate and ecological environment (Croat, 1978; Leigh et al., 1982), and previous studies on seedling recruitment ecology (Garwood, 1983, 1986; Augspurger, 1984a,b; De Steven and Putz, 1984; Howe, 1984, 1990; Sork, 1987; Schupp, 1988; Kitajima and Augspurger, 1989).

Quantifying cotyledon photosynthesis

I quantified the morphology and photosynthetic function of cotyledons for ten tree species with epigeal phanerocotylar seedlings, sampling a wide range of cotyledon thickness from 0.2 to 5 mm (Kitajima, 1992b). Maximum photosynthetic rates (i.e. light and CO_2 saturated) and dark respiration rates of detached cotyledons soon after their full expansion were measured with an oxygen electrode. Gross photosynthetic rates per unit area were high (ca. 16 μmol O_2 m^{-2} s^{-1}) and did not differ significantly among species with various thicknesses. Dark respiration rates per unit mass were similar among cotyledons of different thicknesses, indicating similar respiration rates for storage cells and photosynthetic cells. As the ratio of storage cells to photosynthetic cells increased with increasing cotyledon thickness, dark respiration rates per unit area increased; it was as high as 10 μmol O_2 m^{-2} s^{-1} in cotyledons thicker than 2 mm. Thus, photosynthesis by thick epigeal cotyledons is likely to be important in supplying energy required for non-photosynthetic functions of cotyledons, e.g. modification and export of stored reserves, even though its net carbon gain is negligibly small.

198

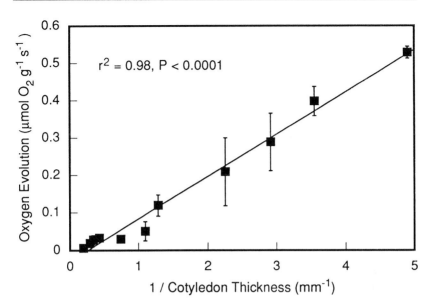

Figure 8.3 Form and function relationship among cotyledons of ten tropical tree species in Panama. Each point is a species mean for three to five seedlings with ± SD. The inverse of cotyledon thickness is a good predictor of the maximum net photosynthesis rates per unit mass of cotyledons measured as the oxygen evolution rates at light and CO_2 saturation

Photosynthetic rate per unit mass is a measure of the average degree of photosynthetic differentiation of cotyledon tissue, i.e. the ratio of photosynthetic cells to storage cells. Thin cotyledons (e.g. 0.2 mm) had very high rates of gross photosynthesis per unit mass (e.g. 0.6 μmol O_2 g^{-1} s^{-1}), while cotyledons thicker than 1 mm had photosynthetic rates just high enough to balance respiration and achieve a small but positive net photosynthesis. This relationship is best described as a simple linear correlation between photosynthetic rate per unit mass and the inverse of cotyledon thickness (Figure 8.3). Net photosynthesis per unit mass was also correlated with the inverse of cotyledon thickness because dark respiration rate per unit mass was not related to cotyledon thickness. Thus, the reciprocal of cotyledon thickness [1/cotyledon thickness] is the best morphological predictor of the degree of photosynthetic differentiation of cotyledon tissues.

Relationship between seed size and cotyledon functional morphology

Given the strong relationship between thickness and photosynthetic capacity per unit mass of cotyledons, it was possible to examine the relationship between mass of seed contents and cotyledon functional morphology, treating both as continuous variables (Figure 8.4). For seventy-four woody species,

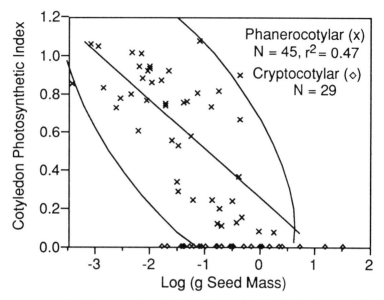

Figure 8.4 Relationship between $\log_{10}$(seed mass in grams) and cotyledon photosynthetic index in arbitrary unit estimated from cotyledon thickness (= $\log_{10}[1/\text{cotyledon thickness} + 1]$) for seventy-four tropical woody species in Panama. For cyptocotylar species, zeros are assigned arbitrarily since they lack photosynthetic capability. Regression analysis includes only phanerocotylar species; the ellipse indicates the 95 per cent confidence limits for a bivariate normal distribution and the straight line indicates the simple linear regression

including eight liana species, I determined oven dry mass of individual seeds excluding seed coats and cotyledon thickness of seedlings raised in a growth house (Kitajima, 1992a). Cotyledon photosynthetic index was calculated as $\log_{10}[1/\text{cotyledon thickness} + 1]$. Log transformation was applied to improve the normality of the distribution and one was added to facilitate arbitrary assignment of zeros to cryptocotylar species. A strong negative relationship existed between seed mass and cotyledon photosynthetic index, regardless of whether cryptocotylar species were included or not in the regression analysis ($p < 0.0001$). This indicates that species with larger seed reserve mass tend to have higher ratios of storage cells to photosynthetic cells in their cotyledons.

This relationship is essentially the same as the categorical associations between cotyledon functional morphology groups and seed length class found in an African forest by Miquel (1987) and Hladik and Miquel (1990); however, the analysis presented in Figure 8.4 is a more direct examination of the underlying functional relationships between seed reserve size and cotyledon morphology. Also this result indicates that there is a wide range of cotyledon functional morphology for a given seed mass (and also a wide range of seed mass for a given type of cotyledon functional morphology).

Resource concentration in seeds *versus* cotyledon functional morphology

Concentrations of energy and nitrogen in a seed are likely to influence the initial seedling size or the duration of support of seedlings by seed reserves. I define energy concentration as heat of combustion per unit seed mass, which should be a linear function of the ratio of lipids (ca. $39\,kJ\,g^{-1}$) to starch ($17.5\,kJ\,g^{-1}$) in the carbon reserves (Williams et al., 1987). Ratios of lipids to starch in seed carbon reserves vary widely among tropical tree species (Barclay and Earl, 1974). Levin (1974) hypothesized the possible advantage of high energy concentration in seeds for establishment in shaded environments; however, the effect of seed energy concentration on seedling growth has not been examined quantitatively. Nitrogen, most of which is stored in the form of storage proteins in seeds, is used for synthesis of various enzymes necessary during seedling development. Development of photosynthetic enzyme systems in photosynthetic cotyledons or the first leaves is likely to require high nitrogen availability.

Two alternative hypotheses are possible about the evolution of seed size and resource concentration in seeds. Energy and nitrogen concentrations may have become negatively correlated with seed mass so that concentration (quality) compensates for mass (quantity) as a result of natural selection for smaller seed mass for better dispersal. Alternatively, natural selection may have favoured a larger seed reserve size by increasing both seed mass and concentration of resources in an environment where greater parental investment is favoured. Similarly, two alternative relationships between resource concentration in seeds and cotyledon functional morphologies may be hypothesized. Seeds and cotyledons of species with mostly storage-type cotyledons may have high energy concentration because cotyledon storage is the only source of energy supply for seedling growth until sufficient development of leaves. Conversely, extensive and rapid construction of new tissue that must take place in photosynthetic cotyledons may require a higher energy concentration in seeds. Nitrogen concentration in seeds is likely to be higher for species with photosynthetic cotyledons whose photosynthetic enzyme systems usually develop before extensive root development.

In order to examine whether such interspecific correlations exist among tropical tree species, energy and nitrogen concentrations in seeds were examined for twelve tropical woody species, three to five in each of three families, Bignoniaceae, Bombacaceae and Leguminosae (Figure 8.5, Kitajima, 1992a). Families were selected so that a wide variation in cotyledon functional morphologies, as indicated by the thickness and the maximum photosynthetic rates, could be examined within each family. Also, among the twelve species, seed mass excluding seed coats differed more than 1,000-fold. Heat of combustion per dry mass of seeds varied substantially among species (CV = 19 per cent); however, seed energy concentration had no clear relationship with cotyledon functional morphology (Figure 8.5, top) or seed mass

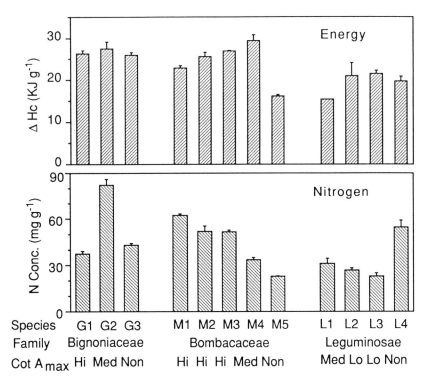

Figure 8.5 Concentrations of energy (= heat of combustion) and nitrogen (= Kjeldahl nitrogen) of seed excluding seed coat for twelve tropical woody species in three families in Panama. Mean and SD of three plants each. Within each family, species are shown in the order of their cotyledons' maximum photosynthetic rates (Cot A_{max}): High: >0.2, Med: 0.1–0.2, Low: 0–0.1 $\mu mol\ g^{-1}\ s^{-1}$. G1, *Tabebuia rosea* DC.; G2, *Callichlamys latifolia* K. Schum.; G3, *Pithecoctenium crucigerum* A. Gentry; M1, *Ochroma pyramidale* Urban.; M2, *Pseudobombax septenatum* Dug.; M3, *Cavanillesia platanifolia* H.B.K.; M4, *Bombacopsis sessilis* Pitt.; M5, *Quararibea asterolepis* Pitt.; L1, *Tachigalia versicolour* Standl. and Wms.; L2, *Ormosia macrocalx* Ducke; L3, *Dipteryx panamensis* Rec and Mell; L4, *Platypodium elegans* J. Vogel

(data not shown). Nitrogen concentration varied more widely among species (CV = 43 per cent) than energy. Nitrogen concentration in seeds was higher with an increasing degree of photosynthetic differentiation of cotyledons in species of Bombacaceae, as expected previously, but not in the other two families (Figure 8.5, bottom). In summary, energy and nitrogen concentrations in seeds vary widely among species; however, this variation is largely independent of cotyledon functional morphology or seed mass. None of the earlier four hypotheses is supported, possibly because the opposite trends predicted by the alternative hypotheses are cancelling each other. This apparent lack of association of resource concentration in seeds with seed mass or cotyledon type should make it statistically easier to detect the effect of resource concentration in seeds on seedling growth and development.

Based on the theory of biochemical cost of tissue construction (Penning de Vries and Van Laar, 1977), a unit seed mass with a high ratio of lipid to starch should be converted into a greater seedling mass. In a theoretical calculation, an increase of lipid content from 0 per cent to 50 per cent in seed means a 63 per cent increase in energy concentration from $17.5 \, \text{kJ} \, \text{g}^{-1}$ to $28.5 \, \text{kJ} \, \text{g}^{-1}$, which should result in a 38 per cent increase in seedling mass produced per unit seed mass (Kitajima, 1992a). The relatively smaller increase in seedling mass is the result of a lower efficiency of energy retrieval from lipids than from starch (Goodwin and Mercer, 1983; Chapin, 1989). These calculations assume that all carbon reserves are utilized as building blocks and for growth respiration, but not for a prolonged period of maintenance respiration. Alternatively, higher energy concentration in a seed may support the seedling's metabolic demands for a longer period. In an experiment in which ten species were grown in deep shade (2 per cent of full sun available), there was a weak but significant correlation between energy concentration in seed and seedling mass produced per unit seed mass after full expansion of cotyledons but immediately before the true leaf development in shade ($r = 0.66$, $p < 0.04$, Kitajima, 1992a). Thus, a species with a higher energy concentration tends to produce larger seedlings by the end of seed reserve dependency period than another species of the same mass but with lower energy concentration. Despite the lower energetic efficiency of retrieving energy from lipids than from starch, seeds of some species contain high proportions of lipids. This must indicate a strong evolutionary advantage of increasing lipid content when both increase in carbon reserve size and decrease in seed mass are favoured, for example, when both large initial seedling size and long dispersal distance are selected for. However, possible change in energy concentration is more constrained than possible change in mass; energy concentration can differ up to threefold while seed mass can differ over 10^5-fold among species.

Duration of seed reserve dependency

Duration of support of seedlings by seed reserves is frequently tied to discussions of the evolutionary advantage of seed size (Fenner, 1987; Thompson, 1987) or cotyledon functional morphologies (Garwood, 1983). However, the actual duration of seed reserve dependency has not been compared among species, partly because it is difficult to define clearly what to measure. Two aspects of the transition from seed reserve dependency to dependency on external resources need to be considered in defining the period of seed reserve dependency. First, this transition occurs gradually. Initially, after radicle emergence, a developing seedling acquires all resources from seed reserves and the rate of its development is independent of the level of external resources. Following the development of organs necessary for uptake of external resources, the seedling starts to utilize external resources (= end of the 'complete' dependency = beginning of switch to external resources). For a certain period, seedlings utilize both seed-derived and external resources, with increasing dependency on the latter, until all seed reserves disappear (= end of transitional period = beginning of complete autotrophy). The second problem is that this transition is likely to occur at different times for different resources, e.g. carbon, nitrogen, phosphorus (Fenner, 1987).

I have developed an experimental method to determine when seedling growth starts to depend on individual external resources based on the following set of three predictions (Kitajima, 1992a):

(1) Growth rate of seedlings should be independent of the external availability of a particular resource as long as they depend solely on seed reserves for this resource;

(2) As seedlings start utilizing external resources, seedling growth rate is expected to respond to the level of external resources; and

(3) If growth curves are constructed from frequent harvests, the growth curve for seedlings growing under the condition deficient in a single resource is expected to start falling below the reference growth curve for seedlings without deficiencies when seed reserve of that particular resource is no longer sufficient to support the maximum rate growth.

This method was applied in a study of dependency on energy (= the major above-ground resource) and nitrogen (= the major below-ground resource) in seed reserves versus from external sources for three woody species with contrasting cotyledon functional morphologies in the Bignoniaceae (Table 8.1). The study's objectives were: first, to examine whether the switch of dependency from seed reserves to external sources occurs earlier for energy or nitrogen, and second, to examine whether the timing when seedlings start depending on the external sources of energy or nitrogen differs for species with different functional morphologies of cotyledons. I had two predictions prior to the experiment. The first was that species with photosynthetic cotyledons would start depending on light availability earlier than those with storage cotyledons which have to wait until the development of true leaves for utilizing light energy. My second prediction was that species with photosynthetic cotyledons also start depending on external nitrogen earlier than species with storage cotyledons, because the extensive modification of cotyledons into photosynthetic organs and the resulting high relative growth rate at an earlier time may require high nitrogen supplies.

Seedlings were raised individually for forty-five days from the time of radicle emergence in plastic pots filled with a sand and vermiculite mixture under optimal growth conditions with high light and nutrient availability (= reference) or under conditions deficient in either light or nitrogen supply. Nitrogen supply was controlled by a daily supply of nutrient solutions differing

Table 8.1 Characteristics of seeds and seedling cotyledons of three woody species of Bignoniaceae with contrasting cotyledon functional morphologies after germination. Seeds of these species have no endosperm. How long seedlings depend solely on energy and nitrogen reserves in seeds was determined as the duration from radicle emergence until the growth curves started to be negatively affected by the deficiency of light and soil nitrogen (Kitajima, 1992a)

Species	Tabebuia rosea		Callichlamys latifolia		Pithecoctenium crucigerum	
	n	Mean ± SD	n	Mean ± SD	n	Mean ± SD
Seed characteristics						
Seed mass (mg)	12	39.4 ± 2.8	12	187.2 ± 17.8	12	46.1 ± 17.8
N concentration (mg g^{-1})	3	37.4 ± 1.8	3	82.3 ± 3.8	3	43.1 ± 1.1
Energy concentration (kJ g^{-1})	3	27.2 ± 0.8	3	28.3 ± 1.7	3	26.8 ± 0.6
Cotyledon characteristics						
Position		epigeal		epigeal		hypogeal
Exposure		phanerocotylar		phanerocotylar		cryptocotylar
Morphology		papyraceous		coriaceous		coriaceous
Area at radicle emergence (cm^2)*	6	1.5 ± 0.2	7	3.7 ± 0.5	7	1.7 ± 0.2
Area at full expansion (cm^2)*	51	10.4 ± 1.7	47	4.5 ± 0.8	28	2.1 ± 0.4
Thickness at centre (mm)†	5	0.42 ± 0.05	6	1.76 ± 0.11	6	1.05 ± 0.0
Net A$_{max}$ (μmol O$_2$ g^{-1} s^{-1})‡	3	0.51 ± 0.06	3	0.07 ± 0.04		NA
Age at abscission (days)		> 80		30 – 80		30 – 80
Duration of sole dependency on seed reserves						
On seed energy reserves (days)		7		20		13
On seed nitrogen reserves (days)		14		> 45		16

* Total area of the two cotyledons

† Measured at 20, 7 and 12 days after radicle emergence, respectively

‡ Light and CO$_2$ saturated net photosynthesis rates per unit area or dry mass measured at 22 and 23 days after radicle emergence, respectively. Gas exchange was not measured for non-green cotyledons of *P. crucigerum*

only in nitrogen concentration (complete solution for reference and complete solution minus nitrogen for nitrogen-deficient condition). Shade cloth was used to cut the light availability to 2 per cent of full sun to create conditions deficient in the external energy supply; the reference for comparison had no shade cloth. Three plants were harvested every day or every other day from each treatment for each species. Then, total seedling dry mass was plotted against time after radicle emergence in order to identify the day when the growth curves of plants raised under conditions deficient in light or nitrogen started to drop below the reference curve of each species (Table 8.1, bottom).

Biomass growth of all species responded to light availability earlier than to soil nitrogen availability. For example, in *Tabebuia rosea*, the biomass of nitrogen-fed seedlings in shade started to fall below the biomass of nitrogen-fed seedlings in sun at seven days after germination, while the growth of nitrogen-deficient seedlings in sun started to fall below the growth of nitrogen-fed seedlings in sun at about fourteen days. Thus, the transition from complete dependency on seed reserves to a significant dependency on external resources occurred earlier for energy (carbon) than for nitrogen. Seedlings of these species have intermediate to high shade tolerance and most of their seeds naturally germinate in shade. In all species, external nitrogen availability had no effect on seedling growth in shade for at least forty days (data not shown). Thus, it appears that seeds of these tropical woody species contain enough nitrogen to meet the seedling nitrogen demand in shade during the early seedling establishment stage.

Among species, the duration of sole dependency on energy and nitrogen reserves in seeds differed (Table 8.1). Although the results did not exclude a possibility of a positive contribution of seed mass to a prolonged support by seed reserves, the results indicate the effect of cotyledon photosynthetic differentiation on the timing of the switch to light as the energy source and the effect of seed nitrogen concentration on the timing of switch to soil nitrogen. The response to light availability occurred earlier in *Tabebuia rosea*, the species with thinner photosynthetic cotyledons than in the other two species whose cotyledons' primary function is storage. Having photosynthetic cotyledons enables seedlings to maximize their relative growth rate at very early time after germination. In contrast, the switch to soil nitrogen was not related to cotyledon functional morphology, but rather to the nitrogen concentration in seeds. *Callichlamys latifolia* had twice as high nitrogen in seeds as the other two species and it started to respond to soil nitrogen more than twice as late as the other species.

CONCLUSION

The evolutionary significance of differences in mass and types of seed reserves can be evaluated properly only in relation to how seedlings use them.

Seed mass and cotyledon functional morphology are two important traits that are strongly associated with each other and determine the utilization patterns of seed reserves. On the other hand, concentrations of energy and nitrogen in seeds vary widely but rather independently of seed mass or cotyledon functional morphology. Seed energy concentration has a significant effect on size of seedlings established in shade, although the seedling size is largely determined by the seed mass. The higher the nitrogen concentration in seeds, the longer the seedlings depend on nitrogen reserves in seeds without a need to utilize the external nitrogen in soil. Cotyledon functional morphology *per se* does not have a significant effect on seedling mass at the end of the pre-leaf cotyledonous stage in shade; however, species with photosynthetic cotyledons start utilizing light as the energy source earlier than those with less photosynthetic cotyledons. Regardless of the cotyledon functional morphology or seed mass, the external acquisition of resources starts earlier for energy resources than for nitrogen resources.

These findings add to our mechanistic understandings of what traits are important in differentiating regeneration niches among tropical tree species at the early seedling stage with regard to light environment. There is a negative interspecific correlation between relative growth rates of young seedlings and their survivorship in the shaded understorey (Kitajima, 1994). It appears that species specialized for regeneration in high-light environments have a suite of traits that lead to faster growth rates, while species selected for establishment of seedling banks in the understorey have a suite of traits that lead to higher survivorship at the expense of growth rate. Having photosynthetic cotyledons is probably a result of selective pressures for the species to grow fast in a competitive environment, i.e. light gaps, at the earliest possible time after germination. It should be viewed as a part of the general allocation traits that lead to high relative growth rates, such as low leaf mass per unit area and high leaf area ratios. In fact, even after expansion of true leaves, species with photosynthetic cotyledons continue to have lower leaf area ratios and grow faster than species with storage cotyledons (Kitajima, 1992a). In contrast, having greater seed mass combined with storage cotyledons provide survival advantage in shade at the expense of relative growth rates. The primary advantage of a larger seed is probably to secure a certain seedling size in energy limited environment without sacrificing allocation for physical and chemical defence and storage necessary for repairs after accidental loss of tissue. Future research should evaluate the cost and benefit of defence and storage allocation during and after seed reserve dependency period.

ACKNOWLEDGEMENTS

I am deeply indebted to Carol Augspurger and Nancy Garwood for their advice and encouragement. Carol Augspurger, John Cheeseman, Shahid Naeem, and an anonymous reviewer provided helpful comments on the manuscript. This research was supported by a predoctoral fellowship from the Smithsonian Institution and logistic supports from the Smithsonian Tropical Research Institute.

REFERENCES

Aide, T.M. (1987). Limbfalls: a major cause of sapling mortality for tropical forest. *Biotropica*, **19**, 284–5.

Augspurger, C.K. (1984a). Seedling survival of tropical tree species; interactions of dispersal distance, light gaps and pathogens. *Ecology*, **65**, 1705–12.

Augspurger, C.K. (1984b). Light requirements of neotropical tree seedlings: a comparative study of growth and survival. *Journal of Ecology*, **72**, 777–95.

Augspurger, C.K. (1986). Morphological and dispersal potential of wind-dispersed diaspores of neotropical trees. *American Journal of Botany*, **73**, 353–63.

Barclay, A.S. and Earl, F.R. (1974). Chemical analyses of seeds III. Oil and protein content of 1253 species. *Economic Botany*, **28**, 178–236.

Bawa, K.S. and Hadley, M. (1991). *Reproductive Ecology of Tropical Forest Plants.* UNESCO/Parthenon, Paris/Carnforth.

Bokdam, J. (1977). *Seedling morphology of some African Sapotaceae and its taxonomical significance.* Mededelingen Lanbouwhogeschool, Wageningen.

Brokaw, N.V.L. (1985). Treefalls, regrowth and community structure in tropical forest. In Picket, S.T.A. and White, P.S. (eds.), *The Ecology of Natural Disturbance and Patch Dynamics*, pp. 53–69. Academic Press, New York.

Brokaw, N.V.L. and Scheiner, S. (1989). Species composition in gaps and structure of a tropical forest. *Ecology*, **70**, 538–41.

Burger Hzn., D. (1972). *Seedlings of Some Tropical Trees and Shrubs, Mainly of South East Asia.* Centre for Agricultural Publishing and Documentation (PUDOC), Wageningen.

Chapin, F.S. (1989). The cost of tundra plant structures: evaluation of concepts and currencies. *American Naturalist*, **133**, 1–19.

Croat, T.B. (1978). *Flora of Barro Colorado Island.* Stanford University Press, Stanford.

De Steven, D. and Putz, F.E. (1984). Impact of mammals on early recruitment of a tropical canopy tree, *Dipteryx panamensis,* in Panama. *Oikos*, **43**, 207–16.

de Vogel, E.F. (1980). *Seedlings of Dicotyledons.* Centre for Agricultural Publishing and Documentation (PUDOC), Wageningen.

Duke, J.A. (1965). Keys for the identification of seedlings of some prominent woody species in eight forest types in Puerto Rico. *Annals of the Missouri Botanical Garden*, **52**, 314–50.

Fenner, M. (1987). Seedlings. *New Phytologist*, **106**, 35–47.

Foster, S.A. and Janson, C.H. (1985). The relationship between seed size and establishment conditions in tropical woody plants. *Ecology*, **66**, 773–80.

Garwood, N.C. (1983). Seed germination in a seasonal tropical forest in Panama: a community study. *Ecological Monographs*, **53**, 150–81.

Garwood, N.C. (1986). Constraints on the timing of seed germination in a tropical forest. In Estrada, A. and Flemin, T.H. (eds.), *Frugivores and Seed Dispersal*, pp. 347–55. W. Junk, Dordrecht.

Grime, J.P. and Jeffrey, D.W. (1965). Seedling establishment in vertical gradients of sunlight. *Journal of Ecology*, **53**, 621–42.

Goodwin, T.W. and Mercer, E.I. (1983). *Introduction to Plant Biochemistry*, 2nd edn. Pergamon, Oxford.

Harris, M., Mackender, R.O. and Smith, D.L. (1986). Photosynthesis of cotyledons of soybean seedlings. *New Phytologist*, **104**, 319–29.

Hladik, A. and Miquel, S. (1990). Seedling types and plant establishment in an African rain forest. In Bawa, K.S. and Hadley, M. (eds.), *Reproductive Ecology of Tropical Forest Plants*, pp. 261–82. UNESCO/Parthenon, Paris/Carnforth.

Howe, H.F. (1984). Early Consequences of seed dispersal for a neotropical tree (*Virola surinamensis*). *Ecology*, **66**, 781–91.

Howe, H.F. (1990). Survival and growth of juvenile *Virola surinamensis* in Panama: effects of herbivory and canopy closure. *Journal of Tropical Ecology*, **6**, 259–80.

Kitajima, K. (1992a). *The importance of cotyledon functional morphology and patterns of seed reserve utilization for the physiological ecology of neotropical tree seedlings*. Ph.D. Dissertation, University of Illinois, Urbana-Champaign.

Kitajima, K. (1992b). Relationship between photosynthesis and thickness of cotyledons for tropical tree species. *Functional Ecology*, **6**, 582–9.

Kitajima, K. (1994). Relative importance of photosynthetic traits and allocation patterns as correlates of seedling shade tolerance of 13 tropical tree species. *Oecologia*, **98**, 419–28.

Kitajima, K. and Augspurger, C.K. (1989). Seed and seedling ecology of a monocarpic tropical tree, *Tachigalia versicolour*. *Ecology*, **70**, 1102–14.

Leigh, E.G. Jr., Rand, S.A. and Windsor, D.M. (eds.) (1982). *The Ecology of a Tropical Forest: Seasonal Rhythms and Long-term Changes*. Smithsonian Institution Press, Washington, DC.

Levin, D.A. (1974). The oil content of seeds: an ecological perspective. *American Naturalist*, **108**, 193–206.

Lovell, P. and Moore, K. (1971). A comparative study of the role of the cotyledons in seedling development. *Journal of Experimental Botany*, **22**, 153–62.

Miquel, S. (1987). Morphologie fonctionnelle de plantules d'espèces forestières du Gabon. *Bulletin du Muséum National d'Histoire Naturelle, Paris, 4ème série, section B, Adansonia*, **9**, 101–2.

Molofsky, J. and Augspurger, C.K. (1992). The effect of leaf litter on early seedling establishment in a tropical forest. *Ecology*, **73**, 68–77.

Ng, F.S.P. (1978). Strategies of establishment in Malayan forest trees. In Tomlinson, T.B. and Zimmerman, H.M. (eds.), *Tropical Trees as Living Systems*, pp. 129–62, Cambridge University Press, Cambridge.

Ng, F.S.P. (1992). *Manual of Forest fruits, Seeds and Seedlings*. Vol. 1 and 2. Forest Research Institute of Malaysia, Kepong.

Olofinboba, M.O. (1975). Studies on seedlings of *Theobroma cacao* L., variety F3 Amazon. I. Role of cotyledons in seedling development. *Turrialba*, **25**, 121–7.

Penning de Vries, F.W.T. and Van Laar, H.H. (1977). Substrate utilization in germinating seeds. In Landsberg, J.J. and Cutting, C.V. (eds.), *Environmental Effects on Crop Physiology*, pp. 217–28. Academic Press, London.

Schupp, E.G. (1988). Seed and early seedling predation in the forest understory and in treefall gaps. *Oikos*, **51**, 71–8.

Smith, C.C. and Fretwell, S.D. (1974). The optimal balance between size and number of offspring. *American Naturalist,* **108**, 499–506.

Sork, V.L. (1987). Effects of predation and light on seedling establishment in *Gustavia superba*. *Ecology*, **68**, 1341–50.

Swaine, M.D. and Whitmore, T.C. (1988). On the definition of ecological species groups in tropical rain forest. *Vegetatio*, **75**, 81–6.

Thompson, K. (1987). Seeds and seed banks. *New Phytologist*, **106** (Suppl.), 23–34.

Westoby, M., Jurado, E. and Leishman, M. (1992). Comparative evolutionary ecology of seed size. *Trends in Ecology and Evolution*, **7**, 368–72.

Whitmore, T.C. (1989). Canopy gaps and the two major groups of forest trees. *Ecology*, **70**, 536–8.

Williams, K., Percival, F., Merino, J. and Mooney, H.A. (1987). Estimation of tissue construction cost from heat of combustion and organic nitrogen content. *Plant, Cell and Environment*, **10**, 725–34.

Revised manuscript received April 1994

CHAPTER 9

DIFFERENTIAL RESPONSES TO NUTRIENTS, SHADE AND DROUGHT AMONG TREE SEEDLINGS OF LOWLAND TROPICAL FOREST IN SINGAPORE

David F.R.P. Burslem

INTRODUCTION

Both stochastic and biological factors have been implicated in the maintenance of species richness in tropical rain forest (Denslow, 1987; Whitmore, 1974, 1975). The biological factors include density- or distance-dependent mortality of seedlings (Hubbell et al., 1990) or niche-differentiation during the regeneration phase (Grubb, 1977a), while the alternative hypotheses emphasize the roles of chance and history (Hubbell and Foster, 1986a,b, 1987).

One expression of the idea that differences in the regeneration characteristics of tropical tree species promotes coexistence is the hypothesis that different species are adapted to exploit canopy gaps of different sizes (Denslow, 1980; Hartshorn, 1978; Whitmore, 1978). Short-term experiments designed to test this hypothesis have not found support for it (Barton, 1984; Brown and Whitmore, 1992), although observations over longer periods will be required to clarify the outcome of these experiments. There is some evidence that within-gap heterogeneity may contribute to the maintenance of species richness (Barton, 1984; Brandani et al., 1988). Field experiments conducted so far have investigated only some components of the regeneration niche as originally defined (Grubb, 1977a) and cannot be regarded as complete tests of the hypothesis. Species differ in aspects such as reproductive phenology (Appanah, 1985; Fleming, 1985), germination (Raich and Gong, 1990), seed size and establishment conditions (Molofsky and Augspurger, 1992), and seedling allometry (King, 1990; Kohyama, 1987; Kohyama and Hotta, 1990), as well as seedling responses to forest patchiness at many different scales. Of particular interest for the explanation of the maintenance of the large group of tropical tree species which are both variably shade-tolerant as seedlings and demanding of a gap to complete growth to maturity (Whitmore, 1975) are the processes operating before the canopy opens. As occupancy of a gap may be strongly linked to seedling size at the time of gap creation (Brown and Whitmore, 1992) it is important to focus on the factors that influence seedling size or longevity in the understorey, either directly, such as seed size

(Osunkoya et al., 1993), or indirectly through differences in seedling allometry (King, 1990; Kohyama, 1987; Kohyama and Hotta, 1990) or physiology (see, for example, Pearcy, 1983; Pearcy and Calkin, 1983; Pearcy et al., 1983).

In order to determine the relative importance of differences in seedling growth for the maintenance of tropical tree species richness it is necessary to answer a series of interrelated questions.

(1) What are the resources for which plants compete?

(2) What is the extent of heterogeneity in the availability of these resources under natural conditions?

(3) Are plants differentiated in their responses to heterogeneity in these resources and to interactions between colimiting resources?

(4) Is this differentiation important for species coexistence?

This chapter presents an overview of recent research based on a lowland dipterocarp rain forest site in Singapore. I first place the research in context by describing the results of an analysis of the nutrient status of the forest in Singapore where it was conducted, and then I outline a series of shade house experiments designed to address the first and third of these questions in some detail and the second question in much less detail. The final question underlines the point that differences between species which emerge from ecological experimentation are not direct evidence that different species occupy different regeneration niches. In the final section of the paper the questions are re-examined and a procedure is outlined for testing the predictions arising from earlier experiments. For a more detailed description of the experiments discussed here the reader is referred to papers to be published elsewhere (Burslem et al., 1994, 1995; Grubb et al., 1994).

THE NUTRIENT STATUS OF COASTAL HILL DIPTEROCARP FOREST IN SINGAPORE

The study site was located in the Republic of Singapore (103° 50'E, 1° 20'N), and was a remnant fragment of coastal hill dipterocarp rain forest (*sensu* Symington, 1943) in Bukit Timah Nature Reserve on Singapore's highest hill (163 m). The Republic of Singapore has a typical tropical diurnal climate with mean monthly temperatures in the range 26.4–27.8°C (Dale, 1963) and annual rainfall of about 2,400 mm (Watts, 1955). No month has a mean rainfall less than 140 mm (Corlett, 1990), but year-to-year variation may dictate that evaporation exceeds precipitation for periods of up to six months in some years (Nieuwolt, 1965). Coastal regions of the Malay Peninsula experience a higher frequency of dry periods than equivalent sites further inland because of higher average wind speeds and reduced cloudiness (Nieuwolt, 1965). Two-thirds of the 71 ha forest is primary (Corlett, 1988) and has a species-rich tree flora with an abundance of the Dipterocarpaceae, Euphorbiaceae and Rubiaceae (Corlett, 1990; Wong, 1987). Coastal hills of the Malay Peninsular are characterized by the abundance of the dipterocarp *Shorea curtisii* close to sea-level; further inland this species occurs on ridges at altitudes above 225 m (Burgess, 1975; Whitmore, 1975). At Bukit Timah another dipterocarp, *Dipterocarpus caudatus* ssp. *penangianus* occurs in near equal abundance to *Shorea curtisii* (Wong, 1987).

The parent material at Bukit Timah is granite (Thomas, 1991), which gives rise to Typic Paleudult soils of the Rengam series (Ives, 1977). The nutrient status of the forest was determined by chemical analysis of soil, leaves and leaf litter; the amount of litter on the forest floor and the distribution of fine roots in the soil profile were also obtained to aid comparison with forests elsewhere. Soil was collected from three pits in April 1990 and taken by air immediately to Cambridge, UK, where it was analysed for pH, loss-on-ignition, total N, P and K concentrations and N mineralization rates using standard techniques (for details see Grubb et al., 1994). The amount of litter was determined at these three sites and at a further ten selected at random throughout the forest in August, 1991; as there was not a significant difference between the mean values at the two sampling dates the data are combined for presentation here. Apart from these two sampling dates, temporal changes in the amount of litter were not characterized, but variation through the year did not appear to be great. Samples of fresh litter from the L_1 layer of these thirteen sites were analysed for their N, P, K, Mg and Ca concentrations. Samples of living 'shade' leaves were collected from twenty of the most abundant species in April, 1990; they were oven-dried immediately and taken to Cambridge for nutrient content analysis as above.

Soil chemical characteristics by depth in the profile are presented in detail elsewhere (Grubb et al., 1994); they are summarized for 0–20 cm and compared with other published descriptions of lowland dipterocarp forests in Tables 9.1 and 9.2. From the comparisons made here it is clear that Bukit Timah soils are more acidic and lower in total N and P than most other lowland dipterocarp forests and at the low end of the ranges for other hill dipterocarp forests (Table 9.1), and that hill dipterocarp forests possess soils of lower pH and lower total concentrations of N and P than those of other forms of lowland dipterocarp forests (Table 9.2).

The amount of litter is presented in Table 9.3 and compared with data from a coastal hill dipterocarp forest in Penang, Peninsular Malaysia (Gong and Ong, 1983), and a lowland dipterocarp forest in Pasoh (Yoda, 1978). The accumulation of litter at Bukit Timah was considerably greater than at either of these sites and the contrast with Bukit Timah is greater for the lowland forest site than the hill forest site. The nutrient concentrations in fresh litter (Table 9.4) reflect to varying degrees the concentrations of major nutrients in soil.

Table 9.1 The ranges of pH and total concentrations of N and P (mg g^{-1}) in soil at Bukit Timah with mean values for other hill dipterocarp forests (HDF) and lowland dipterocarp forests (LDF) of the Malay Peninsula and Borneo

Forest type and location	Sample depth (cm)	pH	Total N (mg g^{-1})	Total P (mg g^{-1})	Reference
HDF Bukit Timah, Singapore.	0–20	3.5–4.2	0.49–1.88	0.03–0.08	This study
HDF, Bukit Timah, Singapore	0–20	4.1	1.6	0.06	Sim et al., 1992
HDF, Peninsular Malaysia.	0–14	3.8	2.8	0.11	Chandler, 1985
HDF, Semangok, Peninsular Malaysia	0–30	4.3	1.4	0.07	Fong, 1977
Dipterocarp forest, hill sites, Andalau, Sarawak	0–1	3.8	5.1	0.06	Ashton, 1964
	1–30	4.4	5.1	0.13	
LDF, Peninsular Malaysia	0–14	4.0	2.6	0.09	Chandler, 1985
LDF, Pasoh, Peninsular Malaysia	0–2	4.5	2.7	0.29	Allbrook, 1973
	2–20	4.3	1.7	0.20	
LDF, Pasoh, Peninsular Malaysia	0–1	4.3	2.7	0.20	Allbrook, 1973
	1–25	4.4	0.4	0.01	
Dipterocarp forest, valley sites, Andalau, Sarawak	15–20	4.2	4.3	0.19	Ashton, 1964
LDF, Belalong, Sarawak	13	4.4	2.9	0.24	Ashton, 1964
LDF, Mulu, Sarawak	0–10	4.1	5.1	0.12	Proctor et al., 1983
	10–30	4.7	1.5	0.14	
LDF, Lempake, E. Kalimantan (Cited in Sim et al., 1992)	0–10	3.4	4.0	0.14	Riswan, 1989

Table 9.2 The ranges of pH and total concentrations of N and P in soil at Bukit Timah (0–20 cm), with comparative data for other hill dipterocarp forests (HDF) and lowland dipterocarp forests (LDF) of the Malay Peninsula and Borneo. For references see Table 9.1

	Bukit Timah	Other HDF	Other LDF
pH	3.5–4.2	3.8–4.4	4.0–4.7
Total N (mg g^{-1})	0.49–1.88	1.4–5.1	0.4–5.1
Total P (mg g^{-1})	0.03–0.08	0.06–0.13	(0.01–) 0.09–0.29

Table 9.4 shows that the mean N concentration (14.1 mg g^{-1}) was not particularly low compared to the range observed in other lowland tropical forests (Proctor, 1984), while that of P (0.22 mg g^{-1}) was at the low end of the ranges for both lowland tropical forests in general (Proctor, 1984) and to the subset of that dataset on oxisol and ultisol soils (Vitousek and Sanford, 1986). Data for K concentrations should be interpreted with caution because of the rapid leaching of K from fallen litter, but the mean value for Bukit Timah falls in

Table 9.3 Mean amounts (t ha^{-1}) of leaf litter and total litter for coastal hill dipterocarp forests (HDF) at Bukit Timah (Singapore) and Penang (Peninsular Malaysia) and for lowland diptero-carp forest (LDF) at Pasoh (Peninsular Malaysia). Data for Penang is given for two successive years during wet and dry seasons. Standard errors in parentheses; n = sample size

		Leaf litter	Total litter	n	Reference
HDF, Bukit Timah, Singapor		7.6 (0.6)	12.2 (1.3)	13	This study
HDF, Penang, Peninsular Malaysia					
Dry season	1980	2.4 (0.2)	4.6 (0.3)	20	Gong and
	1981	1.5 (0.2)	2.9 (0.5)	14	Ong, 1983
Wet season	1980	4.7 (0.4)	6.5 (0.5)	20	
	1981	3.8 (0.4)	5.6 (0.6)	4	
LDF, Pasoh, Peninsular Malaysia		1.7 (0.2)	4.3 (0.3)	4	Yoda, 1978

Table 9.4 Mean concentrations (mg g^{-1}) of N, P, K, Ca and Mg in freshly-fallen litter at Bukit Timah (standard error in parentheses; n = 13) with ranges given by Proctor (1984) for other lowland tropical rain forests and by Vitousek and Sanford (1986) for lowland tropical forests on oxisols and ultisols

Element	Bukit Timah	Other lowland tropical forests	Other forests on oxisols/ultisols
N	14.1 (0.9)	5–21	9.5–16.5
P	0.22 (0.04)	0.1–1.2	0.15–0.7
K	5.0 (1.2)	1–10	—
Ca	5.1 (0.9)	1.5–31	1.5–14
Mg	2.1 (0.1)	1.1–5.4	—

the middle of the range for lowland tropical forests (Table 9.4), while the means for Ca (5.1 mg g^{-1}) and Mg (2.1 mg g^{-1}) lie at the bottom of the ranges reported for lowland tropical rain forest (Table 9.4).

Nutrient concentrations in living leaves at Bukit Timah and other forests on oxisol and ultisol soils are compared in Table 9.5. The mean values for N (19.5 mg g^{-1}) and P (0.81 mg g^{-1}) are above the ranges given for forests on oxisol and ultisol soils by Vitousek and Sanford (1986). Values for K, Ca and Mg should be treated with some caution because most published data are for well-illuminated leaves which may have either higher or lower concentrations of nutrients than leaves developed in the shade (Bongers and Popma, 1988; Shorrocks, 1962); nevertheless, the results for Bukit Timah suggest considerably higher mean concentrations than those found for other forests on oxisol and ultisol soils (Table 9.5).

In comparisons of foliar N concentrations between the two functional groups of tropical trees recognized by Swaine and Whitmore (1988) a consistent trend of higher concentrations in species defined below as 'gap-demanding' has been observed (Coley, 1983; Popma et al., 1992). The same trend

Table 9.5 Mean concentrations (mg g^{-1}) of N, P, K, Ca and Mg in living shade leaves of twenty species* at Bukit Timah Nature Reserve, Singapore, for well-lit leaves of ten species[†] at Kepong, Peninsular Malaysia (Grubb, 1977b) and the range of values for other lowland tropical forests on oxisols and ultisols given by Vitousek and Sanford (1986). Standard errors are given in parentheses

	Bukit Timah	Kepong	Tropical forests on oxisols/ultisols
N	19.4 (1.1)	15.5 (1.0)	13–19
P	0.80 (0.05)	0.71 (0.05)	0.5–0.7
K	12.1 (1.0)	7.1 (0.9)	3.8–5.4
Ca	9.8 (1.7)	5.8 (0.9)	1.1–5.0
Mg	3.1 (0.3)	1.8 (0.3)	1.0–2.9

*Species sampled in Singapore were: *Gluta wallichii* (Anacardiaceae), *Cyathocalyx ridleyi* (Annonaceae), *Canarium patentinervium* (Burseraceae), *Hopea griffithii*, *Shorea curtisii* (Dipterocarpaceae), *Diospyros buxifolia* (Ebenaceae), *Baccaurea parviflora* (Euphorbiaceae), *Calophyllum ferrugineum* (Guttiferae), *Cinnamomum iners* (Lauraceae), *Pternandra echinata* (Melastomataceae), *Knema communis* (Myristicaceae), *Rhodamnia cinerea* (Myrtaceae), *Urophyllum hirsutum* (Rubiaceae), *Alstonia angustifolia* (Apocynaceae), *Macaranga conifera*, *Macaranga heynei*, *Macaranga hypoleuca*, *Macaranga triloba* (Euphorbiaceae), *Ficus fistulosa*, *Ficus grossularioides* (Moraceae)
[†]Species sampled at Kepong were: *Alstonia angustiloba* (Apocynaceae), *Dillenia grandifolia* (Dilleniaceae), *Dipterocarpus baudii*, *Dryobalanops aromatica*, *Shorea parvifolia* (Dipterocarpaceae), *Elateriospermum tapos* (Euphorbiaceae), *Calophyllum ferrugineum* (Guttiferae), *Koompassia malaccensis* (Leguminosae), *Fragraea fragrans* (Loganiaceae), *Pentace* sp. (Tiliaceae)

Table 9.6 Mean concentrations (mg g^{-1}) of N, P, K, Ca and Mg in living shade leaves of seven gap-demanding species and thirteen shade-tolerating trees at Bukit Timah Nature Reserve, Singapore (standard errors in parentheses) and similar data for species of lowland tropical rain forests in Panama (Coley, 1983) and Mexico (Popma et al., 1992). For the definition of 'gap-demanding' and 'shade-tolerant' categories see text. The twenty species sampled in Singapore are listed beneath Table 9.5; the first thirteen in this list were classified as 'shade-tolerant' and the remaining seven as 'gap-demanding'

		Gap-demanding species	Shade-tolerant species	Reference
N	Bukit Timah	23.6 (1.0)	17.1 (1.1)	This study
	Barro Colorado Island, Panama	25	22	Coley, 1983
	Los Tuxtlas, Mexico	20.0 (1.3)	14.9 (1.0)	Popma et al., 1992
P	Bukit Timah	1.03 (0.05)	0.68 (0.05)	This study
	Los Tuxtlas, Mexico	1.47 (0.11)	1.16 (0.12)	Popma et al., 1992
K	Bukit Timah	15.1 (2.3)	10.5 (0.8)	This study
	Los Tuxtlas, Mexico	10.3 (0.8)	11.0 (0.9)	Popma et al., 1992
Ca	Bukit Timah	15.0 (4.0)	7.0 (1.1)	This study
Mg	Bukit Timah	3.3 (0.4)	3.0 (0.4)	This study

was observed for N, P, K and Ca in this study in a comparison of seven gap-demanding species and thirteen shade-tolerating species (Table 9.6), although differences in the mean age of leaves between species of the two groups would tend to confound the comparison based on establishment conditions. The two groups are defined as follows: 'gap-demanders' are those which are found as adults only with their crowns in direct sunlight, and which appear to grow to maturity only in tree-fall gaps, even though for at least some species seedlings up to about 30-cm height may be found in deep shade (c. 1 per cent of diffuse light under cloudy conditions); 'shade-tolerant' species become established in shade and all appear to be able to persist for some years in shade, although there is wide variation within the group as to how much opening of the canopy is needed for onward growth to maturity. The trend of higher foliar nutrient concentrations among gap-demanding trees is supported by the tendency for higher N concentrations (on a mass basis) in leaves of trees with shorter leaf life spans and greater maximum photosynthetic rates in a variety of ecosystems (Reich et al., 1991, 1992).

It may be concluded that the forest at Bukit Timah has developed on an acidic soil with low total nutrient concentrations. The nutrient concentrations in fresh litter parallel the low nutrient status of the soil, particularly that of P, but nutrient concentrations in living leaves are not particularly low. The large amount of litter may reflect low decomposition rates as a consequence of the low concentration of P in the litter and/or the occurrence of periodic drought.

RESPONSES OF SEEDLINGS TO INCREASED NUTRIENT SUPPLY

Shade house experiments were conducted to determine the range of response to elevated nutrient supply among species representative of the coastal hill dipterocarp forest described above. In theory, these species might be differentiated by quantitative variation in growth in response to increased nutrient supply, by limitation by different nutrient(s) or by variation in the patterns of distribution of dry mass in response to nutrient addition. The experiments described here were designed to address the following questions:

(1)   What nutrient(s) limit the growth of seedlings?

(2)   Are there interactions between nutrients on seedling growth?

(3)   How does a restricted water supply influence nutrient limitation to growth at an irradiance representative of the forest understorey?

(4)   How does variation in nutrient supply influence dry mass allocation, both within species and within a group of coexisting, ecologically similar species?

Responses in terms of growth are presented here; further details of all experiments will be presented elsewhere (Burslem, 1993; Burslem et al., 1994, 1995).

Responses of *Melastoma malabathricum* L.

Melastoma malabathricum L. was selected as a test species to answer the first two questions listed above. *Melastoma malabathricum* is a colonizing species on degraded former agricultural land (Holttum, 1954; Sim et al., 1992), and of forest–river edges in less altered landscapes; it is found in tree-fall gaps in the Bukit Timah Nature Reserve, a small reserve now surrounded by secondary vegetation so that the abundance of at least some gap-demanders is probably greater than it would be in a pristine landscape. It has bird-dispersed fruits which are produced continuously and contain numerous very small seeds (mean dry mass 33 µg, D.J. Metcalfe, personal communication) embedded in a purple fleshy pulp.

Two experiments were conducted in a glasshouse supplying 11.2–12.5 per cent of full daylight photosynthetically active radiation (PAR). In the first experiment seedlings were raised from seed, transplanted into pots containing 866 ml of sieved primary forest soil from Bukit Timah Nature Reserve and arranged in a randomized design on a glasshouse bench. The experiment consisted of ten replicates of eight treatments, as follows: (1) control, i.e. forest soil with no nutrient additions; (2–6) the same with total additions of 93 mg/pot N as $0.037 \, M \, NH_4NO_3$, 103 mg/pot P as $0.037 \, M \, Na_2HPO_4$, 113 mg/pot K as $0.032 \, M \, KCl$, 20 mg/pot Mg as $0.009 \, M \, MgSO_4.7H_2O$, 18 mg/pot Ca as $0.005 \, M \, CaCl_2.2H_2O$ respectively; (7) a micronutrient solution containing $2.86 \, g \, l^{-1} \, H_3BO_3$, $1.81 \, g \, l^{-1} \, MnCl_2.4H_2O$, $0.22 \, g \, l^{-1}$ $ZnSO_4.7H_2O$, $0.08 \, g \, l^{-1} \, CuSO_4.5H_2O$ and $0.025 \, g \, l^{-1} \, Na_2MoO_4.2H_2O$; (8) with additions of all nutrients in treatments (2–7). Additions consisted of 10 ml of each nutrient solution and were carried out on nine occasions mostly before the seedlings were transplanted. Seedlings were harvested after 44 days. For a more detailed description of methods see Burslem et al. (1994).

All seedlings in both treatments to which micronutrients (treatments 7 and 8) had been added had died before the end of the experiment. Otherwise, results (Figure 9.1) are expressed as relative growth rates (RGR) between transplantation and the final harvest assuming a uniform dry mass of 0.07 mg at the time of transplantation (mean dry mass of thirty seedlings). RGR was calculated as follows:

$$RGR = 1,000 * [\ln \text{dry mass (µg) at harvest} - \ln 70]/44 \, [\mu g \, mg^{-1} \, day^{-1}]$$

The effects of the treatments on RGR were the same as those on other measures of plant growth in this experiment and show that under the experimental conditions the growth of *Melastoma* seedlings was limited by the availability of P and no other single macronutrient (Figure 9.1A).

In the second experiment seedlings of *Melastoma* were transplanted into pots containing 400 ml of sieved forest soil and treated in replicates of ten as follows: (1) unfertilized control; (2) the same with additions of $0.025 \, M$ Na_2CO_3 to raise the pH to 4.0; (3) + Na_2HPO_4; (4–8) + Na_2HPO_4 and with

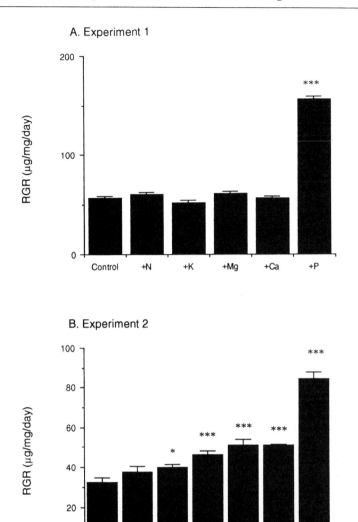

A. Experiment 1

B. Experiment 2

Figure 9.1 Mean relative growth rate (RGR μg mg^{-1} day^{-1}) of seedlings of *Melastoma mala-bathricum* in pots of Bukit Timah forest soil with no nutrient additions (Control) or with additions of N (+N). P (+P), K (+K), Ca (+Ca), Mg (+Mg), P and N (+PN), P and K (+PK), P and Ca (+PCa), P and Mg (+PMg), P and micronutrients (+PMicros) or N, P, K, Ca, Mg and micronutrients (+All) as described in the text between transplantation and harvesting of experiment 1 (A) or between harvest 1 (day 67) and harvest 2 (day 94) of experiment 2 (B). Bars represent 1 standard error of the mean; $n = 10$ in most cases. The significance of differences between the Control mean and any other treatment mean in experiment 1 and between the +P treatment mean and any other treatment mean in experiment 2 (*t*-tests following one-way analysis of variance) are indicated as follows: * $p < 0.05$; ** $p < 0.01$; *** $p < 0.001$

NH_4NO_3, KCl, $CaCl_2.2H_2O$, $MgSO_4.7H_2O$ and micronutrients respectively; (9) complete fertilizer (all nutrients in treatments 3–8); (10) + 'Roots'. In treatment (10) coarse and fine roots of adult *Melastoma* plants growing in the forest were collected and buried in a ring surrounding the roots of the transplanted seedlings in order to facilitate mycorrhizal infection. The concentrations of all nutrient solutions in treatments (3–9) were as experiment 1 except for the micronutrient solution in which all components were a factor of ten less concentrated; additions of 10 ml of each solution were made on ten occasions at intervals of at least one week after transplantation. Thus treatments (3–9) received a total of 126 mg/pot P; treatments (4–7) received in addition (mg/pot) 114 N, 138 K, 22 Ca and 24 Mg respectively; treatment (8) received in addition (mg/pot) 4 B, 4 Mn, 0.40 Zn, 0.16 Cu and 0.79 Mo; and treatment (9) received in addition all nutrients in treatments (4–8). Harvesting for relative growth rate analysis was carried out after 67 and 94 days; at both harvests leaf area and the dry weights of separate plant parts were determined, and at the second harvest samples of fine lateral root were fixed in FAA for later examination for mycorrhizal infection.

Relative growth rates were calculated by ranking individuals within treatments and then comparing individuals of like rank at the two harvests using the following formula (see Hunt, 1978):

$$RGR = 1{,}000 * [\ln \text{ dry mass (mg) at harvest 2} - \ln \text{ dry mass (mg) at harvest 1}]/27 \ [\mu g\,mg^{-1}\,day^{-1}]$$

Relative growth rates between 67 and 94 days (Figure 9.1B) show that once the primary limitation by P is overcome then any other macronutrient (except Ca) and a mixture of micronutrients became limiting to plant growth. Elsewhere I have shown that Ca does have a statistically significant effect on the height growth of *Melastoma* in the presence of adequate P-supply (Burslem et al., 1994). Neither raising the pH nor providing a source of inoculum for mycorrhizal infection increased growth or survival over the control (Burslem et al., 1994). Mycorrhizae were not observed on any of the root samples collected at the end of this experiment, although heavy infection by vesicular-arbuscular mycorrhizae was visible for roots of three established individuals (c. 1 m tall) of *Melastoma malabathricum* growing at Bukit Timah Nature Reserve.

Responses of shade-tolerant species to elevated nutrient supply

The first two experiments explored the responses of a shrub of disturbed or degraded sites to the addition of nutrients; a further three experiments were conducted to widen the investigation to include the much larger group of species that may be described as variably shade-tolerant as seedlings. The six species were *Antidesma cuspidatum* M.A. (Euphorbiaceae), *Calophyllum tetrapterum* Miq. (Guttiferae), *Dipterocarpus kunstleri* King (Dipterocarpaceae), *Garcinia scortechinii* King (Guttiferae), *Hopea griffithii* Kurz. and *Vatica maingayi* Dyer (both Dipterocarpaceae) and were selected on the basis of the availability of seed or seedlings. Very little is known of the ecology of any of these species, although *Antidesma cuspidatum, Calophyllum tetrapterum* (= *C. floribundum*, Stevens, 1980), *Garcinia scortechinii* and *Vatica maingayi* have all been recorded in swamp forest of Singapore or southern Peninsular Malaysia (Corner, 1978) and both *Antidesma* and *Calophyllum* occur in tall secondary forest in Singapore (Corlett, 1992).

In the third experiment seedlings of unknown age were dug-up from seedling 'carpets' growing in the understorey of primary forest at Bukit Timah (for details of the methodology employed in the following three experiments see Burslem et al., in press). They were subsequently transferred to PVC tubes containing 393 ml of primary forest soil and arranged in a randomized design within a shade-screen which transmitted about 3 per cent of full daylight irradiance (PAR) at a red:far-red quotient of 0.9. The experiment involved nutrient additions (all concentrations of nutrient solutions as experiment 1, above) to twelve replicates of each of three treatments as follows: (1) unfertilized control; (2) with total additions of 51.6 mg/pot P as Na_2HPO_4; (3) with total additions of 46.6 mg/pot N as NH_4NO_3, 51.6 mg/pot P as Na_2HPO_4, 25.0 mg/pot K as KCl, 10.9 mg/pot Mg as $MgSO_4$ and 10.0 mg/pot Ca as $CaCl_2$. Plants were harvested after 24 weeks and processed as described for *Melastoma*, above.

Results for mean leaf area paralleled the responses of the other measures of plant growth in this experiment (Burslem et al., 1995) and suggest that *Antidesma* may be distinguished from *Calophyllum* and *Garcinia* in its responsiveness to the addition of nutrients (Figure 9.2). Seedlings of *Antidesma* to which all macronutrients had been added had a significantly greater leaf area than control seedlings, whilst seedlings which received P alone did not (Figure 9.2). Neither of the nutrient addition treatments increased growth of *Calophyllum* or *Garcinia* seedlings over the control.

A fourth experiment was conducted using seedlings of *Dipterocarpus kunstleri* which were obtained from fruit collected in a relict patch of primary forest on the shores of MacRitchie Reservoir, Singapore. The seeds were germinated on damp newspaper on the floor of a glasshouse and then transferred to polypots containing 393 ml of Bukit Timah forest soil. The seedlings were then integrated with those of *Antidesma, Calophyllum* and *Garcinia* in the design of experiment 3, above, and fertilized according to the same three treatments. When experiment 3 was harvested after 6 months, the *Dipterocarpus* seedlings were re-potted into larger containers using soil from appropriate treatments of the previous experiment and two further additions of 25 ml of each nutrient solution were made. A year after the experiment was established the shade-screen was modified to reduce the heterogeneity in the light environment within it; however, this also involved a reduction in irradiance to

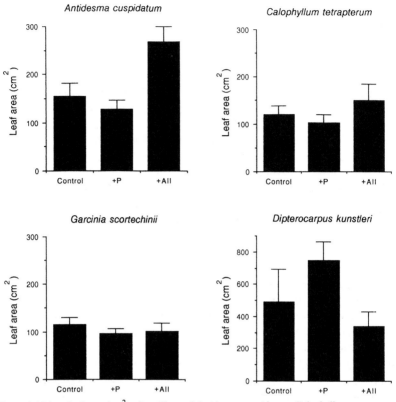

Figure 9.2 Mean leaf area (cm²) of seedlings of *Antidesma cuspidatum, Calophyllum tetrapterum* and *Garcinia scortechinii* grown for six months and for seedlings of *Dipterocarpus kunstleri* grown for seventeen months in pots of Bukit Timah forest soil with no nutrient additions (Control), with additions of P (+P) and with additions of N, P, K, Ca and Mg (+All) as described in the text. Bars represent 1 standard error of the mean ($n = 11$ or 12 for *Antidesma, Calophyllum* and *Garcinia* and 6 or 8 for *Dipterocarpus*)

1.3 per cent of full daylight transmission and in the red:far-red ratio to 0.3. The experiment was harvested after seventeen months.

Seedlings of *Dipterocarpus kunstleri* in this experiment responded in a similar manner to those of *Calophyllum* and *Garcinia* in the previous experiment (Figure 9.2) despite the additional year of growth and the attempts to reduce heterogeneity in the light environment within the shade-screen. In common with other measures of plant growth, leaf area did not increase significantly in response to either nutrient addition treatment (Figure 9.2).

A fifth experiment was conducted to answer the question 'How does nutrient limitation to growth vary with variation in soil water supply and at an irradiance representative of the forest understorey?' The species used were *Antidesma cuspidatum*, which responded to nutrients at 3 per cent of full daylight in experiment 3, and the dipterocarps *Hopea griffithii* and *Vatica maingayi*. Seedlings of *Antidesma* and *Hopea* were obtained from the forest understorey at Bukit Timah Nature Reserve and the Singapore Botanic Garden's Jungle respectively and transferred immediately into PVC tubes (as experiment 3) of forest soil. Seedlings of *Vatica* were obtained from fruit produced during the mast-fruiting of August 1990; these had been germinated on the surface of forest soil, stored in trays for fourteen months at low irradiance and then transplanted into PVC tubes of forest soil prior to the start of the experiment. The potential effects of differences in age at the time of collection and of differential periods of storage before use are unknown. The shade-screen where the experiment was conducted transmitted 0.5–0.9 per cent of full daylight (PAR) at a red:far-red quotient of 0.6. Under these conditions all three species would have been strongly limited by light; the main interest of this experiment was to determine the extent of simultaneous limitation by nutrient supply and soil moisture under conditions which simulated those of the forest understorey.

The experiment consisted of ten replicates of four treatments which were common to the three species and ten of a further six treatments in *Antidesma*. Seven treatments for *Antidesma* were carried out under a frequent-watering regime, as follows: (1) unfertilized control; (2–6) with total additions of 72.6 mg/pot N as NH_4NO_3, 80.2 mg/pot P as Na_2HPO_4, 56.3 mg/pot K as KCl, 16.4 mg/pot Mg as $MgSO_4.7H_2O$ and 15.0 mg/pot Ca as $CaCl_2.2H_2O$ respectively; (7) with additions of all nutrients in treatments (2–6). Treatments (1), (3) and (7) were repeated under a low-frequency watering regime (treatments (8), (9) and (10) respectively). The treatments applied to *Hopea* and *Vatica* were numbers (1), (7), (8) and (10) of the *Antidesma* experiment, i.e. the four possible combinations of presence or absence of complete nutrient addition and two watering regimes. Water was applied to field capacity every second day in the high-frequency watering treatment and was withheld until a plant 'wilted' (defined as a leaf orientation $>90°$ to the perpendicular) in the low-frequency watering treatment. When a plant wilted in the latter treatment, sufficient water was added until the total mass of the pot increased by 30 g after ten minutes of free drainage. During this experiment plants in the high frequency watering treatment were watered seventy times, while those in the low-frequency treatment were watered on average four times (range 0–10). The plants were harvested 22 weeks after the first addition of nutrients and processed as described above. During harvesting, pre-dawn and midday xylem pressure potential measurements were made for all plants from the low-frequency watering treatments and corresponding treatments from those watered frequently using a pressure chamber with whole seedlings (Model 650, PMS Instrument Co., 2,750 N.W. Royal Oaks Drive, Corvallis, Oregon 97330, USA).

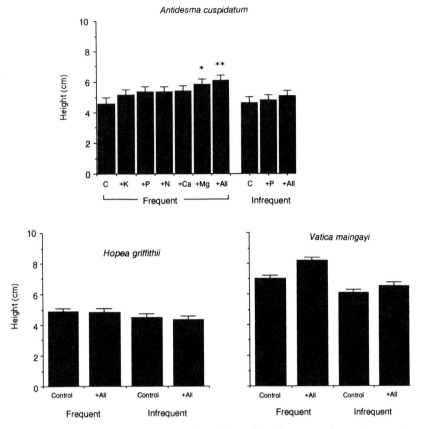

Figure 9.3 Least-squares mean height (cm) of seedlings of *Antidesma cuspidatum, Hopea grif-fithii* and *Vatica maingayi* following growth in pots of Bukit Timah forest soil for 22 weeks without nutrient additions (C, Control) or with additions of N (+N), P (+P), K (+K), Ca (+Ca), Mg (+Mg) or N, P, K, Ca and Mg (+All) and watered either frequently (Frequent) or infrequently (Infrequent) as described in the text. For *Antidesma*, significance of difference between a nutrient-addition treatment mean and its corresponding Control mean is indicated as follows: * $p < 0.05$; **$p < 0.01$

The response of seedling growth to treatments was determined by analysis of those measures of plant size for which initial plant size could be incorporated as a covariate. For the *Antidesma* and *Vatica*, adjusted mean height increased following the addition of all macronutrients and decreased in response to low-frequency watering (Figure 9.3), although the latter effect was statistically significant for the *Vatica* only. Experimental treatments tended not to influence height growth in the *Hopea*. The wider set of treatments for the *Antidesma* under a frequent-watering regime suggested that the most important limiting macronutrient was magnesium (Figure 9.3).

Despite the limited effects on growth, watering treatments did have an impact on the pattern of dry mass distribution in all three species. There were significant increases in root mass ratio (root dry mass as a proportion of total seedling dry mass) in *Antidesma* and *Vatica* and a non-significant increase in *Hopea* in response to low-frequency watering, and a significant increase in the proportion of root dry mass as lateral roots in *Antidesma*. Likewise, leaf area per plant was lower for plants watered less frequently in all three species and mean leaf number was lower in seedlings of *Antidesma* and *Vatica* in this treatment. A further effect was a significant reduction in specific leaf area in response to the low-frequency watering treatment in seedlings of *Antidesma* and *Hopea*. Interpretation of experiments which attempt to simulate affects of drought on tree seedlings in pots is difficult unless some aspect of soil or plant water status is available for comparison between field and experimental conditions. In this case, comparisons of the soil water content at which plants 'wilted' in pots of forest soil with the results of a survey of topsoil (0–10 cm) water content carried out during 1990 shows that a soil water content sufficiently low to induce 'wilting' of the three species in pot experiments was found in the field on most of the sampling occasions (Burslem et al., 1995). Although changes in soil structure during disturbance may mean that soil in pots and from an undisturbed profile are unlikely to have the same soil water potential at a given soil water content, the outcome of this study is suggestive of a potential influence of moisture availability on seedling performance under field conditions (see Discussion).

RESPONSES OF SEEDLINGS TO THE INTERACTION BETWEEN SHADE AND WATER SUPPLY

The seedlings of the shade-tolerant species used in the experiments described above were not strongly differentiated in their growth in response to variation in nutrient supply, except that the *Antidesma* was responsive to increased nutrient supply while seedlings of most other species were not (Figure 9.2). A further experiment was designed to determine whether the seedlings of four of the species used above were differentiated in their responses to the interaction between irradiance and soil moisture status. These factors are predicted to have interactive effects on plant growth because they are both known to influence patterns of dry mass allocation; decreasing irradiance tends to cause an increase in the relative proportion of plant dry mass as shoots and/or leaves (Björkman, 1981), while a reduction in the availability of water leads to a greater relative emphasis on roots (Bradford and Hsaio, 1982). If both irradiance and water supply are limiting during plant development then growth and survival may well depend on the processes by which competing demands for internal resources of carbon are met.

Experiments on plant responses to shade and drought may be hampered by the methodological problems of inadequate replication of light treatments and a lack of independence between irradiance and soil or plant water status. The first problem is encountered when light treatments are replicated within a limited number of shade-screens or glasshouses (often just one per treatment); differences between shade-screens in their transmission properties may be confounded with differences due to other factors, such as exposure, so that a design such as this is pseudo-replicated (Hurlbert, 1984). The second problem arises because increasing solar radiation tends to increase water loss by evapotranspiration, which may reduce the availability of water at higher irradiance treatments irrespective of differences in the frequency of watering. An apparatus was designed to eliminate the effects of pseudo-replication and the lack of independence between light and watering (Figure 9.4). It involved the use of randomly-assigned shade 'towers' for individual plants and imposing drought treatments on tree seedlings in part by means of root competition with the grass *Axonopus compressus* (Swartz) Beauv. The height of the grass canopy was manipulated to impose the variable root competition treatments, although differential watering frequencies were also necessary.

Seedlings of *Antidesma*, *Calophyllum* and *Garcinia* (species as above) were obtained from 'carpets' of seedlings growing in the shaded understorey at Bukit Timah and transplanted immediately into PVC tubes of forest soil as above; those of *Hopea* were collected similarly from the Singapore Botanic Garden's Jungle (for details see Burslem, 1993). The tubes were sunk into a soil/vermiculite mixture contained within a black perforated polythene bag and possessing a newly-germinated grass sward. After a period of time for seedling acclimation and ramification of the grass roots throughout the soil/vermiculite mixture and into the soil within the tubes, shade 'towers' of wire mesh were applied to seedlings in two of the three irradiance treatments. Differential shade treatments were applied using green polyester filter and muslin attached in one of two ways to the towers: in the deepest shade treatment irradiance was reduced by a double layer of muslin over a single layer of polyester filter and a conical 'roof' of polyester filter, while the intermediate treatment possessed the 'roof' only. Seedlings in the highest irradiance treatment were exposed within the shelter where the experiment was conducted. Measurements of irradiance showed that the 'light', 'medium' and 'dark' treatments transmitted 10.3, 5.6 and 0.3 per cent of full daylight (PAR)

Figure 9.4 Schematic diagrams for the apparatus used in experiment 6 to create a factorial combination of three irradiance treatments and two watering treatments. The two watering treatments are high-frequency watering with low root competition (right of the dashed line) and low-frequency watering with high root competition (left of the dashed line) and these were combined with 'light' (top), 'medium' (middle) and 'dark' (bottom) irradiance treatments

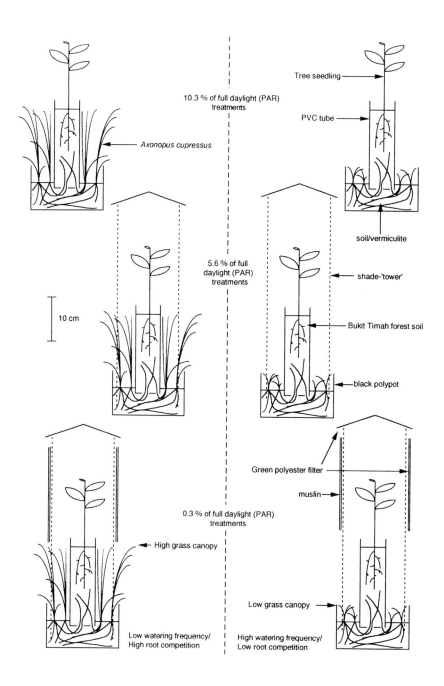

respectively and measurements of the red : far-red quotient gave mean values of 0.6 in the 'dark' treatment and 0.9 in the 'medium' and 'light' treatments.

Watering treatments were applied by maintaining the height of the grass canopy at 4 cm or by allowing it to grow up to a maximum height of 15 cm. The aim of creating differences in the total area of grass canopy between these two treatments was to impose differences in the amounts of water removed by transpiration of the grass and thereby influence the degree of competition for water in the pot. The technique was supplemented by watering the 4 cm and 15 cm grass canopy height treatments at frequencies of 2 and 7–9 days respectively to ensure differences in soil water status between the two treatments.

The experiment consisted of a factorial combination of the three light treatments and the two watering treatments with eight replicates for *Hopea* and ten for the other three species. The seedlings were allowed to grow under experimental conditions for three months and were then harvested and processed as described for previous experiments. The biomass of grass roots in each pot was also determined. Xylem pressure potential measurements were made during pre-dawn and midday measurement periods in a manner that enabled comparison between species and between watering treatments (Burslem, 1993).

Leaf areas at the beginning of the experiment were estimated from their measured dimensions using regression equations obtained for leaves at the end of the experiment. Estimated initial leaf area and measured values of seedling height and stem diameter were used to estimate the intial dry mass of each seedling using forward stepwise linear regression equations describing the relationship between these variables and dry mass at the end of the experiment (for an application of a similar procedure see Putz and Canham, 1992). The equations used to derive initial dry mass (DM) were as follows:

Antidesma: Initial DM[g] = (0.00375*leaf area[cm^2]) + (0.0642*stem diameter[mm]) + (0.00723*height[cm]) – 0.0574   [r^2 = 0.65]

Calophyllum: Initial DM[g] = (0.0110*leaf area[cm^2]) + (0.119*stem diameter [mm]) – 0.0383   [r^2 = 0.79]

Garcinia: Initial DM[g] = (0.010*leaf area[cm^2]) + (0.164*stem diameter [mm]) – 0.0916   [r^2 = 0.83]

Hopea: Initial DM[g] = (0.0258*height[cm]) + 0.0058   [r^2 = 0.85]

Relative growth rates were calculated as described previously. Estimated relative growth rates were influenced by the irradiance treatments but not watering treatments in this experiment (Figure 9.5), although watering treatments did affect xylem pressure potential in *Antidesma* and *Garcinia* (Figure 9.6). Relative growth rates were much higher in *Antidesma* than the other species, possibly because the seedlings were younger. All species increased growth in response to an increase in irradiance from 0.3 per cent to 5.6 per cent of full daylight PAR under both watering treatments. However, a significant

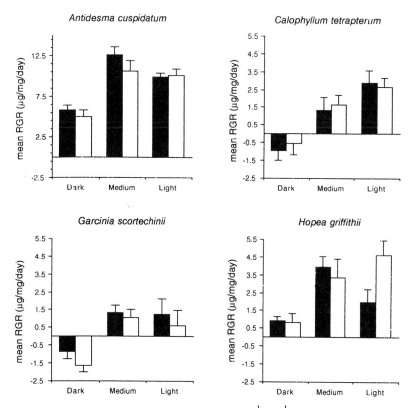

Figure 9.5 Mean estimated relative growth rates ($\mu g\,mg^{-1}\,day^{-1}$) for seedlings of *Antidesma cuspidatum, Calophyllum tetrapterum, Garcinia scortechinii* and *Hopea griffithii* grown for three months at 10.3 per cent (Light), 5.6 per cent (Medium) or 0.3 per cent (Dark) of full daylight PAR and under either high (filled bars) or low (open bars) frequency watering regimes. Bars represent 1 standard error of the mean (n = 9, 10 or 11 for *Antidesma*, 9 or 10 for *Calophyllum*, 10 for *Garcinia* and 7 or 8 for *Hopea*)

additional increase in growth in response to a further increase in irradiance to 10.3 per cent of full daylight PAR was observed only in *Calophyllum* (Figure 9.5). For *Hopea* the response to irradiance was dependent on the watering treatment: mean RGR increased with increasing irradiance in the low-frequency watering treatment but showed a maximum at 5.6 per cent of full daylight irradiance when watered frequently. There was considerable interspecific variation in RGR in deep shade (Figure 9.5) and in xylem pressure potential in response to the same watering treatments (Figure 9.6).

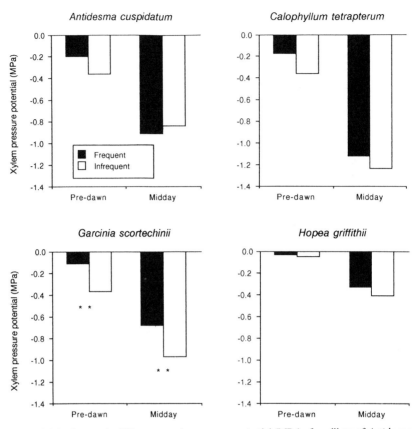

Figure 9.6 Predawn and midday mean xylem pressure potential (MPa) of seedlings of *Antidesma cuspidatum, Calophyllum tetrapterum, Garcinia scortechinii* and *Hopea griffithii* under high (filled bars) or low (open bars) frequency watering treatments. The significance of the difference between watering treatments during a given measurement interval is indicated as follows: **$p < 0.01$

DISCUSSION

What are the resources for which tropical tree seedlings compete?

Plants are likely to compete for resources which limit their growth, such as light, nutrients and water. Experiment 1 showed that the gap-demanding shrub *Melastoma malabathricum* was strongly limited by the availability of P when grown in pots of forest soil (Figure 9.1A); under conditions of adequate P supply growth increased in response to any other macrontrient or a mixture of micronutrients (Figure 9.1B and Burslem et al., 1994). Since the *Melastoma* seedlings were non-mycorrhizal in these experiments and it is well-established that a primary ecological role of mycorrhizae is in the uptake of P

230

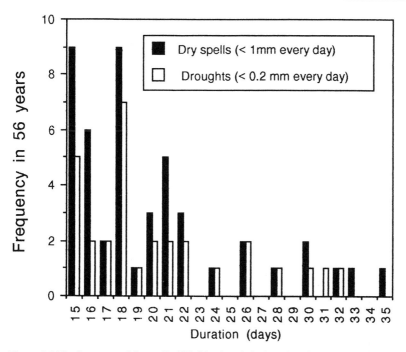

Figure 9.7 The frequency of dry spells (filled bars) and absolute droughts (open bars) in Singapore for the years 1929–1941 and 1948–1990 (total 56 years). A dry spell is defined as a period of at least 14 days duration during which there is less than 1 mm of rainfall every day; a drought occurs when there is less than 0.2 mm of rainfall every day. Data supplied by the Singapore Meteorological Service

(Harley and Smith, 1983), it is likely that mycorrhizal *Melastoma* seedlings growing in the forest are limited by more than one macronutrient. In contrast, among the six shade-tolerant species examined only *Antidesma cuspidatum* was limited by nutrient supply in pots of forest soil, and in that case the limiting nutrient was not P (Figure 9.2). Seedlings of *Antidesma cuspidatum*, *Calophyllum tetrapterum* and *Garcinia scortechinii* possessed vesicular-arbuscular mycorrhizae in experiment 3 and those of *Dipterocarpus kunstleri* may have possessed ectomycorrhizae in experiment 4 (although this was not examined explicitly).

These results only partially support the hypothesis that plants of moist lowland tropical forest are limited by the availability of P (Vitousek, 1984). The initial evidence in support of this hypothesis was derived from the observation that litterfall productivity was more strongly positively correlated with litterfall P concentration than with that of either N or Ca for a group of fifty-five tropical forest sites (Vitousek, 1984); similarly, for a variety of tropical forest soils N mineralization rates have been found to be high (De Rham, 1970; Marrs et al., 1991; Robertson, 1984; Vitousek and Denslow, 1986). Direct tests of this hypothesis have only found support for it when the test species was not characteristically mycorrhizal (e.g. *Phytolacca rivinoides*, Denslow et al., 1987) or when not mycorrhizal under experimental conditions (e.g. *Melastoma malabathricum*, Figure 9.1A). In other experiments, plant growth in pots has been limited by nutrients other than P (e.g. species of *Miconia* and *Piper*, see Denslow et al., 1987; *Antidesma cuspidatum*, Figure 9.2; *Dryobalanops aromatica*, *Dryobalanops oblongifolia*, Sundralingham, 1983) or not limited by nutrient supply at all under experimental conditions (*Calophyllum tetrapterum*, *Garcinia scortechinii* and *Dipterocarpus kunstleri*, Figure 9.2).

If the responses of plants in these experiments are representative then the prevalence of limitation by the availability of P is low among tree seedlings of lowland tropical rain forest, possibly because the prevalence of mycorrhizal infection is high (Janos, 1983; Alexander, 1989). Extrapolation of findings for pot bioassays to field conditions should be conducted with caution because tree seedlings growing in the understorey of tropical forest are subjected to competition from adult trees which may reduce nutrient availability relative to that in pots. Nevertheless, field fertilization experiments have not shown a positive response to nutrient addition for either cuttings of the same species of *Miconia* and *Piper* growing in lowland tropical rain forest in Costa Rica which were shown previously to be responsive to nutrient addition in pots of forest soil (Denslow et al., 1987, 1990), or for seedlings of dipterocarps in the understorey of lowland rain forests in Malaysia (Turner et al., 1993).

In experiment 6, plant growth increased if irradiance increased from about 0.3 per cent to about 5.6 per cent of full daylight PAR. These treatments were designed to simulate the light climate of the forest understorey and a small gap in lowland dipterocarp rain forest respectively (see Ashton, 1992; Raich, 1989; Whitmore and Wong, 1959; Yoda, 1974). The results show that shade-tolerant seedlings growing in the forest understorey would be limited by the availability of light, a point which has been shown repeatedly for seedlings in shade house or controlled environment experiments (e.g. Bongers et al., 1988; Fetcher et al., 1983, Thompson et al., 1992a), by planting seedlings into different forest habitats (Denslow et al., 1990), gap-creation experiments (Healey, 1990; Brown and Whitmore, 1992) and by monitoring seedling populations in the field (Osunkoya et al., 1993; Turner, 1990a), although in many field studies it is not possible to differentiate between the effects of release from suppression by shade and a reduction in root competition in newly-created gaps (Sanford, 1989, 1990). The physiological mechanism for this process is well-known: at light levels below the photosynthetic light saturation point the rate of photosynthesis increases linearly with increases in irradiance (Björkman, 1981). Plants in the forest understorey are exposed to levels of PAR considerably below this point for most of the time and to only occasional periods of direct radiation ('sunflecks') during which they conduct a large proportion of their total carbon assimilation (Chazdon, 1988). Seedlings

232

in the understorey of an evergreen forest in Hawaii showed a linear relationship between relative growth rate and the potential daily duration of sunflecks (Pearcy, 1983).

In experiment 5 some seedlings of three species were exposed to drying treatments in pots of forest soil over a period of five months. Re-watering occurred only in response to a plant wilting and when it was carried out the amount of water added was only just sufficient to reverse wilting. The minimum gravimetric soil water contents the seedlings were exposed to in this experiment were within the range of values determined for top-soil samples (0–10 cm) at ten understorey sites in Bukit Timah Nature Reserve during a survey of soil water content over eight months in 1990 (Burslem et al., in press).

As shown in Figure 9.3 height growth of seedlings of two species was reduced by the low-frequency watering treatments imposed in this experiment. The correspondence between the soil moisture conditions in the drying treatment and values for the forest understorey suggest that seedling growth may have been limited by the supply of water in the understorey of Bukit Timah Nature Reserve during April–November 1990 (although it is important to recognize that differences in the structure of soil in the field and in pots may lead to differences in soil water potential at a given soil water content). Further experiments are needed to test this possibility.

Singapore has an 'everwet' aseasonal climate (Whitmore, 1975), but examination of long-term climatic data has led to speculation that plants growing in such climates may be occasionally subject to limitation by low water availability (Baillie, 1976; Brünig, 1969; Nieuwolt, 1965; Whitmore, 1975). Data supplied by the Singapore Meteorological Service support this hypothesis for Singapore (Figure 9.7): a dry spell or drought of at least one-month duration occurs about once a decade in Singapore, and it is possible that when they occur these events have major effects on the survival and growth of tree seedlings.

A dry spell of this duration did not occur during the period of the soil moisture survey in the understorey at Bukit Timah, and yet the gravimetric soil water content at some sites was as low as that required to cause wilting of seedlings under experimental conditions and a reduction in height growth in two species. In the experiment seedlings were watered as soon as they wilted and so the period during which carbon assimilation would have been restricted by stomatal closure was not great during any part of the watering cycle (Bradford and Hsiao, 1982). In the forest understorey soil water content remained below this 'wilting point' for extended periods and so it is possible that positive carbon gain would have been severely restricted over several weeks for seedlings at these sites. This hypothesis requires testing for tree seedlings of aseasonal tropical forests.

Experiment 5 also provided indirect evidence of the operation of selection to withstand drought in the tree seedlings examined. Although effects of the watering treatments on dry mass yield were not detected at the end of the experiment, there were significant effects on the distribution of dry mass in response to low-frequency watering. These responses were a decrease in leaf area and leaf number, a reduction in specific leaf area, an increase in the distribution of plant dry mass to roots and an increase in the distribution of root dry mass to lateral roots. Most of these phenotypic responses are identical to those described as evolutionary responses of crop plants to drought (Bradford and Hsiao, 1982) and suggest that the species examined here have evolved mechanisms to cope with drought. Fisher et al. (1991) and Wright (1991) have shown that dry season soil water availability may influence the survival and growth of tree and shrub seedlings of seasonally dry tropical forest in Panama, but whether similar constraints exist for tree seedlings of aseasonal tropical forest is unknown.

Are coexisting tropical tree seedlings differentiated in responses to heterogeneity in the resources which limit their growth?

A degree of differentiation in response to increased nutrient supply was observed for shade-tolerant tree seedlings in experiment 3: one of four species tested was responsive to 'all macronutrients' although the responsiveness was much reduced at 0.5–0.9 per cent of full daylight irradiance (Figure 9.3). It remains unclear whether differentiation in response to increased nutrient supply occurs for shade-tolerant tree seedlings of lowland tropical forest; many species tested are not responsive at low irradiance (Burslem et al., in press; Denslow et al., 1987, 1990; Turner et al., 1993), but it remains a possibility that a spectrum of responsiveness exists to release from root competition in canopy gaps of increasing size. Field experiments are required to determine whether the effects of root competition are to increase the prevalence of limitation by nutrient supply relative to that found in pot experiments.

Two aspects of differentiation in response to irradiance must be considered: both species-specific irradiance optima for plant growth and variable degrees of responsiveness to a unit increase in irradiance. Of the three light treatments in experiment 6 there were limited differences between species in the light regime for maximum growth, but major differences in responsiveness of growth to an increase in irradiance from 0.3 to 5.6 per cent of full daylight PAR and in relative growth rates in the shade (Figure 9.5). Other experiments have failed to demonstrate that coexisting species possess different radiation optima for growth, beyond the finding that irradiance for the maximum relative growth rate of gap-demanding species is greater than that for shade-tolerators (Denslow et al., 1990). In contrast, the degree of responsiveness to a unit increase in irradiance and the survivorship of tree seedlings in shade may show considerable variation between species (Augspurger, 1984). However, in drawing this contrast it is important to recognize the difficulties associated with applying uniform irradiance treatments under artificial conditions. The variance within shade-screens is often likely to be significant relative to that between shade-screens, in which case a very high degree of replication is required to confirm subtle differences between species. Conclusive experiments have yet to be carried out.

Experiments on the responses of tree seedlings to variation in water supply have not been conducted for seedlings of the aseasonal tropics, despite speculation that rare, unpredictable droughts may have an effect on tree growth and survival (Baillie 1976; Brünig, 1969; Whitmore, 1975). Differentiation between species occurred in experiment 6 to a much greater extent in terms of xylem pressure potential (Figure 9.6) than growth (Figure 9.5), although many more treatments would be required to determine the range of interspecific patterns of growth to variation in soil water supply.

For many species of tropical trees it is possible that more than one factor limits growth simultaneously. For seedlings growing in the understorey this is particularly likely because limitation by low light is combined with competition for water and nutrients with the roots of saplings and trees, particularly in seasonally dry tropical forests (Fisher et al., 1991; Wright, 1991), but also in aseasonal tropical forest as argued above. Under these circumstances variance in the availability of resources that do not covary leads to an increase in the heterogeneity of the forest environment. Whether or not spatial variation exists in soil moisture content, variation in annual rainfall may create a temporal component of soil moisture variability, in which case there is a potential for interactions to occur in seedling growth between spatial variation in irradiance and temporal variation in soil moisture supply. An interaction between irradiance and soil moisture is suggested by the ability of black cherry (*Prunus serotina*) to grow in deeper shade on more mesic sites in North America (Abrams et al., 1992). Interaction between irradiance and water availability was shown for seedling growth of only one of the four species of tropical trees examined in experiment 6 (Figure 9.5), but an interaction between nutrient supply and irradiance on growth and photosynthesis have been shown for tree seedlings of rain forest in Northern Queensland (Thompson et al., 1992a,b) and for photosynthesis in tree seedlings from West Africa (Riddoch et al., 1991).

The maintenance of species richness

There can be little doubt that the biological differences between 'pioneer' and 'climax' species (*sensu* Swaine and Whitmore, 1988) contribute to the maintenance of the two groups in tropical forest, although the latter group is very broad and contains a large proportion of the total tree flora (Whitmore, 1975).

Monitoring of tree populations over long periods has demonstrated interspecific differences in mortality and growth through time and in response to disturbance (Clark and Clark, 1992; Whitmore, 1974, 1989), but short-term experiments have not yet established the critical factors leading to these differences, beyond a general acceptance of contrasting physiological responses to light. Hence the maintenance of species richness within the two groups remains to be explained.

An alternative mechanism for the maintenance of species richness within the large shade-tolerant group of species is one which emphasizes the role of variable seedling architecture in species differentiation (King, 1990; Kohyama, 1987; Kohyama and Hotta 1990). Kohyama and Hotta (1990) described the spectrum of architectural types for shade-tolerant saplings of lowland tropical forest in Sumatra and labelled representatives of the end-points of this spectrum as 'optimists' and 'pessimists' with respect to the length of time between establishment and gap-creation. The distinction between an extreme 'optimist', such as *Swintonia schwenkii*, and an extreme 'pessimist', such as *Hopea dryobalanoides*, is the outcome of a trade-off between biomass distribution to increase height growth or leaf area respectively. When present, 'optimists' are favoured following gap-creation because tall seedlings are most likely to become established in the gap (Brown and Whitmore, 1992) while 'pessimists' are favoured at a site if the time between germination and gap-creation is long relative to the survivorship of the 'optimist' seedlings in the shade (Kohyama, 1987). A diverse community of shade-tolerant plants would be maintained because gap-creation at a given site is an unpredictable, stochastic event (Hubbell and Foster, 1986b). The hypothesis may be extended for species growing in forests subjected to periodic drought to include an architectural spectrum which reflects the trade-off between root development for the exploration of a large volume of soil during periods of soil water deficit and shoot development for maximization of height growth or leaf area expansion. Aspects of the hypothesis are being explored using the data obtained from experiment 6 and from a field experiment; results indicate that contrasting allometry is one determinant of seedling growth and survival in relation to estalishment conditions for shade-tolerant tree seedlings in Singapore, including dipterocarps (Burslem, 1993).

Elements of the original hypothesis of Kohyama (1987) have already been tested for tree seedlings of tropical forest. The necessary diversity in aboveground architecture exists (Kohyama and Hotta, 1990) and there is considerable interspecific differentiation in the pattern of survivorship of shade-tolerant tree seedlings in the shade (Augspurger, 1984; Turner, 1990b). In addition, gap-creation is unpredictable in time and space (Hubbell and Foster, 1986a), and so seedlings which do not become established in a gap as a consequence of seed dispersal or photoblastic germination are exposed to understorey light conditions for an unpredictable length of time. It is likely that physiological differences also contribute to interspecific variation in seedling survivorship in the shade (Chazdon, 1988), although comparisons have tended to be between species from the 'pioneer' and 'climax' classes (e.g. Ramos and Grace, 1990; Riddoch et al., 1991) rather than within the latter class. The mechanism for the maintenance of species richness for shade-tolerant tree species proposed here illustrates how both stochastic factors (the probability of time to gap-creation over a given seedling) and biological factors (architectural and probably physiological differences) are likely to be involved; a similar point has been made previously for tree species of tropical rain forests in the Solomon Islands (Whitmore, 1974, 1989) and Panama (Hubbell and Foster, 1986b), as well as other types of vegetation (Grubb, 1986).

Future work and applied considerations

In order to test whether differences in the regeneration niches of different species contribute to the maintenance of species richness it is necessary to determine whether the differences which emerge over the time-scales of ecological experiments (typically a few months to several years) are manifested as long-term maintenance of a species-rich community of reproductive adults. For tropical rain forest there are in existence a number of long-term records of the population dynamics of trees in permanent plots (e.g. Connell et al., 1984; Crow, 1980; Hubbell and Foster, 1986a,b, 1987; Lieberman et al., 1990; Whitmore, 1989) and it is important to make use of records of recruitment and mortality at these sites as tests of predictions arising from ecological experimentation. As pointed out by Canham (1989) and Poulson and Platt (1989) the focus of this kind of study should be on comparisons between species which are able to establish in shade, rather than the more usual comparisons between those which are capable of establishment in shade with those which are not. Doing so would help to answer the fourth question in the list presented in the Introduction and allow a complete test of the regeneration niche concept as applied here to seedling growth.

Understanding the mechanism of the maintenance of species richness in tropical forest is essential if the forests are to be managed artifically for the preservation of species richness or for repeatable timber extraction. For instance, silvicultural systems based on the hypothesis that the regeneration of a suite of desirable species is enabled by the creation of gaps of a range of sizes would be very different from those based on the hypothesis that regeneration of the mixture of species is ensured by a variable frequency of gap creation. Fundamental questions need to be answered before prescriptions for forest management can be made on an ecological basis, irrespective of the status of the economic criteria which usually dictate the selection of forest management practices.

ACKNOWLEDGEMENTS

The research described here was carried out at the Department of Botany, National University of Singapore; I thank Professor C.J. Goh and Professor G.L. Lim for making that possible and the National Parks Board for permission to conduct research in Bukit Timah Nature Reserve. I am particularly grateful to Dr P.J. Grubb and Dr I.M. Turner for their help and guidance throughout my doctoral research and to them, Dr T.C. Whitmore and Dr M.D. Swaine for comments on the manuscript. I thank the Natural Environment Research Council and UNESCO for funding to conduct the research and to attend the workshop respectively.

REFERENCES

Abrams, M.D., Kloeppel, B.D. and Kubiske, M.E. (1992). Ecophysiological and morphological responses to shade and drought in two contrasting ecotypes of *Prunus serotina*. *Tree Physiology*, **10**, 343–55.

Alexander, I. (1989). Mycorrhizae in tropical forests. In Proctor, J. (ed.), *Mineral nutrients in Tropical Forest and Savanna Ecosystems*, pp. 169–88. Blackwell Scientific Publications, Oxford.

Allbrook, R.F. (1973). The soils of Pasoh Forest Reserve, Negri Sembilan. *Malaysian Forester*, **36**, 22–3.

Appanah, S. (1985). General flowering in the climax rain forests of South-east Asia. *Journal of Tropical Ecology*, **1**, 225–40.

Ashton, P.S. (1964). *Ecological Studies in the Mixed Dipterocarp Forests of Brunei State*. Oxford Forestry Memoirs, **25**. Clarendon Press, Oxford.

Ashton, P.M.S. (1992). Some measurements of the microclimate within a Sri Lankan tropical rainforest. *Agricultural and Forest Meteorology*, **59**, 217–35.

Augspurger, C.K. (1984). Light requirements of neotropical tree seedlings: a comparative study of growth and survival. *Journal of Ecology*, **72**, 777–95.

Baillie, I.C. (1976). Further studies on drought in Sarawak, East Malaysia. *Journal of Tropical Geography*, **43**, 20–9.

Barton, A.M. (1984). Neotropical pioneer and shade-tolerant tree species: do they partition treefall gaps? *Tropical Ecology*, **25**, 196–202.

Bongers, F. and Popma, J. (1988). Is exposure-related variation in leaf characteristics of tropical rain forest species adaptive? In Werger, M.J.A., van der Aart, P.J.M., During, H.J. and Verhoeven, J.T.A. (eds.) *Plant Form and Vegetation Structure*, pp. 191–200. SPB Academic Publishing, The Hague.

Bongers, F., Popma, J. and Iriarte-Vivar, S. (1988). Response of *Cordia megalantha* seedlings to gap environments in tropical rain forest. *Functional Ecology*, **2**, 379–90.

Björkman, O. (1981). Responses to different quantum flux densities. In Lange, O.L., Nobel, P.S., Osmond, C.B. and Ziegler, H. (eds.) *Encyclopaedia of Plant Physiology New Series Volume 12A: Physiological Plant Ecology I. Responses to the Physical Environment*, pp. 57–107. Springer-Verlag, Berlin.

Bradford, K.J. and Hsiao, T.C. (1982). Physiological responses to moderate water stress. In Lange, O.L., Nobel, P.S., Osmond, C.B. and Ziegler, H. (eds.) *Encyclopaedia of Plant*

Phsiology New Series Volume 12B, Physiological Plant Ecology II Water Relations and Carbon Assimilation, pp. 263–324. Springer-Verlag, Berlin

Brandani, A., Hartshorn, G.S. and Orians, G.H. (1988). Internal heterogeneity of gaps and species richness in Costa Rican tropical wet forest. *Journal of Tropical Ecology*, **4**, 99–119.

Brown, N.D. and Whitmore, T.C. (1992). Do dipterocarp seedlings really partition tropical rain forest gaps? *Philosophical Transactions of the Royal Society*, Series B, **335**, 369–78.

Brunig, E.F. (1969). On the seasonality of droughts in the lowlands of Sarawak (Borneo). *Erdkunde*, **23**, 127–35.

Burgess, P.F. (1975). Silviculture in the hill forests of the Malay Peninsula. *Malaysian Forestry Department Research Pamphlet* **66**.

Burslem, D.F.R.P. (1993). *Differential Responses to Limiting Resources among Tree Seedling of Lowland Tropical Rain Forest in Singapore*. PhD dissertation, University of Cambridge.

Burslem, D.F.R.P., Turner, I.M. and Grubb, P.J. (1994). Mineral nutrient status of coastal hill dipterocarp forest and adinandra belukar in Singapore: bioassays of nutrient limitation. *Journal of Tropical Ecology*, **10**, 579–99.

Burslem, D.F.R.P., Grubb, P.J. and Turner, I.M. (1995). Responses to nutrient addition among shade-tolerant tree seedlings of lowland tropical forest in Singapore. *Journal of Ecology*, **83**, 113–122.

Burslem, D.F.R.P., Grubb, P.J. and Turner, I.M. (in press). Responses to simulated drought and elevated nutrient supply among shade-tolerant tree seedlings of lowland tropical forest in Singapore. *Biotropica.*

Canham, C.D. (1989). Different responses to gaps among shade tolerant tree species. *Ecology*, **70**, 548–50.

Chandler, G. (1985). Mineralization and nitrification in three Malaysian forest soils. *Soil Biology and Biochemistry*, **17**, 347–53.

Chazdon, R.L. (1988). Sunflecks and their importance to forest understorey plants. *Advances in Ecological Research*, **18**, 1–63.

Clark, D.A. and Clark, D.B. (1992). Life history diversity of canopy and emergent trees in a neotropical rain forest. *Ecological Monographs*, **62**, 315–44.

Coley, P.D. (1983). Herbivory and defensive characteristics of tree species in a lowland tropical rain forest. *Ecological Monographs*, **53**, 209–33.

Connell, Tracey, J.G. and Webb, L.J. (1984). Compensatory recruitment, growth and mortality as factors maintaining rain forest tree diversity. *Ecological Monographs*, **54**, 141–64.

Corlett, R.T. (1988). Bukit Timah: the history and significance of a small rain-forest reserve. *Environmental Conservation*, **15**, 37–44.

Corlett, R.T. (1990). Flora and reproductive phenology of the rain forest at Bukit Timah, Singapore. *Journal of Tropical Ecology*, **6**, 55–63.

Corlett, R.T. (1992). Plant succession on degraded land in Singapore. *Journal of Tropical Forest Science*, **4**, 151–61.

Corner, E.J.H. (1978). *The Freshwater Swamp-Forest of south Johore and Singapore*. Botanic Gardens Parks and Recreation Department, Singapore.

Crow, T.R. (1980). A rainforest chronicle: a 30-year record of change in structure and composition at El Verde, Puerto Rico. *Biotropica*, **12**, 42–55.

Dale, W.L. (1963). Surface temperatures in Malaya. *Journal of Tropical Geography*, **17**, 57–71.

De Rham, P. (1970). L'azote dans quelques forêts, savanes et de terrains de culture d'Afrique tropicale humide (Côte d'Ivoire). *Veröffentlichungen des Geobotanischen Institutes, Zürich*, **45**, 1–127.

Denslow, J.S. (1980). Gap partitioning among tropical rain forest trees. *Biotropica*, **12** (suppl.), 47–55.

Denslow, J.S. (1987). Tropical rain forest gaps and tree species diversity. *Annual Review of Ecology and Systematics*, **18**, 431–51.

Denslow, J.S., Schultz, J.C., Vitousek, P.M. and Strain, B.R. (1990). Growth responses of tropical shrubs to treefall gap environments. *Ecology*, **71**, 165–79.

Denslow, J.S., Vitousek, P.M. and Schultz, J.C. (1987). Bioassays of nutrient limitation in a tropical rain forest soil. *Oecologia*, **74**, 370–6.

Fetcher, N., Strain, B.R. and Oberbauer, S.F. (1983). Effects of light regime on the growth, leaf morphology and water relations of seedlings of two species of tropical trees. *Oecologia*, **58**, 314–19.

Fisher, B.L., Howe, H.F. and Wright, S.J. (1991). Survival and growth of *Virola surinamensis* yearlings: water augmentation in gap and understorey. *Oecologia*, **86**, 292–7.

Fleming, T.H. (1985). Coexistence of five sympatric *Piper* (Piperaceae) species in a tropical dry forest. *Ecology*, **66**, 688–700.

Fong, F.W. (1977). Edaphic conditions under bertram (*Eugeissona tristis* Griff.) on seraya ridge forests. *Tropical Ecology*, **18**, 60–70.

Gong, W.K. and Ong, J.E. (1983). Litter production and decomposition in a coastal hill dipterocarp forest. In Sutton, S.L., Whitmore, T.C. and Chadwick, A.C. (eds.) *Tropical Rain Forest: Ecology and Management*, pp. 275–85. Blackwell Scientific Publications, Oxford.

Grubb, P.J. (1977a). The maintenance of species richness in plant communities: the importance of the regeneration niche. *Biological Reviews*, **52**, 107–45.

Grubb, P.J. (1977b). Control of forest growth and distribution on wet tropical mountains: with special reference to mineral nutrition. *Annual Review of Ecology and Systematics*, **8**, 83–107.

Grubb, P.J. (1986). Problems posed by sparse and patchily distributed species in species-rich plant communities. In Diamond, J. and Case, T.J. (eds.), *Community Ecology*, pp. 207–25. Harper and Row, New York.

Grubb, P.J., Turner, I.M. and Burslem, D.F.R.P. (1994). Mineral nutrient status of coastal hill dipterocarp forest and adinandra belukar in Singapore: analysis of soil, leaves and litter. *Journal of Tropical Ecology*, **10**, 559–77.

Harley, J.L. and Smith, S.E. (1983). *Mycorrhizal Symbiosis*. Academic Press, London.

Hartshorn, G.S. (1978). Tree falls and tropical forest dynamics. In Tomlinson, P.B. and Zimmermann, M.H. (eds.), *Tropical Trees as Living Systems*, pp 617–38. Cambridge University Press, Cambridge.

Healey, J.R. (1990). *Regeneration in a Jamaican Montane Tropical Rain Forest*. Ph.D. dissertation, University of Cambridge, Cambridge.

Holttum, R.E. (1954). Adinandra belukar. *Journal of Tropical Geography*, **3**, 27–32.

Hubbell, S.P. and Foster, R.B. (1986a). Canopy gaps and the dynamics of a neotropical forest. In Crawley, M.J. (ed.) *Plant Ecology*, pp. 77–96. Blackwell Scientific Publications, Oxford.

Hubbell, S.P. and Foster, R.B. (1986b). Biology, chance and history and the structure of tropical rain forest tree communities. In Diamond, J. and Case, T.J. (eds.) *Community Ecology*, pp. 314–29. Harper and Row, New York.

Hubbell, S.P. and Foster, R.B. (1987). The spatial context of regeneration in a neotropical forest. In Gray, A.J., Crawley, M.J. and Edwards, P.J. (eds.), *Colonization, Succession and Stability*, pp. 395–412. Blackwell Scientific Publications, Oxford.

Hubbell, S.P., Condit, R. and Foster, R.B. (1990). Presence and absence of density dependence in a neotropical tree community. *Philosophical Transactions of the Royal Society*, Series B, **330**, 269–81.

Hunt, R. (1978). *Plant Growth Analysis*. Edward Arnold, London.

Hurlbert, S.H. (1984). Pseudoreplication and the design of ecological field experiments. *Ecological Monographs*, **54**, 187–211.

Ives, D.W. (1977). Soils of the Republic of Singapore. *New Zealand Soil Survey Report*, **36**.

Janos, D.P. (1983). Tropical mycorrhizae, nutrient cycles and plant growth. In Sutton, S.L., Whitmore, T.C. and Chadwick, A.C. (eds.), *Tropical Rain Forest: Ecology and Management*, pp. 327–45. Blackwell Scientific Publications, Oxford.

King, D.A. (1990). Allometry of saplings and understorey trees of a Panamanian forest. *Functional Ecology*, **4**, 27–32.

Kohyama, T. (1987). Significance of architecture and allometry in saplings. *Functional Ecology*, **1**, 399–404.

Kohyama, T. and Hotta, M. (1990). Significance of allometry in tropical saplings. *Functional Ecology*, **4**, 515–21.

Lieberman, D., Hartshorn, G.S., Lieberman, M. and Peralta, R. (1990). Forest dynamics at La Selva Biological Station, 1969–1985. In Gentry, A.H. (ed.), *Four Neotropical Rainforests*, pp. 509–21. Yale University Press, New Haven.

Marrs, R.H., Thompson, J., Scott, D. and Proctor, J. (1991). Nitrogen mineralization and nitrification in terra firme forest and savanna soils on Ilha de Maracá, Roraima, Brazil. *Journal of Tropical Ecology*, **7**, 123–37.

Molofsky, J. and Augspurger, C.K. (1992). The effect of leaf litter on early seedling establishment in a tropical forest. *Ecology*, **73**, 68–77.

Nieuwolt, S. (1965). Evaporation and water balances in Malaya. *Journal of Tropical Geography*, **20**, 34–53.

Osunkoya, O.O., Ash, J.E., Graham, A.W. and Hopkins, M.S. (1993). Growth of tree seedlings in tropical rain forests of North Queensland, Australia. *Journal of Tropical Ecology*, **9**, 1–18.

Pearcy, R.W. (1983). The light environment and growth of C_3 and C_4 tree species in the understory of a Hawaiian forest. *Oecologia*, **58**, 19–25.

Pearcy, R.W. and Calkin, H.W. (1983). Carbon dioxide exchange of C_3 and C_4 tree species in the understory of a Hawaiian forest. *Oecologia*, **58**, 26–32.

Pearcy, R.W., Osteryoung, K. and Calkin, H.W. (1983). Photosynthetic responses to dynamic light environments by Hawaiian trees. *Plant Physiology*, **79**, 896–902.

241

Popma, J., Bongers, F. and Werger, M.J.A. (1992). Gap dependence and leaf characteristics of trees in a lowland tropical rain forest in Mexico. *Oikos*, **63**, 207–14.

Poulson, T.L. and Platt, W.J. (1989). Gap light regimes influence canopy tree diversity. *Ecology*, **70**, 553–5.

Proctor, J. (1984). Tropical forest litterfall. II. The data set. In Sutton, S.L. and Chadwick, A.C. (eds.), *Tropical Rain Forest: the Leeds Symposium*, pp. 83–113. Leeds Philosophical and Literary Society, Leeds.

Proctor, J., Anderson, J.M., Chai, P. and Vallack, H.W. (1983). Ecological studies in four contrasting lowland rain forests in Gunung Mulu National Park, Sarawak. I. Forest environment, structure and floristics. *Journal of Ecology*, **71**, 237–60.

Putz, F.E. and Canham, C.D. (1992). Mechanisms of arrested succession in shrublands: root and shoot competition between shrubs and tree seedlings. *Forest Ecology and Management*, **49**, 267–75.

Raich, J.W. (1989). Seasonal and spatial variation in the light environment in a tropical Dipterocarp forest and gaps. *Biotropica*, **21**, 299–302.

Raich, J.W. and Gong, W.K. (1990). Effects of canopy openings on tree seed germination in a Malaysian dipterocarp forest. *Journal of Tropical Ecology*, **6**, 203–17.

Ramos, J. and Grace, J. (1990). The effects of shade on the gas exchange of seedlings of four tropical trees from Mexico. *Functional Ecology*, **4**, 667–77.

Reich, P.B., Uhl, C., Walters, M.B. and Ellsworth, D.S. (1991). Leaf lifespan as a determinant of leaf structure and function among 23 tree species in Amazonian forest communities. *Oecologia*, **86**, 16–24.

Reich, P.B., Walters, M.B. and Ellsworth, D.S. (1992). Leaf life-span in relation to leaf, plant and stand characteristics among diverse ecosystems. *Ecological Monographs*, **62**, 365–92.

Riddoch, I., Lehto, T. and Grace, J. (1991). Photosynthesis of tropical tree seedlings in relation to light and nutrient supply. *New Phytologist*, **119**, 137–47.

Riswan, S. (1989). Trend of soil nutrient movements in two different soil types after clear-cut with or without burnt in Kalimantan, Indonesia. In van der Heide, J. (ed.), *Nutrient Management for Food Crop Production in Tropical Farming Systems*, pp. 261–70. Institute for Soil Fertility, Haren.

Robertson, G.P. (1984). Nitrification and nitrogen mineralization in a lowland rainforest succession in Costa Rica, Central Amazonia. *Oecologia*, **61**, 99–104.

Sanford, R.L.Jr. (1989). Fine root biomass under a tropical forest light gap opening in Costa Rica. *Journal of Tropical Ecology*, **5**, 251–6.

Sanford, R.L.Jr. (1990). Fine root biomass under light gap opening in an Amazonian rain forest. *Oecologia*, **83**, 541–5.

Shorrocks, V.M. (1962). Leaf analysis as a guide to the nutrition of *Hevea brasiliensis* II. Sampling technique with mature trees: variations in nutrient composition of the leaves with position on the tree. *Journal of the Rubber Research Institute of Malaya*, **17**, 91–101.

Sim, J.W.S., Tan, H.T.W. and Turner, I.M. (1992). Adinandra belukar: an anthropogenic heath forest in Singapore. *Vegetatio*, **102**, 125–37.

Stevens, P.F. (1980). A revision of the old world species of *Calophyllum* (Guttiferae). *Journal of the Arnold Arboretum*, **61**, 117–424.

Sundralingham, P. (1983). Responses of potted seedlings of *Dryobalanops aromatica* and *Dryobalanops oblongifolia* to commercial fertilizers. *Malaysian Forester*, **46**, 86–92.

Swaine, M.D. and Whitmore, T.C. (1988). On the definition of ecological species groups in tropical rain forests. *Vegetatio*, **75**, 81–6.

Symington, C.F. (1943). *Foresters Manual of Dipterocarps*. Malayan Forest Record **16**.

Thomas, G.S.P. (1991). Geology and geomorphology. In Chia, L.S., Rahman, A. and Tay, D.B.H. (eds.), *The Biophysical Environment of Singapore*, pp. 50–88. Singapore University Press, Singapore.

Thompson, W.A., Kriedemann, P.E. and Craig, I.E. (1992a). Photosynthetic response to light and nutrients in sun-tolerant and shade-tolerant rainforest trees. I. Growth, leaf anatomy and nutrient content. *Australian Journal of Plant Physiology*, **19**, 1–18.

Thompson, W.A., Huang, L.-K. and Kriedemann, P.E. (1992b). Photosynthetic response to light and nutrients in sun-tolerant and shade-tolerant rainforest trees. II. Leaf gas exchange and component processes of photosynthesis. *Australian Journal of Plant Physiology*, **19**, 19–42.

Turner, I.M. (1990a). Tree seedling growth and survival in a Malaysian rain forest. *Biotropica*, **22**, 146–54.

Turner, I.M. (1990b). The seedling survivorship and growth of three *Shorea* species in a Malaysian tropical rain forest. *Journal of Tropical Ecology*, **6**, 469–78.

Turner, I.M., Brown, N.D. and Newton, A.C. (1993). Effect of fertilizer application on dipterocarp seedling growth and mycorrhizal infection. *Forest Ecology and Management*, **57**, 329–37.

Vitousek, P.M. (1984). Litterfall, nutrient cycling and nutrient limitation in tropical rain forests. *Ecology*, **65**, 285–98.

Vitousek, P.M. and Denslow, J.S. (1986). Nitrogen and phosphorus availability in treefall gaps of a lowland tropical rainforest. *Journal of Ecology*, **74**, 1167–1178.

Vitousek, P.M. and Sanford, R.L. (1986). Nutrient cycling in moist tropical forest. *Annual Review of Ecology and Systematics*, **17**, 137–67.

Watts, I.E.M. (1955). Rainfall of Singapore Island. *Journal of Tropical Geography*, **7**, 1–71.

Whitmore, T.C. (1974). *Changes with time and the role of cyclones in tropical rain forest on Kolombangara, Solomon Islands*. Commonwealth Forestry Institute Paper **46**.

Whitmore, T.C. (1975). *Tropical Rain Forests of the Far East*. Clarendon Press, Oxford.

Whitmore, T.C. (1978). Gaps in the forest canopy. In Tomlinson, P.B. and Zimmerman, M.H. (eds.), *Tropical Trees as Living Systems*, pp. 639–55. Cambridge University Press, Cambridge.

Whitmore, T.C. (1989). Changes over twenty-one years in the Kolombangara rain forests. *Journal of Ecology*, **77**, 469–83.

Whitmore, T.C. and Wong, Y.K. (1959). Patterns of sunfleck and shade in tropical rain forest. *Malayan Forester*, **22**, 50–62.

Wong, Y.K. (1987). Ecology of the trees of Bukit Timah nature reserve. *Garden's Bulletin, Singapore*, **40**, 45–76.

Wright, S.J. (1991). Seasonal drought and the phenology of understorey shrubs in a tropical moist forest. *Ecology*, **72**, 1643–57.

Yoda, K. (1974). Three-dimensional distribution of light intensity in a tropical rain forest of West Malaysia. *Japanese Journal of Ecology*, **24**, 247–54.

Yoda, K. (1978). Organic carbon, nitrogen and mineral nutrients stock in the soil of Pasoh forest. *Malayan Nature Journal*, **30**, 229–51.

Revised manuscript received January 1994

CHAPTER 10

SEEDLING GROWTH OF SHOREA *SECTION* DOONA *(DIPTEROCARPACEAE) IN SOILS FROM TOPOGRAPHICALLY DIFFERENT SITES OF SINHARAJA RAIN FOREST IN SRI LANKA*

C.V.S. Gunatilleke, G.A.D. Perera, P.M.S. Ashton, P.S. Ashton and I.A.U.N. Gunatilleke

---

INTRODUCTION

There are two apparently incompatible hypotheses which seek to explain the maintenance of species richness in tropical forests. In one, dubbed the equilibrium hypothesis by Hubbell and Foster (1983), every species occupies a specific ecological niche; in other words, each performs better than all other species in the forest at least in one respect. Evidence for this hypothesis has been presented in respect of soils (Ashton, 1969), predation, herbivore and pathogen specificity (Janzen, 1970; Connell, 1971), to the disturbance regimes (Grubb, 1977), and in respect to competition for seed dispersers (Snow, 1966) and pollinators (Ashton, 1989). Hubbell and Foster (1983), in contrast, hold to a non-equilibrium hypothesis. They have refined the views of many early authors that rain forest species, although assorted into ecological guilds, are generalists within these guilds and that forest composition is unpredictable at all spatial and temporal scales. They attribute composition to the vagaries of extinction and the chance opportunities for immigration and spread (Hubbell, 1979; Hubbell and Foster, 1983).

These alternatives clearly have profound implications for management. The equilibrium hypothesis implies that site-specific silvicultural prescriptions will be necessary, but the non-equilibrium hypothesis does not. As Hubbell and Foster (1983) have already indicated, the latter hypothesis predicts, on the basis of island biogeography theory, that any diminution in forest area will lead to some extinctions. The larger a germplasm preserve the better. The equilibrium hypothesis, by contrast, implies that species composition is predictable, and returns to its former quantitative as well as qualitative composition after perturbation (provided nearby seed sources persist); and that, because the landscape is already subdivided into ecological islands, a few preserves of moderate size, chosen to have adequate representation of all site conditions, may allow permanent conservation of most if not all species. By 'adequate' we mean areas sufficiently large enough for breeding populations of most species, however rare, to persist and to survive the periodic natural perturbations which occur.

In Sri Lanka, the canopy of the endemic-rich rain forests of the steeply undulating lowlands and mid-elevations of the wet zone is dominated by tree species belonging to the families Dipterocarpaceae, Clusiaceae, Myrtaceae and Sapotaceae (Gunatilleke and Ashton, 1987). Among the dipterocarps, the genus *Shorea* section *Doona* includes ten species, all endemic to the lowland and sub-montane rain forests (up to 1,800 m) of the wet zone of Sri Lanka, where they dominate the canopy of the *Mesua–Doona* community at altitudes of 300–600 m. Among these *Shorea* species, *S. gardneri* (Thw.) P. Ashton and *S. zeylanica* (Thw.) P. Ashton are restricted to the sub-montane forests where they form almost pure stands. The remaining eight species are ecologically partially sympatric. In the lowlands the drought tolerant *S. worthingtonii* P. Ashton is more abundant on the upper slopes and ridges, the light demanding *S. megistophylla* P. Ashton, *S. trapezifolia* (Thw.) P. Ashton, *S. congestiflora* (Thw.) P. Ashton and *S. cordifolia* (Thw.) P. Ashton are common along valleys, water courses and lower slopes, *S. affinis* (Thw.) P. Ashton is abundant on midslopes and *S. disticha* P. Ashton has a wide distributional amplitude along the soil catena (Ashton, P.S., 1988; Ashton, P.M.S., 1992). The distribution of some species has also been found to be correlated with inorganic soil phosphorous and magnesium concentrations (Gunatilleke and Ashton, 1987). *S. ovalifolia* (Thw.) Ashton, thought to be extinct, has been recorded in the past from the coastal lowlands.

A comparative analysis of ecological strategies of eight of these phylogenetically related species allows us to test in species-rich tropical rain forests Darwin's (1859) surmise, elaborated and tested by Gause (1934), that closely related species never share the same site and ecology. This hypothesis is based on the fact that closely related taxa are by definition those which share the greatest genetic similarity. By implication these species should also be the most ecologically similar. Consequently, if species-specific competition does occur, it is among such species groups that it should be most severe. The existence of a clade of endemic canopy tree species whose geographical ranges completely overlap in one small region also provides an exceptional opportunity to test the equilibrium hypothesis for the maintenance of tree species richness in tropical forests.

Among the most important ecological specializations that might contribute to the maintenance of this partially sympatric clade are differences among juveniles in their response to light (quality, quantity and duration), moisture (quantity and periodicity) and the physico-chemical status of the soil. Existence of such specializations would imply that species composition and rank order of abundance is predictable at community level and species richness is maintained by competitive interactions, with each species occupying a distinct niche within which it has competitive advantage (Ashton, 1969; Grubb, 1977).

Although many previous studies have demonstrated floristic variation in moist tropical forests associated with broad topographic and edaphic variations (Ashton, 1964; Poore, 1968; Austin et al., 1972; Baillie and Ashton, 1983; Baillie et al., 1987; Tracey, 1969; Williams et al., 1969), the small-scale distribution of individual species has rarely been investigated (Basnet, 1992; Pemadasa and Gunatilleke, 1981). Local topographic variations that create a mosaic of microhabitats have been seen as exerting considerable effect on interspecific ecological specialization with different species exploiting distinct niches in a complex heterogeneous environment (Ashton, 1969, 1976; Austin et al., 1972; Whitmore, 1978, 1984; Lugo, 1988).

In this study we test, in respect of one set of environmental variables, two hypotheses: first, that different species within a clade possess distinct ecological ranges in conformity with the equilibrium hypothesis; and second that every ecologically sympatric species manifests superiority of performance over close relatives under certain conditions. Specifically, in this paper we test the prediction that seedlings of every sympatric species of *Shorea* section *Doona* exhibit a characteristic growth response to the nutrient levels in four soils from different sites underlain by similar geology, but differing in nutrient levels.

TEST SPECIES, SITE CHARACTERISTICS AND EXPERIMENTAL DESIGN

The eight *Shorea* species studied were *S. affinis, S. congestiflora, S. cordifolia, S. disticha, S. gardneri, S. megistophylla, S. trapezifolia* and *S. worthingtonii.*

The experiment was conducted in Sinharaja rain forest, a Man and the Biosphere Reserve and a World Heritage Site in Sri Lanka. The climate, geology, soils, vegetation and human impact in the area have been previously described (Gunatilleke and Gunatilleke, 1983, 1985 and references therein). The reserve, 335–915 m in elevation, consists of parallel ridges of Precambrian schists and gneisses overlain by ultisols. The mean annual rainfall at the field research station records 4,780 mm with an aseasonal perhumid climate.

An experiment was set up in an artificial shelter near the field research station located at 460 m on a flat, open well-drained site, about 15 m × 25 m in size and cleared of vegetation. Shading was provided by enclosing the site on all sides by shade cloth that allowed 800 $\mu mol\,m^{-2}\,s^{-1}$ photosynthetic photon flux density (PPFD) at noon on sunny days as measured with radiation sensors (Li-Cor 190SA and 190SZ attached to Li-Cor 1,000 data logger, Lincoln, Nebraska, USA). All plants were exposed to the normal rainfall that permeated through shade cloth having a mesh size of 10 mm. During relatively dry weather when moisture stress was evident, all plants were uniformly watered once every 5 days. This had earlier been found sufficient to ensure that water was never limiting (Ashton, P.M.S., 1990).

Mature fruits of each of the eight *Shorea* spp. were collected from several tree populations within and around Sinharaja reserve from June to August of the mast fruiting year, 1989. For each species fruit samples were pooled, germinated and grown in forest soil in a partially shaded nursery for a period of one to three months before transplanting to the experimental soils. At the time of transplanting the seedlings satisfactory infection of ectotrophic mycorrhizae was evident in them.

Soils were collected from three sites on a forested hillock within the reserve, and from a single midslope site in an 11-year old *Pinus caribaea* plantation about 3 km from the hillock in the buffer zone. The three forest sites were within 200 m of one another and represented a valley, midslope and ridge top of a single soil catena along an altitudinal gradient of 85 m. While all the forest sites had characteristic multi-tiered vegetation profiles, the *P. caribaea* plantation had an overstorey of uniformly spaced 7–10 m tall trees with a mixed understorey of ferns, herbs and shrubs typical of early successional vegetation. At each site litter-free soils to 30 cm depth, including both humus and upper mineral soil layers, were collected from an area of 5–10 m^2. The seedlings were potted in well mixed soils from each site in 15-cm diameter, 30 cm high black polythene containers.

The experiment was set up in a split-plot design, with four replicates per soil treatment for species; each replicate had twenty-five even-sized seedlings for each species selected from the nursery and transplanted into polythene bags. Each main treatment (four soil types) therefore included eight subtreatments (eight *Shorea* species). The periodic measurement of height growth of all species (not presented in this paper) indicated that, at the end of twenty-four months, the seedlings were still in their logarithmic phase of growth and showed no evidence of root confinement.

The growth performance was examined by measuring height of seedlings to the tip of the leader and total leaf number per seedling, one month and twenty-four months after initiation of the experiment, for twelve randomly selected individuals per species per replicate. In addition, dry mass of the stem, leaves, tap root and laterals with fine roots were taken, after twenty-four months from three randomly selected plants per replicate per species, after washing and drying at 85°C for 48 hours.

Three soil samples, each of them a composite of six augur samples taken randomly from each site were analysed for pH, bulk density, organic C and total N, P, K, Ca and Mg. These analyses were done for pH using a water extract, for organic C by the Walkley–Black method and for total elements by wet digestion at 450°C, followed by micro-Kjeldahl for N, and flame-atomic absorption spectrophotometric determination for K, Ca and Mg. Total P was determined by spectrophotometric determination at 420 nm of the molybdate–vanadate complex, using a flow injection analyser. Air dried soil samples were air freighted to the Institut für Waldökologie, Universität für Bodenkulter, Vienna, Austria, where all soil analyses were carried out. The rest of the analyses took place at the Institute of Fundamental Studies, Sri Lanka.

The data were subjected to analyses of variance using the GLM procedure of SAS (Littell et al., 1991). Two- and one-way analyses of variance were carried out using natural logarithm-transformed data for each of the growth attributes measured (height increment, leaf number, total and component dry mass) to compare the growth performance of species in different soils. As the differences among replicates were not significant, data in them were pooled for analyses. Multiple comparisons of means among species were performed by Tukey's Honest Significant Difference method where $\alpha = 0.05$. Back transformed means of values from analyses of logarithmically transformed data are presented.

RESULTS

Soil characteristics

The pH values showed significant differences among each of the four soil types even though the range in variation among them was relatively small (Table 10.1). *Pinus* soil recorded the highest soil pH, followed in turn by that in the valley, ridge and midslope. In contrast to pH, organic C showed a reverse trend, with significantly higher values in the natural forest soils compared to that in *Pinus*. Bulk density was highest in the ridge soil and lowest in the midslope soil and the values in each of the four soils were not significantly different.

The concentration of total N in the valley soil was significantly higher than that in the midslope soil (Table 10.1). The concentrations of P in the three natural forest soils were not significantly different from each other, and that in the *Pinus* was significantly lower only from that in ridge soil. The concentration of total K in the *Pinus* soil was significantly higher than that in the valley and midslope soils, which themselves were similar. The concentration of total Mg in *Pinus* soil was significantly higher than that in any of the natural forest soils, where the concentrations in the valley and ridge soils were similar and both significantly higher than that in the midslope soil. In contrast to the above nutrients, concentrations of Ca in the four soils showed no significant difference.

Among the natural forest soils, the C:N ratio in the midslope soil was three times and in the ridge twice the value of that in the valley soil. In the *Pinus* soil, the C:N ratio was only slightly higher than that of the valley soil.

Considering the elements analysed overall, *Pinus* and valley soils are relatively richer in nutrients than the ridge soil and in turn all of them are better than the midslope soil.

Table 10.1 pH, bulk density (BD, g/cm^3), organic carbon (OC, per cent), mean percentage concentrations of total nutrients and their standard deviations (in brackets) from a valley, midslope and ridge of the natural forest and a midslope in a *Pinus* plantation in the buffer zone of Sinharaja and their C:N ratios (OC:N). Letters beside values indicate statistical similarities (same letter) and differences (different letters) for each attribute across soil types

	Pinus	Valley	Ridge	Midslope
pH	4.91 (0.072)a	4.77 (0.047)b	4.54 (0.112)c	4.41 (0.088)d
BD	1.788 (0.267)a	1.705 (0.360)a	1.811 (0.242)a	1.515 (0.306)a
OC	3.045 (0.145)c	3.398 (0.273)b	4.452 (0.755)a	4.730 (0.746)a
N	0.159 (0.025)ab	0.218 (0.028)a	0.131 (0.013)ab	0.097 (0.037)b
P	0.033 (0.003)b	0.038 (0.002)ab	0.045 (0.004)a	0.035 (0.002)ab
K	0.137 (0.018)a	0.063 (0.011)a	0.103 (0.003)ab	0.085 (0.010)bc
Ca	0.018 (0.006)a	0.015 (0.002)a	0.009 (0.0004)a	0.062 (0.041)a
Mg	0.099 (0.002)a	0.073 (0.002)b	0.072 (0.002)b	0.044 (0.006)c
OC:N	19.11	17.21	34.07	49.00

Seedling performance

In presenting the results of seedling growth in different soils, the statistical analysis of each performance measure has been given in the following order where relevant: performance of species, collectively and individually among soils; relative performance among species in soils collectively, and within each soil. The effects of species and soils on height, total and component dry mass, leaf number and unit leaf mass are given in Table 10.2. Significant interactions between species and soils were observed for total dry mass, leaf number and other (= lateral and fine) root dry mass.

Mean height growth

The mean height growth of all eight *Shorea* species collectively was significantly different in the four soils (Figure 10.1). Each species showed similar height growth in valley and *Pinus* soils, except *S. trapezifolia* which grew significantly taller in valley than in *Pinus* soil (Figure 10.1 and Table 10.3). Likewise, all species showed similar mean height growth in ridge and midslope soils, except *S. worthingtonii* which grew significantly taller in ridge soil as compared to midslope soil. Mean height growth of each species in soils collectively ranked *S. disticha* the tallest and *S. megistophylla* the shortest (Figure 10.2). Based on the relative mean height growth of species in each of the four soils, three broad groups of species can be recognized. *S. disticha*, *S. trapezifolia* and *S. affinis* had the greatest height growth although their relative positions interchanged among soils. *S. cordifolia*, *S. worthingtonii*, *S. congestiflora* and *S. gardneri* consistently grouped together as those with medium height growth, and *S. gardneri* and *S. megistophylla* showed the least height growth in all soils (Figure 10.1). Broadly similar trends in height growth of all the species in each of the four soils are reflected in the absence

Table 10.2 Values for the F statistic and the levels of significance (* = 0.05, ** = 0.01, *** = 0.001 level) from the two-way and one-way analyses of variance carried out for each attribute of seedling performance for the *Shorea* species tested. For height and leaf no. $n = 48$ and for total and each component dry mass measure $n = 12$

Treatment effects	Height	Total dry mass	Leaf No.	Unit leaf mass	Stem dry mass	Leaf dry mass	Tap root dry mass	Other root dry mass
Main treatments								
Total	10.56***	10.76***	44.80***	28.80***	9.70***	12.08***	6.77***	8.51***
Soils	69.85***	88.84***	208.15***	20.38***	76.42***	100.85***	47.00***	62.27***
Species	15.23***	4.46***	102.03***	114.26***	6.60***	5.94***	4.52***	2.81**
Soils x species	0.54	1.71*	2.36***	1.05	1.20	1.43	1.77	2.81***
Sub treatments by species among soils								
S. affinis	20.40***	6.70***	23.42***	41	6.19**	10.18***	4.09*	2.47
S. congestiflora	10.20***	17.84***	19.59***	14.47***	15.26***	14.94***	16.52***	14.26***
S. cordifolia	27.80***	16.39***	34.92***	1.46	14.37***	14.73***	8.79***	18.23***
S. disticha	37.67***	11.69***	43.18***	3.45*	11.48***	14.36***	3.03*	7.61***
S. gardneri	19.90***	9.58***	39.22***	2.90*	6.11**	15.09***	5.49***	10.89***
S. megistophylla	12.53***	14.95***	12.21***	2.94*	14.54***	19.63***	5.88***	19.09***
S. trapezifolia	31.48***	18.65***	29.73***	4.84**	19.96***	17.16***	10.63***	10.68***
S. worthingtonii	16.66***	7.04***	19.78***	3.35*	6.91***	5.89***	4.45**	2.67
Species performance within each soil								
Pinus	13.04***	0.95	41.32***	32.16***	0.98	1.75	0.81	1.65
Valley	15.06***	2.88**	35.78***	29.25***	3.33**	3.18**	2.98**	2.37*
Ridge	5.54***	1.09	21.72***	18.40***	1.99	1.12	0.77	1.91
Midslope	5.17***	4.89***	18.10***	46.32***	3.97***	5.22***	5.56***	5.21***

Table 10.3 Tukey rankings (row-wise) for growth attributes of each of the *Shorea* species among soils (P = *Pinus*, V = valley, R = ridge, M = midslope). The rankings indicate statistical similarities (similar letters) and differences (different letters) in their performance at the 5% level. See Table 10.2 for values of *n*

Species	P	V	R	M	P	V	R	M
		Height				Total dry mass		
S. megistophylla	ab	a	bc	c	a	a	b	b
S. disticha	a	a	b	b	a	a	b	b
S. cordifolia	a	a	b	b	a	a	b	b
S. worthingtonii	a	a	b	c	a	a	ab	b
S. trapezifolia	b	a	c	c	b	a	c	c
S. congestiflora	a	a	b	b	a	a	b	c
S. affinis	a	a	b	b	a	ab	b	b
S. gardneri	a	a	b	b	a	ab	bc	c
		Leaf number				Unit leaf mass		
S. megistophylla	a	ab	bc	c	a	a	a	a
S. disticha	b	a	c	c	a	ab	b	ab
S. cordifolia	a	a	b	c	a	a	a	a
S. worthingtonii	a	a	b	c	ab	a	ab	b
S. trapezifolia	a	a	b	c	ab	a	b	b
S. congestiflora	a	a	b	b	a	a	a	b
S. affinis	a	a	b	b	a	a	a	a
S. gardneri	a	a	b	c	a	a	a	a
		Stem dry mass				Leaf dry mass		
S. megistophylla	ab	a	b	c	a	a	b	c
S. disticha	a	a	b	b	a	a	b	b
S. cordifolia	a	a	b	b	a	a	b	b
S. worthingtonii	a	a	ab	b	a	a	ab	b
S. trapezifolia	b	a	c	c	ab	a	bc	c
S. congestiflora	a	a	b	c	a	a	b	b
S. affinis	a	ab	b	b	a	ab	bc	c
S. gardneri	a	ab	bc	c	a	ab	b	c
		Tap root dry mass				Fine root dry mass		
S. megistophylla	ab	a	b	b	a	ab	b	c
S. disticha	a	a	a	a	ab	a	c	bc
S. cordifolia	ab	a	bc	c	a	a	b	b
S. worthingtoni	a	a	ab	b	a	a	a	a
S. trapezifolia	ab	a	b	b	a	a	b	b
S. congestiflora	ab	a	b	c	ab	a	b	c
S. affinis	a	a	b	ab	a	a	a	a
S. gardneri	a	a	ab	b	a	ab	bc	c

of a significant interaction between soil and species for height growth (Table 10.2). The principal difference among sites was that variations in height growth among species were greater in valley and *Pinus* soils than midslope and ridge soils, as exemplified by *S. disticha* and *S. affinis* which grew better than the other species in the former two.

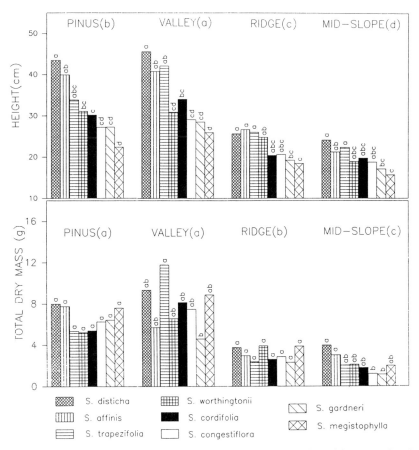

Figure 10.1 Mean height ($n = 48$) and mean dry mass ($n = 12$) of seedlings of the test species after twenty-four months growth under shade house conditions, in soils obtained from a valley, midslope and ridge of the natural forest, and a midslope of a nearby *Pinus* plantation. Letters above each histogram indicate statistical differences among species within a given soil. Letters next to each soil and above each set of histograms represents differences among soils. Species or soil bearing the same letter are not significantly different from each other at the 0.05 level

Mean total dry mass

Mean total dry mass of all species collectively was similar in valley and *Pinus* soils (Figure 10.1). These soils produced significantly greater total dry mass than in ridge soil, and all of them were significantly greater than that in the midslope soils. The mean total dry mass of each species in each soil indicated that the performance of *S. trapezifolia* was significantly greater in the valley soil than in the *Pinus* soil, but the performance of all other species in these two soils was similar (Table 10.3). Dry mass in valley and *Pinus* soils is significantly greater than that in ridge and midslope soils for five species, and

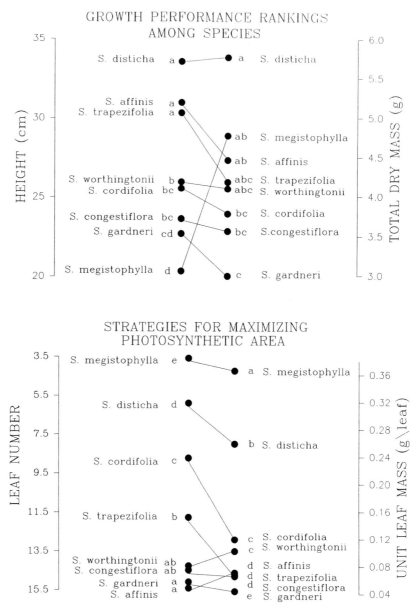

Figure 10.2 Comparison of growth performance rankings (Tukey) between species based on their mean heights, dry mass, leaf number and unit leaf mass (total leaf dry mass divided by leaf number per seedling) for soils collectively. Letters next to species denote statistical differences (different letters) or similarities (same letter) among them at the 0.05 level. Note inverted scale on *Y* axis for leaf number. For height and leaf number *n* = 48; and for dry mass and unit leaf mass *n* = 12

254

only from midslope soil for *S. worthingtonii* and *S. gardneri*; it was similar in all three forest soils only for *S. affinis*. *S. congestiflora* alone showed a significantly higher mass in the ridge soil than in midslope soil (Table 10.3). The rank order of total dry mass gain among species over all soils was *S. disticha* with the highest, followed by *S. megistophylla*, *S. affinis*, *S. trapezifolia*, *S. worthingtonii*, *S. cordifolia*, *S. congestiflora* and *S. gardneri* (Figure 10.2). In the valley soil, *S. trapezifolia* had the largest dry mass gain and *S. gardneri* the least (Figure 10.1). In both *Pinus* and ridge soils, there was no significant difference among mean dry mass of different species. In the midslope soil however, the relative ranking among species was distinctly different from that in valley soils which is also reflected in their significant interaction for this attribute (Table 10.2, Figure 10.1). The largest mean dry mass was in *S. disticha* and the least in *S. gardneri*.

Component dry mass

The mean dry mass allocation to stems, leaves, tap roots and other roots of all species collectively was similar in valley and *Pinus* soils, each of which was in turn significantly greater than that in ridge and midslope soils (Table 10.4).

The relative allocations to different parts in the latter two soils were significantly different, except for dry mass of tap roots. Most species showed a trend similar to that found collectively. However, tap root dry mass in *S. disticha* and other root dry mass of *S. worthingtonii* and *S. affinis* were similar in all four soils.

Stem dry mass in valley and *Pinus* soils was significantly different in *S. trapezifolia*. *S. megistophylla* and *S. congestiflora* showed significant differences between ridge and mid-slope soils for three of the component dry mass attributes. In the remaining species, differences between them were non-significant (Table 10.3).

The relative performance of species in soils collectively showed that *S. disticha* ranks highest (Table 10.4). Greater variation among species was observed for above than for below ground dry mass components. Within each soil, differences among species with respect to each dry mass component were least in the *Pinus* soil and most accentuated in the midslope soil (Table 10.4).

Variation in allocation to above- and below-ground dry mass components among species in the four soils reveal different patterns of resource allocation (Figure 10.3). Overall, *S. trapezifolia* showed the largest dry mass increment, from relatively nutrient-poor midslope soils to nutrient-rich valley and *Pinus* soils. In *S. worthingtonii*, however, allocation of dry mass to each component showed relatively little variation across the nutrient gradient.

Table 10.4 Tukey ratings of dry mass components (stems, leaves, tap root and fine roots), for *Shorea* species collectively in each soil (row-wise), and among species within soils collectively (column-wise) (CL) and separately (P = *Pinus*, V = valley, R = ridge, M = midslope). Statistical similarities (same letter) and differences (different letter) given are at the 5 per cent level ($n = 12$)

Species	CL	P	V	R	M	CL	P	V	R	M
			Stem dry mass					Leaf dry mass		
S. disticha	A	a	a	a	a	A	a	a	a	a
S. affinis	AB	a	ab	ab	ab	AB	a	ab	a	ab
S. trapezifolia	AB	a	a	ab	abc	BC	a	ab	a	abc
S. megistophylla	AB	a	ab	ab	abc	A	a	a	a	abc
S. cordifolia	BC	a	ab	ab	abc	ABC	a	ab	a	abc
S. worthingtonii	BC	a	ab	ab	abc	AB	a	ab	a	ab
S. congestiflora	BC	a	ab	ab	bc	ABC	a	ab	a	bc
S. gardneri	C	a	b	b	c	C	a	b	a	c
All species collectively in each soil		A	A	B	C		A	A	B	C
			Tap root dry mass					Other root dry mass		
S. disticha	A	a	ab	a	a	A	a	a	a	ab
S. affinis	AB	a	ab	a	ab	A	a	a	a	a
S. trapezifolia	AB	a	a	a	abc	AB	a	a	a	abc
S. megistophylla	A	a	ab	a	ab	AB	a	a	a	c
S. cordifolia	AB	a	ab	a	abc	B	a	a	a	bc
S. worthingtonii	B	a	b	a	bc	AB	a	a	a	abc
S. congestiflora	B	a	ab	a	c	AB	a	a	a	bc
S. gardneri	B	a	b	a	bc	B	a	a	a	c
All species collectively in each soil		A	A	B	B		A	A	B	C

Leaf number

The mean leaf number per seedling for all species collectively was similar in valley and *Pinus* soils and significantly greater in both of them than in ridge soil (Figure 10.4). Leaf number in these three soils was significantly greater than in midslope soils. Leaf number per seedling in each of the species, with the exception of *S. disticha*, was similar and relatively high in valley and *Pinus* soils (Table 10.3). It was significantly lower in ridge and midslope soils than in the above soils in all species, except in *S. megistophylla*. The mean number of leaves per seedling among species over all soils collectively was highest in *S. affinis* followed in decreasing order by *S. gardneri*, *S. congesti-flora*, *S. worthingtonii*, *S. trapezifolia*, *S. cordifolia*, *S. disticha* and *S. megistophylla* (Figure 10.2). This rank order in soils collectively was also observed among species in *Pinus* soil (Figure 10.4). However, the five highest ranking species changed their relative positions in the three natural forest soils as reflected in highly significant interaction between them (Table 10.2). The

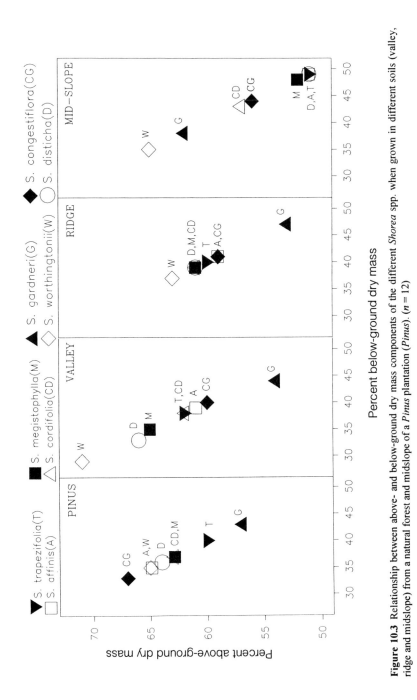

Figure 10.3 Relationship between above- and below-ground dry mass components of the different *Shorea* spp. when grown in different soils (valley, ridge and midslope) from a natural forest and midslope of a *Pinus* plantation (*Pinus*). (*n* = 12)

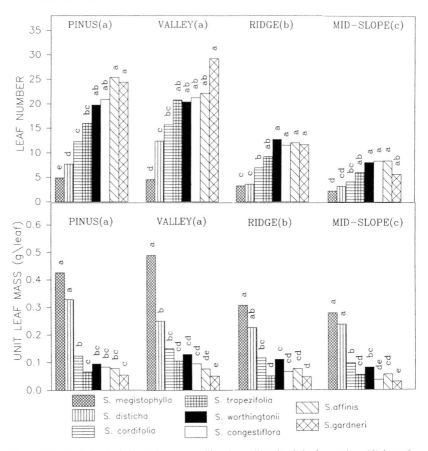

Figure 10.4 Variation in leaf number per seedling (*n* = 48) and unit leaf mass (*n* = 12) in each *Shorea* species grown in different soils. Notation as in Figure 10.1

largest variation in leaf number per seedling among species was observed in the valley and *Pinus* soils, and the least was in midslope soil.

Unit leaf mass

The mean unit leaf mass (mean mass of a single leaf) showed an overall trend opposite to that of leaf number (Figures 10.2 and 10.4).Unit leaf mass for species collectively was highest in valley and *Pinus* soils and least in midslope soil (Figure 10.4). This attribute was similar in valley and *Pinus* soils for all the species (Table 10.3). When the three natural forest soils are considered, the species fall into two groups, (a) where unit leaf mass in the valley soil was significantly higher than in midslope and/or ridge soils (*S. congestiflora*, *S. trapezifolia* and *S. worthingtonii*) and (b) where it was similar in all three soils for the remaining species. The unit leaf mass of each species in soils collectively decreased from *S. megistophylla* to *S. gardneri* (Figure 10.2). Differences in unit leaf mass among species within each soil showed the same trend as that observed in soils collectively with a few exceptions (Figure 10.4). The larger leaved species, *S. megistophylla*, *S. disticha*, *S. cordifolia* and *S. worthingtonii* always ranked among the first four maintaining the same relative position in each soil (Figure 10.4). The smallest leaved *S. gardneri* was always ranked last. The remaining species, *S. affinis*, *S. congestiflora* and *S. trapezifolia* changed their relative positions in each of the soils.

DISCUSSION

Species performance in different soils

We have presented comparisons of seedling performance of eight rain forest tree species in one section of a single genus in four different soils. Our results bear comparison with those of Latham (1992) who compared seedlings of six species of temperate deciduous broad-leaved trees under three light regimes and three concentrations of a fertilizer in which nutrients were maintained in the same proportions. The more or less independent variation in nutrient concentrations among our soils precludes the clarity of interpretation achieved by Latham; a later paper will address the effect of fertilizer applications on our species. However, by selecting eight of the ten known sympatric species of one clade, we are able to focus more narrowly on testing Gause's (1934) hypothesis that closely related taxa will become ecologically differentiated through competitive exclusion.

The overall growth performance of the eight *Shorea* species, as determined by their mean height, leaf number, total and component dry mass including unit leaf dry mass was significantly better at the end of the experiment in nitrogen- and magnesium-rich valley and *Pinus* soils with lower C:N ratios than that in the ridge soil. The general performance was greater in the ridge soil than in midslope soil, which had the lowest levels of nitrogen and magnesium and the highest C:N ratio; however, tap root dry mass was similar in both ridge and midslope soils. Differences in pH, bulk density and organic matter may also contribute to the results observed in this study. In the valley and *Pinus* soils with relatively higher pH and medium bulk density better seedling performances were observed. As all other environmental factors were kept uniform, we conclude that this general trend in growth performance is attributable to inherent fertility characteristics of each soil, although the valley and *Pinus* were not consistently richer than the other two soils in the other elements analysed. Even though the soils were obtained from within a small area of the forest and on the same parent material, the variation in soil characteristics, particularly nutrients, with topography seems to have affected overall seedling growth.

Seedling architecture and height growth

At the end of two years of growth, the tallest group of species, which included *S. disticha*, *S. affinis*, and *S. trapezifolia*, have similar seedling architecture. They have relatively long internodes and greater height relative to branch extensions, and these may have contributed to their large height growth. Furthermore, their seedlings are known to perform relatively well under the partial shade conditions of the experiment (Ashton, P.M.S., 1990 and unpublished data). Species with intermediate seedling height are characterized by the greater growth of their branches relative to their stem in the seedling stages. Of the two shortest species, *S. megistophylla*, which has the largest leaves among all the species, has the smallest stem height; it is one of the most light demanding of the *Shorea* species of section *Doona* (Ashton, P.M.S., 1990). The poor height growth of *S. gardneri* could be attributed to it being the only species which does not naturally grow at the altitude and in the mean monthly temperature range of Sinharaja field station where this experiment was conducted, but it dominates the submontane forests between 900 m and 1,500 m, where mean monthly temperatures are at least 3°C lower. Differences in seedling architecture and growth habit, and differential dry mass allocation to different plant components among the study species, make it difficult to use height growth as a reliable estimator of overall performance. Nevertheless, height still provides valuable information, particularly as an indication of the relative competitiveness of the same species in different soils. Like height, leaf number and unit leaf dry mass have their limitations, but all of them reflect how the different species allocate their resources on the different soils used in this study.

Dry mass and soil nutrients

Rank order among species for dry mass in the three natural forest soils which varied significantly among them, is different. Better performances of *S. trapezifolia*, *S. megistophylla* and *S. disticha* in valley soil and that of *S. worthingtonii* and *S. disticha* in ridge soil reflect the natural distribution of mature individuals along the topographic gradient of Sinharaja forest (Ashton, 1988 and unpublished data). *S. disticha* which perform better than others also has been shown to have wider light and moisture amplitudes (Ashton, P.M.S., 1990). In contrast, better performance of *S. megistophylla* in all but midslope soil suggests that its absence from upper slopes and ridge tops at this elevation must be due to factors other than soil fertility, such as soil moisture stress (Ashton, P.M.S., 1990).

Different proportions of allocation to above and below ground components in these *Shorea* species indicate that species like *S. trapezifolia*, which perform well in nutrient-rich soils reduce their above ground dry mass component relative to their below ground components in nutrient-poor soils. However, in species which perform relatively less well in nutrient-rich soils, the proportion of allocation to above ground components reduces very little as in *S. worthingtonii* or even increases sharply as in *S. gardneri* in nutrient-poor soils (Figure 10.3).

Although the response of species to lower nutrient soils (ridge and midslope), was to reduce their leaf numbers, leaf size and dry mass of stem, and in some cases to increase their relative allocation to root mass, the magnitude of change for each attribute between species was different (Figure 10.3 and Table 10.3). The allocation to above ground dry mass relative to that below ground in the three forest soils was highest in *S. worthingtonii*. It was least in the valley and ridge soils in *S. gardneri* and in the midslope soil in *S. megistophylla, S. disticha, S. affinis* and *S trapezifolia* . Unlike all others, *S. gardneri* increased its allocation to above ground dry mass in the midslope soil. These differences reflect different trade offs in dry mass allocation among species, apparently in response to change in soil fertility.

Leaf attributes

The opposite trends observed in mean leaf numbers and unit leaf mass among the *Shorea* species suggest that different species may exhibit different morphological as well as architectural adaptations and strategies for maximizing photosynthetic area under different environmental conditions which may result in differences between species in survivorship and performance in different ecological niches.

Four of the species, *S. megistophylla, S. cordifolia, S. disticha* and *S. worthingtonii*, locally known as *beraliyas*, have larger leaves, and range along the catena with the largest-leaved, firstmost species mainly in the valleys to the smallest-leaved lastmost on the ridges. The remaining species are known as *thiniyas*. However, each of these groups (*beraliyas* and *thiniyas*) as a whole, do not have characteristic responses to nutrients.

Soil nutrients are just one set of environmental factors among many that may influence species distribution along a topographic gradient in Sinharaja forest. Trends in distribution exhibited by our clade of closely related endemic dipterocarp species in soils from different topographic sites do suggest that their differential performance is at least partly governed by differences in soil nutrients existing in the catena. Consistently good growth performance of all species in *Pinus* soil suggests that, given possible differences between the general environment and those pertaining in the experimental shelters, nutrient status in *Pinus* soil is not a limiting factor for the establishment of these *Shorea* species.

Differences among species

The rank order of height growth and number of leaves in particular, among the species remained remarkably consistent in the different soils, but absolute differences were much greater on the higher nutrient valley and *Pinus* soils than in the other two. Nutrients in the range occurring in our forest apparently lead to an increase in the differences between species in the above ground attributes which would be expected to determine their competitiveness and in particular, between the three fastest growing species and the rest.

Different species with their characteristic physiological and morphological traits are known to exhibit different trade-offs between competitive ability on one hand and tolerance of low resources on the other (Grace, 1990; Latham, 1992). Species that can thrive better under limiting conditions such as in shadier, drier and infertile soils show slower growth rates even under conditions where such factors are less than limiting (Grime, 1977, 1979; Chapin, 1980). Inherently slower growth rate is a consequence of the adaptations exhibited by some species to grow in unfavourable environments. Species whose seedlings out-compete the others under conditions of resource abundance may get displaced when resources are limiting. Such trade-offs among species are considered to be necessary for the maintenance of floristic richness (Latham, 1992).

The results presented here indicate certain patterns that support such a trade-off explanation. There is a significant variation in competitive hierarchies among closely related, congeneric and partially sympatric *Shorea* species. Within this clade, *S. trapezifolia* can be regarded as the most nutrient demanding with greatest competitive ability in nutrient-richer valley soils as judged from its total and component dry mass increases over the two-year study period. It is, on the other hand, one of the least tolerant of nutrient scarcity. At the other extreme is *S. worthingtonii* which is one of the most drought and shade tolerant within the clade (Ashton, P.M.S., 1990; Ashton, P.M.S. and Berlyn, 1992, unpublished data). Consistent with the trade off model, it accrued dry mass more slowly than *S. trapezifolia* in the nutrient-rich valley soils. A strategy to accrue dry mass in relatively nutrient-poor and drought-prone environments such as those in ridge tops and midslopes (Ashton, P.M.S., 1990) has traded off a mechanism of tolerance for poor nutrient levels in *S. worthingtonii* that would increase survival under occasional severe drought conditions that the forest experiences for one that would exhibit a short-term faster growth rate at low nutrient levels. Other species of the clade show a gradient between these two extremes with variable levels of resource allocation to different components along the soil nutrient gradient.

We conclude therefore that, whereas the species are each niche-specific in relation to the combined and various influences of soil, water and light, nutrients appear to influence the degree to which the most competitive species (albeit tested in our experiments in only one light and water regime) can gain dominance. This conclusion is consistent with Tilman's (1982) prediction that species diversity will decline where resources are least limited, because those species most able to avail of them will gain dominance. It also helps explain P.S. Ashton's (1992a,b) observations that tree species richness and dominance

262

of the most abundant species are negatively correlated on the higher nutrient soils in mixed dipterocarp forests in Borneo; and why this correlation does not occur in the forests on the low nutrient soils examined by him.

Whether or not future research demonstrates that our interpretation of the correlations observed are correct, they manifest the existence of consistent interspecific differences in performance among the species and on different soils. This is consistent with the equilibrium hypothesis for the maintenance of mixed species stands in tropical forests. Currently, field transplant and competition experiments are under way which will enable the patterns in the pot experiments described here to be evaluated in relation to patterns in the field.

ACKNOWLEDGEMENTS

This investigation was supported by a grant from USAID to Prof. P.S. Ashton at Harvard University (DPE-5,542-G-SS-8,023–00), subcontracted to the University of Peradeniya, Sri Lanka and was locally administered by the Natural Resources Energy and Science Authority under grant RG/AID/12. The field facilities and permission to work in Sinharaja were given by the Forest Department, Sri Lanka and the soil analyses were carried out in the Institut für Waldokologie, Universität für Bodenkulter, Vienna, Austria and the Institute of Fundamental Studies, Sri Lanka. This manuscript was prepared during the tenure of an associateship of the Arnold Arboretum of Harvard University to CVSG and IAUNG. Many friends and two anonymous reviewers gave much of their time to read and comment on the manuscript of this paper. The authors extend their sincere thanks to all of them.

REFERENCES

Ashton, P.M.S. (1990). *Seedling response of Shorea species across moisture and light regimes in a Sri Lankan rain forest.* Ph.D. Thesis, Yale University, USA.

Ashton, P.M.S. (1992). Establishment and early growth of advance regeneration of canopy trees in moist mixed-species forests. In Kelty, M.J., Larson, B.C. and Oliver, C.D. *The Ecology and Silviculture of Mixed-species Forests*, pp. 101–22. Kluwer Academic Publishers, Dordrecht.

Ashton, P.M.S. and Berlyn, G.P. (1992). Leaf adaptations of some *Shorea* species to sun and shade. *New Phytologist*, **121**, 587–96.

Ashton, P.S. (1964). Ecological studies in the mixed Dipterocarp forests of Brunei state. *Oxford Forestry Memoirs*, **25**.

Ashton, P.S. (1969). Speciation among tropical forest trees: some deductions in the light of recent evidence. *Biological Journal of the Linnean Society*, **1**, 155–96.

Ashton, P.S. (1976). An approach to the study of breeding systems, population structure and taxonomy of tropical trees. In Burley, J. and Styles, B.T. (eds.), *Tropical*

Trees: Variation, Breeding and Conservation, pp. 35–42. Linnean Society Symposium Series No.2. Academic Press, London.

Ashton, P.S. (1988). Dipterocarp biology as a window to the understanding of tropical forest structure. *Annual Review of Ecology and Systematics*, **19**, 347–70.

Ashton, P.S. (1989). Dipterocarp reproductive biology. In Lieth, H. and Werger, M.J.A. (eds.), *Ecosystems of the World*, 14B, *Tropical Rain Forest Ecosystems*, pp. 219–40. Elsevier, Amsterdam.

Ashton, P.S. (1992a). The structure and dynamics of tropical rain forest in relation to tree species richness. In Kelty, M.J., Larson B.C. and Oliver G.C.D. (eds.), *The Ecology and Silviculture of Mixed Species Forests*, pp. 53–64. Kluwer Academic Publishers, Boston.

Ashton, P.S. (1992b). Species richness in plant communities. In Fiedler, P.H. and Jain, S.K. (eds.), *Conservation Biology: The Theory and Practice of Nature Conservation Preservation and Management*, pp. 3–22. Chapman and Hall, New York.

Austin, M.P., Greig-Smith, P. and Ashton, P.S. (1972). The application of quantitative methods to vegetation survey III. A re-examination of rain forest data from Brunei. *Journal of Ecology*, **60**, 305–34.

Baillie, I.C. and Ashton, P.S. (1983). Some soil aspect of the nutrient cycle in Mixed Dipterocarp Forests in Sarawak. In Sutton, S.L. Whitmore, T.C. and Chadwick, A.C. (eds.), *Tropical Rain Forest: Ecology and Management*, pp. 347–56. Blackwell, Oxford.

Baillie, I.C., Ashton, P.S., Court, N.M., Anderson, J.A.R., Fitzpatrick, E.A. and Tinsley, J. (1987). Site characteristics and the distribution of tree species in mixed dipterocarp forests on tertiary sediments in Central Sarawak, Malaysia. *Journal of Tropical Ecology*, **3**, 201–19.

Basnet, K. (1992). Effect of topography on the pattern of trees in Tabanvo (*Dacryoides excelsa*) dominated rain forests in Puerto Rico. *Biotropica*, **24**, 31–42.

Chapin, F.S. (1980). The mineral nutrition of wild plants. *Annual Review of Ecology and Systematics*, **11**, 233–60.

Connell, J.H. (1971). On the role of natural enemies in preventing competitive exclusion in some marine animals and in rain forest trees. In den Boer, P.J. and Gradwell, G.R. (eds.), *Dynamics of Populations*, pp. 298–312. PUDOC, Wageningen.

Darwin, C. (1859). *The Origin of Species* (reprinted in 1958). New American Library of World Literature, New York.

Gause, G.F. (1934). *The Struggle for Existence*. Waverley Press, Baltimore.

Grace, J.B. (1990). On the relationship between plant traits and competitive ability. In Grace, J.B and Tilman, D. (eds.), *Perspectives on Plant Competition*, pp. 51–65. New York, Academic Press.

Grime, J.P. (1977). Evidence for the existence of three primary strategies in plants and its relevance to ecological and evolutionary theory. *American Naturalist*, **111**, 1169–94.

Grime, J.P. (1979). *Plant Strategies and Vegetation Process*. Wiley, London.

Grubb, P.J. (1977). The maintenance of species richness in plant communities: the importance of the regeneration niche. *Biological Reviews*, **52**, 107–45.

Gunatilleke, C.V.S. and Ashton, P.S. (1987). New light on the plant geography of Ceylon II. The ecological biogeography of the lowland endemic tree flora. *Journal of Biogeography*, **14**, 295–327.

Gunatilleke, C.V.S. and Gunatilleke, I.A.U.N. (1983). A forestry case study of the Sinharaja rain forest. In Hamilton, L. (ed.), *Forest and Watershed Development and Conservation in Asia and the Pacific*, pp. 289–358. Westview Press, Colorado.

Gunatilleke, C.V.S. and Gunatilleke, I.A.U.N. (1985). Phytosociology of Sinharaja - a contribution to rain forest conservation in Sri Lanka. *Biological Conservation*, **31**, 21–40.

Hubbell, S.P. (1979). The dispersion, abundance and diversity in a tropical dry forest. *Science*, **213**, 1299–1309.

Hubbell, S.P. and Foster, R.B. (1983). Diversity of canopy trees in a neotropical rain forest and implications for conservation. In Sutton, S.L., Whitmore, T.C. and Chadwick, A.C. (eds.), *Tropical Rain Forest: Ecology and Management*, pp. 25–42. Blackwell, Oxford.

Janzen, D.H. (1970). Herbivores and the number of tree species in tropical forests. *American Naturalist*, **104**, 501–28.

Latham, R.E. (1992). Co-occurring tree species change rank in seedling performance with resources varied experimentally. *Ecology*, **73**, 2129–44.

Littell, R.C., Freund, R.J. and Spector, P.C. (1991). *SAS System for Linear Models*, Third Edition. SAS Institute, Cary.

Lugo, A.E. (1988). Diversity of tropical species. *Biology International* Special Issue, **19**. IUBS, Paris.

Pemadasa, M.A. and Gunatilleke, C.V.S. (1981). Pattern in a rain forest in Sri Lanka. *Journal of Ecology*, **69**, 117–24.

Poore, M.E.D. (1968). Studies in the Malaysian Rain Forest I. The forest on Triassic sediments in the Jengka Forest Reserve. *Journal of Ecology*, **56**, 143–96.

Snow, D.W. (1966). A possible selective factor in the evolution of fruiting seasons in a tropical forest. *Oikos*, **15**, 274–81.

Tilman, D. (1982). Resource competition and community structure. *Monographs in Population Biology*, **17**. Princeton University Press, Princeton.

Tracey, J.G. (1969). Edaphic differentiation of some forest types in eastern Australia I. Soil physical factors. *Journal of Ecology*, **57**, 805–16.

Whitmore, T.C. (1978). Gaps in forest canopy. In Tomlinson, P.B. and Zimmerman, M.H. (eds.), *Tropical Trees as Living Systems*, pp. 639–55. Cambridge University Press, Cambridge.

Whitmore, T.C. (1984). *Tropical Rain Forests of the Far East*, 2nd edn. Oxford University Press, Oxford.

Williams, W.T.G., Lance, G.N., Webb, L.J., Tracey, J.G. and Connell, J.H. (1969). Studies in the numerical analysis of complex rain forest communities IV. A method for elucidation of small-scale forest pattern. *Journal of Ecology*, **57**, 635–54.

Revised manuscript received August 1994

CHAPTER 11

THE SIGNIFICANCE OF SEEDLING SIZE AND GROWTH RATE OF TROPICAL RAIN FOREST TREE SEEDLINGS FOR REGENERATION IN CANOPY OPENINGS

René G.A. Boot

INTRODUCTION

In tropical rain forests, canopy openings created by treefall gaps are important sites for the establishment and growth of trees (Denslow, 1980; Hartshorn, 1980; Brokaw, 1985; Whitmore, 1989). Within gaps new trees grow up, and a mature canopy is eventually attained. Therefore, gaps are a critical phase in the forest cycle because what grows up determines the floristic composition of the future stand. The species most likely to occupy the space in the canopy is still open to question. Some authors hypothesized that the probability of a particular tree species replacing a fallen tree in the canopy is mainly determined by competition for resources among established seedlings and saplings and recently germinated seedlings (Denslow, 1980; Hartshorn, 1980). An alternative hypothesis emphasizes the relative abundance, distribution and size of seedlings and saplings already present in the understorey at the time of gap formation as the key factors determining the species most likely to attain canopy stature in gaps (Hubbell and Foster, 1986; Denslow, 1987 and references therein).

These two pathways of tree replacement after canopy disturbance are reflected in the two main regeneration strategies often distinguished among rain forest trees: the pioneer and climax strategies. Swaine and Whitmore (1988) defined pioneers as those whose seeds and seedlings germinate and survive only in high light environments. In contrast, non-pioneer or climax species are species whose seeds are able to germinate in shade and whose seedlings can survive prolonged periods of shade in the forest understorey. Their growth and survival, however, is greater in canopy openings than in understorey. In large gaps, the light-demanding pioneer species are the first to monopolize resources and space. Small canopy openings, in contrast, seem to favour shade-tolerant climax species, species which are already present in the understorey as seedlings and saplings prior to gap creation.

Natural and logged-over forests differ in the rate and size of gap creation. Gaps in exploited forests are often larger and may appear more frequently than those created under natural conditions (D. Hammond, unpublished results). Therefore, knowledge of the patterns and processes with which species regenerate in small and large gaps can be seen as a prerequisite for the design of forest management systems based on the natural dynamics of tropical rain forests.

In this chapter I investigated inherent differences in survival and seedling size of tree species in deep shade, as related to seed size. Secondly, I studied the growth response of pioneer and climax tree seedlings to different natural light climates associated with the understorey-gap habitat. Thereafter, the results are used in a simple model which aims to evaluate the relative importance of growth in different light climates and differences in seedling size for growth and establishment of tree species in small and large gaps.

The work reported here was carried out as part of the Tropenbos Programme in Guyana at their research site in the Mabura Hill region located in north central Guyana, 235 km south of Georgetown between 5° 16' and 5° 19' North and 58° 40' and 58° 48' West.

SURVIVAL AND GROWTH IN SHADE IN RELATION TO SEED SIZE

Survival in the shaded understorey of a closed canopy forest is an important factor determining the abundance and distribution of tree species in understorey prior to gap creation and thus partly determines the probability that a particular species replaces a fallen tree in the canopy.

Salisbury (1942, 1974) was the first to demonstrate that in moist environments species that become established in closed, shaded habitats tend to have larger seeds than those that typically become established in sunlit, early successional habitats. In an analysis of the Californian flora involving nearly 2,500 taxa, Baker (1972) found a similar relationship for trees, but not for herbs and grasses. However, he attributed the latter result in part to the confounding effects of drought, noting that desiccation stress showed a strong positive correlation with seed size and a negative correlation with the degree of shading. In the lowland tropical forests of the Manu National Park of Peru, Foster and Janson (1985) found that tree species requiring large gaps for seedling establishment tended to have smaller seeds than those that establish beneath closed forest canopies. This difference remained significant even when the species were classified by dispersal syndromes, growth form and plant height.

If we assume that low light intensity is a key factor determining seedling mortality in the shaded understorey, then survival of seedlings in shade is dependent on: first, the total amount of stored reserves in the seed; second, the rate with which these reserves are reallocated to leaves, stems and roots; and third, the rate of carbon fixation and respiration of the seedling under the prevailing light conditions. From this it follows that seedling survival is

Table 11.1 List of rain forest species, their seed mass and seed reserve mass (± SD)

Species	Seed mass (g)	Reserve mass (g)
Chamaecrista adiantifolia (Benth.) Irwin & Barneby var. *pteridophylla* (Sandw.) Irwin & Barneby	0.112 (0.016)	0.102 (0.015)
Peltogyne venosa (Vahl) Benth.	0.305 (0.030)	0.237 (0.024)
Diospyros ierensis Britt.	1.01 (0.05)	0.98 (0.05)
Dicymbe altsonii Sandw.	8.45 (1.54)	8.02 (1.48)
Chlorocardium rodiei (Schomb.) Rohwer, Richter & v.d. Werff	41.6 (6.5)	32.2 (5.7)
Mora excelsa Benth.	53.4 (14.0)	52.5 (13.8)

positively related to seed size only when plants grow at light intensities below their whole-plant light compensation point. If they grow at higher light levels the amount of stored reserves and the rate of reallocation of these reserves will be less important for survival, but of course will still affect growth. In other words, a strong positive relationship between survival and the amount of stored seed reserves among plant species is likely to arise only when plants differing in seed size grow at very low light intensities; the correlation between survival and seed size will become weaker with increasing light intensity. Based on this hypothesis the relationship between survival in deep shade and seed size was investigated.

Methods

For this study, six tree species, differing in seed mass, were selected (Table 11.1). Seeds of these species were placed in trays filled with sand and watered daily. Upon germination 100 seeds (twenty-five per treatment) were randomly assigned to one of the following shade treatments (mean percentages of full sunlight ±SE in shade treatments are presented in brackets): 0 per cent FS (0 per cent full sunlight), 1 per cent FS (0.9±0.1 per cent full sunlight), 2 per cent FS (1.8±0.1 per cent full sunlight) and 4 per cent FS (4.3±0.1 per cent full sunlight). To reduce the amount of solar radiation in the three shade treatments we used layers of black (neutral) shade cloth. For the 0 per cent FS treatment black plastic sheeting, covered with a layer of white plastic to reflect sunlight, was used. Within and between-treatment variation in total daily photon flux density (PPFD) was measured simultaneously and continuously, with four radiation sensors (Li-190SA) and two Li-1,000 DataLoggers (Li-Cor Inc., Lincoln, Nebraska, USA) on thirty-six sunny days (total daily PPFD $>30\,mol\,m^{-2}\,day^{-1}$) in twelve different locations, at two heights, within each shade box. Three sensors were placed in the various shade boxes, except for the 0 per cent FS treatment, and one radiation sensor was mounted on top of the nursery, located in a large clearing, to measure total daily PPFD. The 0 per cent FS treatment was measured independently on other days during the experiment.

Seedling mortality of all species in the various shade treatments was monitored for one year and scored weekly. At the same time the height, the number of leaves and leaflets and the basal stem diameter of all seedlings was measured to assess the relationship between seed size and seedling size of tree species growing in deep shade.

Results

Survival and seed size

Species differed in their ability to survive in shade (Figure 11.1). All species survived in 4 per cent FS, but only one species, *Chlorocardium rodiei*, survived in 0 per cent FS in the first year after germination. Results further showed that *Diospyros, Mora* and *Dicymbe* exhibited an increase in mortality with decreasing light availability (Figure 11.1). Survival in shade and dry seed reserve mass were positively correlated in 0 per cent FS only (Figure 11.2). In this comparison the slope of the linear regression equation of the number of surviving seedling versus time was used as an index of shade tolerance (STI). Note that in addition to the six species presented in Figure 11.1, two more species, *Eperua falcata and Dimorphandra conjugata*, are included in Figure 11.2. Their survival was monitored in 0 per cent FS only, due to space limitations in the other shade boxes. In 1, 2 and 4 per cent FS no such positive relationship between seed mass and survival was found.

The findings for the 1, 2 and 4 per cent FS treatments agree with Augspurger (1984) who found that survival was not related to initial seed reserves of eighteen wind-dispersed tree species studied. Seed masses of species tested in the latter study were very much smaller than the ones used here, and the range in seed size in both studies is small, relative to the full range in seed size often present in tropical moist forest trees. The present results, however, contrast with earlier findings of tree species in which seed mass was positively correlated with the ability to survive in shade (Grime and Jeffrey, 1965; Rabinowitz, 1978). Grime and Jeffrey (1965), however, studied seedling survival in a vertical gradient of sunlight (simulating a low vegetation in which small differences in height are associated with larger changes in light intensity), and thus the light environment of an individual seedling was related to its size. Furthermore, we excluded herbivores and fungi from the experiment and watered the plants weekly, which might have affected the results. Ng (1978), for example, found in his studies on Malaysian seedlings, that

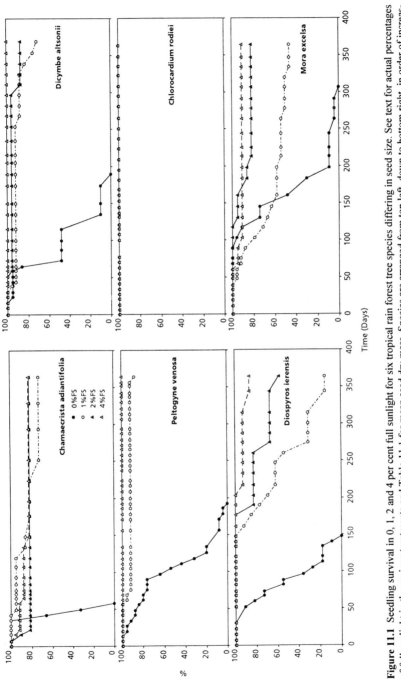

Figure 11.1 Seedling survival in 0, 1, 2 and 4 per cent full sunlight for six tropical rain forest tree species differing in seed size. See text for actual percentages of full sunlight in the various treatments and Table 11.1 for mean seed dry mass. Species are arranged from top left, down to bottom right, in order of increasing seed reserve mass

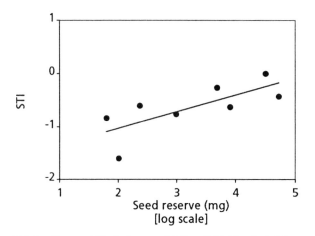

Figure 11.2 Seedling mortality in 0 per cent full sunlight. The shade tolerance index (STI, see text for definition) plotted against the seed reserve mass of eight tropical rain forest tree species. The following species are presented from left to right: *Dimorphandra conjugata, Chamaecrista adiantifolia, Peltogyne venosa, Diospyros ierensis, Eperua falcata, Dicymbe altsonii, Chlorocardium rodiei* and *Mora excelsa*. Regression equation: $y = 0.31x - 1.66$, where x = seed reserve mass ($\log_{10}$ mg), and y = STI (shade tolerance index)); $R = 0.55$, $F = 7.432$, $p < 0.05$

seedlings from small-seeded species were more susceptible to drought and fungal pathogens than those from large-seeded species.

Seedling size and seed size

What other advantages do large seeds confer upon a seedling? Foster (1986) listed a number of possible advantages of large seeds. For example, it might enhance the ability of seeds to persist in reduced light intensities until suitable light or moisture conditions arise by providing for metabolic requirements during quiescent periods. Second, large seeds might provide secondary compounds for defence of persistent seedlings against pathogens and predators during periods of low energy availability. Third, the ability to replace lost or damaged tissue in persistent seedlings may be higher in large-seeded species than in small-seeded species. And finally, large seeds may provide energy for construction of large amounts of photosynthetic tissue needed to maintain a positive carbon balance or enable the plants to grow into higher irradiance strata. An evaluation of the first three mechanisms that might have led to larger seed sizes is discussed in Foster (1986), and will not be dealt with here. The possibility that large seeds provide energy for construction of large amounts of photosynthetic tissue needed to maintain a positive carbon balance is not supported by the present study. Large-seeded species constructed more leaf area after one year in shade than small-seeded species, but leaf area expressed per unit of plant mass (LAR, leaf area ratio, $m^2 kg^{-1}$) demonstrated a reverse relationship with seed reserve mass. For example, *Chlorocardium* and *Mora* had leaf area ratios (mass of seed reserves excluded) of 5.5 and $5.1 \, m^2 \, kg^{-1}$, respectively, after growing for one year in 1 per cent FS, whereas *Chamaecrista* and *Peltogyne* had LAR of 22.9 and $9.9 \, m^2 \, kg^{-1}$, respectively.

Another advantage of large seed reserves might be the greater initial size of seedlings from large-seeded species in comparison with seedlings from small-seeded species. For example, if we compare the development of a *Chlorocardium rodiei* seedling, a large-seeded species, with that of *Peltogyne venosa*, a small-seeded species, *Chlorocardium* reached a greater height and produced more leaves and a thicker stem diameter than *Peltogyne* when grown in 1 per cent FS (Figure 11.3). *Chlorocardium and Peltogyne* first increased rapidly in height to approximately 30 and 9 cm, respectively, thereafter height growth ceased. Furthermore, *Chlorocardium* reached its final seedling height well before it produced its maximum number of leaves. *Peltogyne* demonstrated the same response, but less prominently. Third, the height of both species was similar for all shade treatments, except for the 0 per cent FS. Seedlings in 0 per cent FS grew more slowly and they were higher after 250 days than those growing at higher light intensities (1, 2 and 4 percent FS). Results further revealed that *Chlorocardium* in 0 per cent FS was still increasing in height after 250 days, whilst *Peltogyne* stopped after approximately twenty days.

The number of leaves increased with increasing solar radiation in both species (Figure 11.3). However, *Chlorocardium* produced more leaves than *Peltogyne*. In 0 per cent FS *Chlorocardium* did not produce a single leaf for a very long time, whereas the production of first leaves of *Peltogyne* was not affected by the various shade treatments. *Peltogyne* seedlings produced their first two leaves (four leaflets) in all treatments after the same number of days.

The stem diameter of *Chlorocardium* increased with time in all treatments (Figure 11.3). Seedlings growing at higher light intensities developed a thicker stem than seedlings growing at very low light levels (0 and 1 per cent FS). Results for *Peltogyne* were more difficult to interpret. Seedlings in 0 per cent FS demonstrated a reduction in stem diameter with time, due to lignification of the stem. Lignification in other treatments was compensated for by diameter growth.

Inherent differences in height and stem diameter of fourteen species, including those presented in Figure 11.1, revealed a similar relationship between seed size and seedling size, expressed in height and stem diameter (Figure 11.4). Large-seeded species produced larger seedlings than small-seeded species. This is consistent with the results of Howe and Richter (1982), Howe et al. (1985) and Grime and Jeffrey (1965). For example, Grime and Jeffrey (1965) found a strong positive correlation between log mean weight of seed reserve and log maximum height attained in vertical gradients of sunlight among nine herbaceous and woody species from grasslands and forests. This

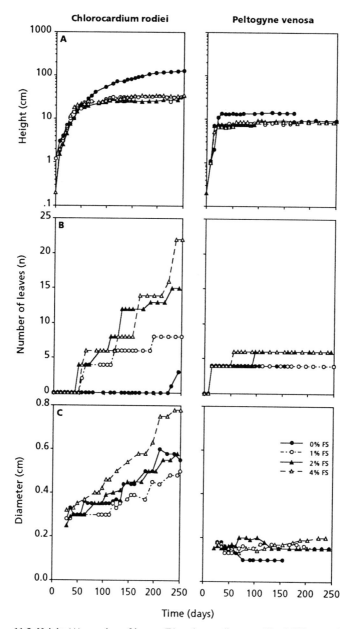

Figure 11.3 Height (A), number of leaves (B) and stem diameter (C) of *Chlorocardium rodiei*, (mean seed reserve dry mass: 32.0 g), and *Peltogyne venosa*, (mean seed reserve dry mass: 0.24 g) versus time in 0, 1, 2 and 4 per cent full sunlight. Of both species the typical development of a seedling is presented

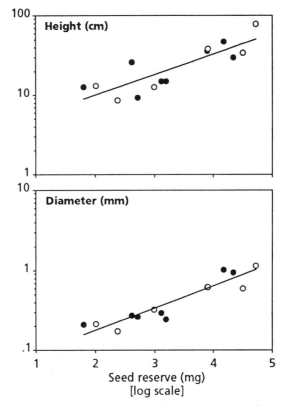

Figure 11.4 Height (cm) and stem diameter (mm) of fourteen tropical rain forest tree species after growing for six months in shade (2 per cent full sunlight, see text for light conditions and actual percentages of sunlight). Open symbols indicate tree species presented in Figure 11.1. Linear regression analysis revealed a significant relationship between these size parameters and seed reserve mass ($p < 0.05$). The following species are presented from left to right: *Dimorphandra conjugata, Chamaecrista adiantifolia, Peltogyne venosa, Parkia nitida, Ormosia coccinea, Diospyros ierensis, Poecilanthe hostmanii, Licania heteromorpha, Ormosia coutinhoi, Dicymbe altsonii, Carapa procera, Catostemma commune, Chlorocardium rodiei* and *Mora excelsa*

result probably explains why these authors found a positive correlation between seed size and survival as reported above. In the vertical sunlight gradients to which the seedlings were exposed, larger individuals experience a higher light environment than the smaller seedlings. A positive correlation between seed size and seedling size was also observed in a comparative study on 200 Malayan forest tree species (Ng, 1978). Howe and Richter (1982) reported on the effects of initial seed mass on seedling characteristics in a Panamanian population of *Virola surinamensis*, a canopy tree in which mean seed mass of different adults ranges from 1.3 to 4.0 g. They found a significant effect of parental source on seedling height, leaf length and dry shoot mass.

SURVIVAL AND GROWTH IN CANOPY OPENINGS

Methods

Growth and survival of seedlings of two pioneer *(Cecropia obtusa* Trécul (Moraceae) and *Goupia glabra* Aublet (Celastraceae)) and four climax tree species (*Chamaecrista apoucouita* (Aublet) Irwin and Barneby (Caesalpinioideae), *Peltogyne venosa* (Vahl) Benth (Caesalpinioideae), *Duguetia neglecta* Sandw. (Annonaceae) and *Oxandra asbeckii* (Pulle) R.E. Fries (Annonaceae) were studied in different natural light climates. Based on height at maturity *Chamaecrista apoucouita* and *Peltogyne venosa* can be classified as canopy trees, and *Duguetia neglecta* and *Oxandra asbeckii* as understorey tree species.

Seedlings of climax species were collected (four leaves and cotyledons still present) in forest understorey and pioneer species (four or five leaves, height less than 3 cm) in medium-sized gaps. Plants were planted in 3-litre plastic bags filled with sand, and watered once a week and supplied with a NPK-fertilizer containing 14 per cent nitrogen, 16 per cent phosphate and 18 per cent potassium and trace elements (DSM Moreels N.V. Ghent Belgium), to ensure non-limiting water and nutrient conditions for all seedlings independent of their size.

After two weeks of acclimation, seedlings were transferred to the understorey of a closed rain forest, and the edge and centre of a multiple-treefall gap. The daily photosynthetic photon flux density (PPFD) on these sites was determined with Li-Cor radiation sensors (Ii-190SA) (Li-Cor Inc., Lincoln, Nebraska, USA) on three sunny days. These values were compared with measurements taken simultaneously in the centre of a large clearing which served as above-canopy readings. The percentage of daily PPFD in understorey, edge and centre were 2.2 per cent (± 2.0 per cent), 9.4 per cent (± 1.3 per cent) and 30.2 per cent (± 0.4), respectively.

Immediately after transferring the seedlings to the various sites, ten randomly selected plants of each species were harvested. Thereafter, six seedlings per species and per treatment were harvested after seven, fifteen and twenty-five weeks, respectively. Harvested plants were separated into leaf blades, leaf petioles, stems and roots. Leaf area was determined with a LI-3100 (Li-Cor Inc., Lincoln, Nebraska, USA). After oven drying at 70°C for 48 h the dry weights of the various plant parts were determined. From these primary data the following parameters were derived: leaf area ratio (LAR, leaf area per unit plant biomass ($m^2 kg^{-1}$)), net assimilation rate (NAR, biomass production per unit leaf area and time ($g m^{-2} day^{-1}$)) and relative growth rate (RGR, biomass production per unit biomass already present per unit of time ($mg g^{-1} day^{-1}$)). For the method of calculating RGR and NAR see Hunt (1982).

Results

Survival and growth in gap and understorey conditions

The climax species survived in the shaded environment of the forest under-storey, whereas the two pioneer species: *Cecropia* and *Goupia*, demonstrated a high mortality under these conditions (Figure 11.5). More than 70 per cent of all *Cecropia* and *Goupia* seedlings died in the understorey during the first fifteen weeks, and none of the *Cecropia* and *Goupia* seedlings survived the full duration of the experiment. Between-treatment differences revealed that the two pioneer species had a lower mortality in the edge and centre of a large gap than in the understorey. Climax species survived equally well in under-storey and gap conditions.

Survival of *Cecropia* and *Goupia* in the edge and centre was less than 100 per cent. This mortality might have been the result of drought, since the initial sizes of *Cecropia* and *Goupia* seedlings, and thus the size of their root sys-tems, were small in comparison with the other species' root systems. They were, therefore, more susceptible to drought at midday, when evapotranspira-tion led to desiccation of the topsoil, despite daily watering.

These results of pioneer and climax species growing in gaps and under-storey conditions are in agreement with earlier findings of Augspurger (1984), Denslow et al. (1990) and Alvarez-Buylla and Martinez-Ramos (1992). For example, in a comparative study on eighteen wind-dispersed tree species Augspurger (1984) found that pioneer species did not survive in shade, even for short periods, and that survival in sunlight was higher than in shade for all study species. This study also revealed a significant positive correlation be-tween survival rates in sun and shade. Augspurger, however, attributed the higher mortality in sun by the light-demanding species to growth-limiting light conditions. Alvarez-Buylla and Martinez-Ramos (1992) found low light conditions to be an important cause of mortality for *Cecropia obtusifolia*, a neotropical pioneer tree. Finally, Denslow et al. (1990) demonstrated in a comparative study on growth responses of three *Miconia* and four *Piper* spp. that mortality of high light adapted *Piper* spp. was significantly higher in un-derstorey environments than in gap centres or gap edges. However, this was not found for *Miconia* species. *M. barbinervis*, a high light species, had low mortality rates in all environments, and mortality rates of *M. gracilis*, a shade-tolerant species, were consistently high across all environments studied.

In the present study climax species showed a positive RGR in shade and a higher RGR in both gap environments (Figure 11.6). The RGR of the two pioneer species was close to zero in shade and their RGR was much higher in the edge and centre of a large gap. High seedling mortality of these species in the understorey resulted in sample sizes too small, and possibly biased to-wards larger individuals, for a reliable calculation of their RGR. They were therefore omitted from Figure 11.6. Results of non-destructive measurements

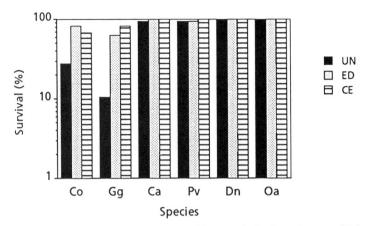

Figure 11.5 Survival (%) of tree seedlings after fifteen weeks in the understorey (UN) of a closed forest and the edge (ED) and centre (CE) of a large gap ($n = 15$ at $t = 0$). See text for details on light climate. Co = *Cecropia obtusa*, Gg = *Goupia glabra*, Ca = *Chamaecrista apoucouita*, Pv = *Peltogyne venosa*, Dn = *Duguetia neglecta* and Oa = *Oxandra asbeckii*

of height, number of leaves and stem diameter, however, showed that the RGR of both species was small and possibly negative (H. Prins and R.G.A. Boot, unpublished data).

Within-species differences in RGR of species growing in the edge and centre of a large gap were rather small. Results further showed that high RGRs do not necessarily coincide with low rates of mortality. For example, *Cecropia* had both a high RGR and a relatively low survival in the centre of a large gap.

The finding that pioneer species increase their RGR to a much greater extent than climax species do with increasing total daily solar radiation, confirmed earlier studies, such as those from Popma and Bongers (1988), Denslow et al. (1990) and King (1991). For example, Denslow et al. (1990) found high-light adapted *Miconia* and *Piper* spp. to have steeper light-response growth curves than low light adapted species of the same two genera.

Growth components

A first step in identifying the morphological and physiological features responsible for inherent and environmentally induced differences in RGR is to factorize the RGR in two components: the net assimilation rate (NAR) and the leaf area ratio (LAR) (Lambers and Poorter, 1992).

Between-species and between-treatment differences in RGR corresponded to differences in NAR (Figure 11.6). The climax species exhibited a positive NAR in shade, and a higher NAR with increasing solar radiation. Secondly, between-site differences in NAR exceeded those in RGR. Results further showed that *Cecropia* had a higher NAR in gap edge and gap centre than

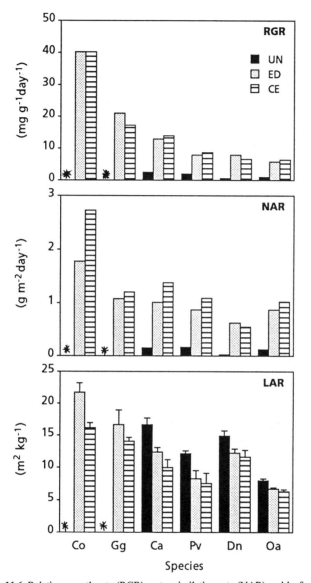

Figure 11.6 Relative growth rate (RGR), net assimilation rate (NAR) and leaf area ratio (LAR) of six rain forest tree species in understorey (UN), gap edge (ED) and gap centre (CE). RGR and NAR are calculated over a period of eight weeks, with dry weight and leaf area data from the second and third destructive harvests. LAR values (mean and standard error) were calculated after fifteen weeks of growth in understorey, gap edge and gap centre. Species are presented from left to right in order of ascending RGR in shade (understorey conditions). Co = *Cecropia obtusa*, Gg = *Goupia glabra*, Ca = *Chamaecrista apoucouita*, Pv = *Peltogyne venosa*, Dn = *Duguetia neglecta* and Oa = *Oxandra asbeckii*. RGR and NAR were not computed for pioneer species (*) for reasons mentioned in the text

those of climax species and all species, except *Duguetia*, had higher NARs in gap centre than in gap edge. Again, the NAR of the two pioneer species in the forest understorey was not computed following arguments stated above.

Cecropia and *Goupia* had a higher LAR in the edge and centre of a mult-iple-treefall gap than the climax species (Figure 11.6) had in the same sites. *Cecropia* and *Goupia* also had a higher LAR in gap edge than in gap centre. The four climax species demonstrated a lower LAR in the centre of a large gap than in the understorey. Thus, the response in LAR of these species was the reverse of the response in NAR. *Chamaecrista apoucouita* responded more strongly to an increase in sunlight than *Oxandra asbeckii*. Furthermore, there were no clear differences in LAR between pioneer and climax species, nor between canopy and understorey trees. Between-treatment differences in RGR were the result of differences in NAR which more than compensated the reverse differences in LAR. Similar findings have been reported by Popma and Bongers (1988), Whitmore and Gong (1983), Okali (1972) and Loach (1970). For example, Popma and Bongers (1988) found in a comparative study of ten tropical tree species from Los Tuxlas, Mexico, that RGR in shade was positively correlated with NAR in shade and a negative relationship was found with LAR in large gaps. Okali (1971) found that fast-growing species (e.g. *Trema, Ochroma, Musanga* and *Ceiba*) had a higher NAR than shade-tolerant ones (*Agathas* spp.) and Loach (1970) found the same for shade-intol-erant temperate forest tree species, but not for shade-tolerant ones.

DISCUSSION

Inherent differences in growth and seedling size: an evaluation of their importance for regeneration

From results reported above it is evident that the absolute difference in RGR between species growing in contrasting light environments increases with in-creasing solar radiation, and thus gap size. For example, the RGR of the study species, which included pioneer and climax species, in the shaded understorey was rather similar. Other authors also found that species-specific differences in RGR when growing in shade or small gaps are rather small. They rarely ex-ceed $10 \, mg \, g^{-1} \, day^{-1}$. In contrast, differences in RGR among species in the high light environment of a large gap are much larger. For example, Ober-bauer and Donnelly (1986) found an absolute difference in RGR between the shade-tolerant *Pentaclethra macroloba* and the pioneer *Ochroma lagopus* of $100 \, mg \, g^{-1} \, day^{-1}$. At the same time, variation in dry weight of seedlings after they have shed their cotyledons or used their food reserves, can vary over sev-eral orders of magnitude, from < 0.001 and $> 10 \, g$ (R.G.A. Boot, unpublished).

To evaluate whether these inherent differences in RGR and seedling size can explain the regeneration success of tree species in small and large gaps I constructed a simple model in which the following assumptions were made:

first, the absolute difference in RGR between pioneer and climax species increases with increasing sunlight; second, pioneer species have a similar or higher RGR than climax species in all light environments; and third, shade-tolerant, large-seeded climax species have larger seedlings than seedlings from small-seeded pioneers. The model now computes the number of days elapsing before the smaller-sized, faster-growing pioneer seedling produces a seedling equal in biomass of that of the larger-sized, slower-growing climax species. For example, if the initial size in dry weight of a climax species is a thousand times that of a pioneer species, and the RGR of the pioneer is $10 \, \text{mg} \, \text{g}^{-1} \, \text{day}^{-1}$ higher than that of the climax species, typical for small gaps, then it will take the pioneer 691 days to produce a seedling equal in size to that of the climax species. However, in large gaps, where the difference in RGR between the fast-growing pioneer and slow-growing climax species is $80 \, \text{mg} \, \text{g}^{-1} \, \text{day}^{-1}$, it will take the pioneer less than three months (eighty-six days) to catch up with the slower-growing, but initially larger, climax species.

From these results, I hypothesize that a high potential RGR is an important feature contributing to the regeneration success in large gaps. In the high light conditions prevailing in these gaps, the high potential RGR of pioneer species is clearly an important attribute enabling the plant to monopolize resources, and successfully fill up the space in the forest canopy. A large seedling size is an important feature increasing the probability of regeneration in small gaps. In these gaps, size differences between the seedlings of climax species already present on the forest floor and newly germinated pioneer species are too large to be compensated for by the marginally increased difference in RGR provoked by the slightly higher light intensities.

However, the model evaluates differences in biomass production per unit biomass and time and seedling mass; it does not take into account the architecture of the seedling or the spatial distribution of its leaves, factors known to be important in competition for light and soil resources between neighbouring plants (Grime, 1979; Caldwell, 1987; Aerts et al., 1991). Consequently, comparing plants on the basis of their biomass production alone, underestimates the potential importance of architectural differences of trees adapted to high or low light environments.

Implications for forest management

These studies further our understanding of which plant features determine the regeneration success of tree species in tropical rain forests in small and large gaps. If we now realize that gaps in logged forests are often larger and created more frequently than those in natural forests (D. Hammond, personal communication), one may expect that the rate of success with which tree species regenerate will differ in natural compared to logged forest. Ultimately, these changes in forest dynamics will affect the future species composition of the forest. This might affect not only species diversity, but also the distribution and abundance of commercial timber trees in production forests, when no silvicultural treatments are applied to avoid these effects. In a logged-over forest we expect faster-growing pioneer species to regenerate more successfully than slower-growing climax species, and their ability to survive or grow in shade and the size of their seeds and seedlings becomes less important under these conditions.

ACKNOWLEDGEMENTS

I wish to thank Herold Prins and Colin Gibson for their contribution to the research discussed in this paper. I am also grateful to Roderick Zagt, Hans Lambers, Marinus Werger, and Wim Dijkman for their comments and helpful suggestions on an earlier draft of this paper. I thank George Walcott for his linguistic advice.

REFERENCES

Aerts, R., Boot, R.G.A. and van der Aart, P.J.M. (1991). The relation between above- and below-ground biomass allocation patterns and competitive ability. *Oecologia*, **87**, 551–9.

Alvarez-Buylla, E.R. and Martinez-Ramos, M. (1992). Demography and allometry of *Cecropia obtusifolia*, a neotropical pioneer tree – evaluation of the climax – pioneer paradigm for tropical rain forests. *Journal of Ecology*, **80**, 275–90.

Augspurger, C.K. (1984). Light requirements of neotropical tree seedlings: a comparative study of growth and survival. *Journal of Ecology*, **72**, 777–95.

Baker, H.G. (1972). Seed weight in relation to environmental conditions in California. *Ecology*, **53**, 997–1010.

Brokaw, N.V.L. (1985). Gap-phase regeneration in a tropical forest. *Ecology*, **66**, 682–7.

Caldwell, M.M. (1987). Plant architecture and resource competition. In Schulze, E.D. and Zwolfer, H. (eds.), *Ecological Studies*, **61**. Springer Verlag, Berlin.

Chazdon, R.L. and Fetcher, N. (1984). Photosynthetic light environment in a lowland tropical rain forest in Costa Rica. *Journal of Ecology*, **72**, 553–64.

Denslow, J.S. (1980). Gap partitioning among tropical rainforest trees. *Biotropica*, **12** (suppl.), 47–55.

Denslow, J.S. (1987). Tropical rainforest gaps and tree species diversity. *Annual Review of Ecology and Systematics*, **18**, 431–51.

Denslow, J.S., Schultz, J.C., Vitousek, P.M. and Strain, B.R. (1990). Growth responses of tropical shrubs to treefall gap environments. *Ecology*, **71**, 165–79.

Foster, S.A. (1986). On the adaptive value of large seeds for tropical moist forest trees: A review and synthesis. *The Botanical Review*, **52**, 260–99.

Foster, S.A. and Janson, C.H. (1985). The relationship between seed size and establishment conditions in tropical woody plants. *Ecology*, **66**, 773–80.

Grime, J.P. (1979). *Plant Strategies and Vegetation Processes*. John Wiley and Sons, Chichester.

Grime, J.P. and Jeffrey, D.W. (1965). Seedling establishment in vertical gradients of sunlight. *Journal of Ecology*, **53**, 621–42.

Hartshorn, G.S. (1980). Neotropical forest dynamics. *Biotropica*, **12** (Suppl.), 23–30.

Howe, H.F. and Richter, W.M. (1982). Effects of seed size on seedling size in *Virola surinamensis*; a within and between tree analysis. *Oecologia*, **53**, 347–51.

Howe, H.F., Schupp, E.W. and Westley, L.C. (1985). Early consequences of seed dispersal for a neotropical tree (*Virola surinamensis*). *Ecology*, **66**, 781–91.

Hubbell, S.P. and Foster, R.B. (1986). Biology, chance, and history and the structure of tropical rain forest tree communities. In Diamond, J. and Case, T.J. (eds.), *Community Ecology*, pp. 314–29. Harper & Row, New York.

Hunt, R. (1982). *Plant Growth Curves. The Functional Approach to Growth Analysis.* Edward Arnold, London.

King, D.A. (1991). Correlations between biomass allocation, relative growth rate and light environment in tropical forest saplings. *Functional Ecology*, **5**, 485–92.

Lambers, H. and Poorter, H. (1992). Inherent variation in growth rate between higher plants: A search for physiological causes and ecological consequences. *Advances in Ecological Research*, **23**, 187–261.

Loach, K. (1970). Shade tolerance in tree seedlings 11. Growth analysis of plants raised under artificial shade. *New Phytologist*, **69**, 273–86.

Ng, F.S.P. (1978). Strategies of establishment in Malayan forest trees. In P.B. Tomlinson and M.H. Zimmerman (eds.), *Tropical Trees as Living Systems*, pp. 129–63. Cambridge University Press, New York.

Oberbauer, S.F. and Donnelly, M.A. (1986). Growth analysis and successional status of Costa Rican rain forest trees. *New Phytologist*, **104**, 517–21.

Okali, D.U.U. (1971). Rates of dry matter production in some tropical forest tree-seedlings. *Annals of Botany*, **35**, 87–97.

Okali, D.U.U. (1972). Growth-rates of some West African forest-tree seedlings in shade. *Annals of Botany*, **36**, 953–9.

Popma, J. and Bongers, F. (1988). The effect of canopy openings on growth and morphology of seedlings of rain forest species. *Oecologia*, **75**, 625–32.

Rabinowitz, D. (1978). Mortality and initial propagule size in mangrove seedlings in Panama. *Journal of Ecology*, **66**, 45–51.

Salisbury, E.J. (1942). *The Reproductive Capacity of Plants.* G. Bell and Sons, London.

Salisbury, E.J. (1974). Seed size and mass in relation to environment. *Proceedings of the Royal Society of London, Biological Sciences*, **186**, 83–8.

Swaine, M.D. and Whitmore, T.C. (1988). On the definition of ecological species groups in tropical rain forests. *Vegetatio*, **75**, 81–6.

Whitmore, T.C. (1989). Canopy gaps and the two major groups of forest trees. *Ecology*, **70**, 536–8.

Whitmore, T.C. and Gong, W.-K. (1983). Growth analysis of the seedlings of Balsa, *Ochroma lagopus. New Phytologist*, **95**, 305–11.

Revised manuscript received November 1993

CHAPTER 12

SEEDLING DEMOGRAPHY IN UNDISTURBED TROPICAL WET FOREST IN COSTA RICA

Mingguang Li, Milton Lieberman and Diana Lieberman

INTRODUCTION

An understanding of the processes that affect regeneration of tropical forest species is of crucial importance to both ecologists and forest managers. As is apparent from the diversity of chapters in this volume, a variety of approaches to the study of tropical seedling ecology has been undertaken and found fruitful. Our approach has been to study the long-term patterns of recruitment, growth and survivorship of tropical seedlings in undisturbed forest.

By including all species, one can assess both community-level and population-level phenomena. For the whole assemblage, one can follow changes in density, recruitment, survivorship, diversity and floristics; for populations, one can evaluate comparative demography, considering differences in distribution, density, recruitment, survivorship and age-class structure among very large numbers of species. By including all species, one is better able to interpret results from individual species. Because the studies have been carried out in permanent forest inventory plots, seedling dynamics can be analysed in the context of the composition and physical structure of the forest stand (Li, 1990). We have followed the fate of tagged seedlings in the study area since June 1983; in this chapter, results are presented for the first six years.

Because seedling stages display very rapid demographic changes, a great deal can be learned over much shorter timespans. Early results of the present study showed certain important differences among seedling groups. It was clear after only two years that seedlings of understorey species germinated abundantly and survived well; subcanopy tree species produced few seedlings, and these had low survivorship; shade-tolerant canopy species had moderate amounts of germination, and the seedlings survived well; and fast-growing, short-lived canopy species had very abundant germination and extremely low survivorship (Lieberman et al., 1990). In the fourth category were included several species considered to be shade-intolerant, such as *Cecropia* spp., which were thought previously to germinate only in light; we found them to germinate under a very wide range of canopy conditions, but most died almost immediately.

Yet certain questions can best be answered with long-term data. How do patterns of recruitment and establishment vary from year to year and from one area to the next? Is there a logarithmic loss of individuals over time? Is early survivorship rate a good indicator of longer-term success of a cohort? How does the survivorship of cohorts vary within and among species? What features of tropical forest species – ecological, morphological or other – are related to patterns of demography and seedling success?

In this chapter we focus on seedling germination and survivorship, considering differences between areas, between dates of germination and between species.

STUDY SITE

The study was carried out at La Selva Biological Station in the Atlantic lowlands of Costa Rica. The station is situated near the confluence of the Rio Puerto Viejo and the Rio Sarapiquí, at the base of the low, steep foothills of Volcán Barva in the Cordillera Central.

Except for abandoned plantations on the alluvial terraces, a small arboretum, and an area of successional strips and young secondary forest along the eastern boundary, the forest in the core area of La Selva has no recent history of human disturbance (Hartshorn, 1978, 1983).

Rainfall during the study period is shown in Figure 12.1. Mean annual rainfall at La Selva (1958–1988) is 3,877 mm (range 2,900–5,600 mm). The two wet seasons (June–August and November–December) produce most of the precipitation, although every month has appreciable rainfall; monthly means range from 148 to 427 mm (Organization for Tropical Studies, unpublished data). Mean annual temperature is 25.4°C (Holdridge et al., 1971).

Residual volcanic soils occur in the southern two-thirds of the reserve; the northern one-third, bordering the Rio Puerto Viejo, bears alluvial deposits (Bourgeois et al., 1972). The soils are deep inceptisols, highly acidic (surface pH in water averages 4.0), fairly rich in organic matter (7 per cent at the surface), but low in cation exchange capacity (less than 4 meq/100 g at the surface), base saturation (25–50 per cent), and exchangeable phosphorus (Parker, 1985). A surface root mat is lacking, but 63 per cent of the total root mass is in the top 20 cm of soil (Raich, 1980). Janos (1975, 1980) has found plants growing at La Selva to be heavily mycorrhizal, and suggests they may be extremely dependent on vesicular–arbuscular mycorrhizae for uptake of phosphorus and other minerals.

La Selva supports tropical wet forest (Holdridge, 1967). Three permanent forest inventory plots totalling 12.4 ha were established in 1969 by the University of Washington College of Forest Resources (Bourgeois et al., 1972). The permanent plots encompass a range of altitudes (32–71 m above sea level), slopes, drainage conditions and soils, but are less than 1.5 km apart.

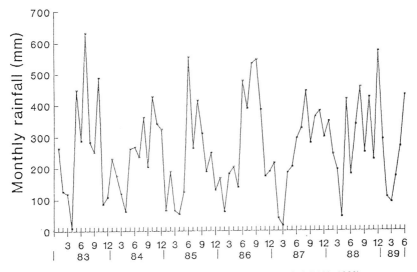

Figure 12.1 Monthly rainfall (mm) at La Selva during the study period (1983–1989)

Previous work in the permanent plots has dealt with population dynamics and regeneration of the dominant canopy tree species *Pentaclethra macroloba* (Hartshorn, 1975); species composition and small-scale floristic variation (Hartshorn, 1983; Lieberman et al., 1985c; Lieberman and Lieberman, 1987; Peralta et al., 1987); tree mortality rates and stand dynamics (Hartshorn, 1978; Lieberman et al., 1985b, 1990; Lieberman and Lieberman, 1987; Peralta et al., 1987); tree growth and longevity (Lieberman et al., 1985a, 1988, 1990; Lieberman and Lieberman, 1987; Peralta et al., 1987); forest canopy structure (Lieberman et al., 1989; Lieberman and Lieberman, 1991); and spatial pattern (Lieberman and Lieberman, 1994). Earlier findings of the seedling studies are reported in Lieberman and Lieberman (1987) and Lieberman et al. (1990).

METHODS

Seedling transects

In June 1983, forty-eight belt transects measuring $10\,m \times 0.5\,m$ were established in the permanent inventory plots (Figure 12.2). Transects were placed at random locations, but were excluded from a buffer zone near the margin of each plot. Plot 1 has fifteen transects; Plot 2 has eighteen transects, with eleven assigned to the swamp and seven to the upland area; and Plot 3 has fifteen transects. For purposes of sampling and analysis, we have treated the swamp and upland portions of Plot 2 separately. Details of forest composition, density and diversity have been evaluated in relation to the mosaic of drainage patterns in this plot by Lieberman et al. (1985c).

287

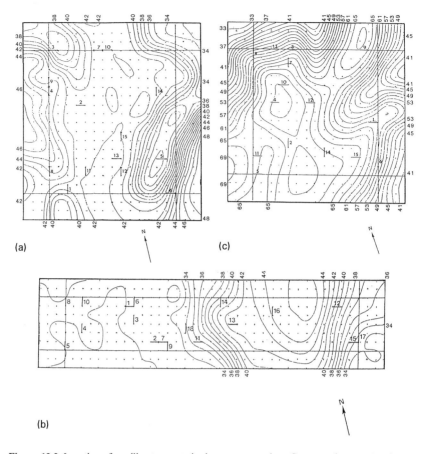

Figure 12.2 Location of seedling transects in the permanent plots. Contours shown at 1 m intervals; grid marks are 10 m apart. (a) Plot 1 (220 × 200 m); buffer zone is 30 m wide. (b) Plot 2 (100 × 400 m); buffer zone is 20 m wide on the north and south margins and 30 m wide on the west and east margins. Transects 1–10 and 18 are in swamp sites. (c) Plot 3 (200 × 200 m); buffer zone is 30 m wide

All seedlings belonging to species capable of reaching 10 cm dbh were included in the study. At the time of the first census, each seedling ≤ 50 cm in height in a transect was tagged, identified, mapped and measured in height from the ground to the highest active meristem. In subsequent censuses, surviving tagged seedlings were remeasured, dead or missing seedlings were recorded, and newly germinated seedlings were tagged, identified, mapped and measured.

Censuses were taken every two months during the first year, and at progressively longer intervals thereafter (Table 12.1). Recruitment, mortality and growth were followed for the first eighteen months (through census 9, December 1984); since that time, mortality and growth have been regularly

288

Table 12.1 Seedling census dates (1983–1989)

Census number	Date	Months since previous census	Total months elapsed	Newly germinated seedlings tagged
1	June 1983	0	0	yes
2	Aug. 1983	2	2	yes
3	Oct. 1983	2	4	yes
4	Dec. 1983	2	6	yes
5	Feb. 1984	2	8	yes
6	Apr. 1984	2	10	yes
7	June 1984	2	12	yes
8	Sep. 1984	3	15	yes
9	Dec. 1984	3	18	yes
10	July 1985	7	25	no
11	Feb. 1986	7	32	no
12	July 1986	5	37	no
13	June 1987	11	48	no
14	June 1988	12	60	no
15	June 1989	12	72	no

recorded but new seedlings have not been tagged. Results are presented here for the first six years of the study, during which time fifteen censuses were carried out.

Seedlings are considered to be members of the cohort in which they were first encountered; thus a cohort includes all seedlings which germinated after the previous census. Seedlings tagged in the first census, however, are of mixed ages, and are not treated as a cohort. Seedlings found dead or missing in censuses 2–15 were considered to have died after the previous census.

Estimation of seedling number between censuses

The number of live seedlings at any census is readily determined; between census dates, however, the number of live seedlings must be estimated. Seedling survivorship curves are close to being log-linear, at least over short periods of time; therefore, we have used log-linear curves as an approximation of the actual cohort survivorship curve between sequential censuses. The change in log-transformed numbers of seedlings is thus linear with respect to time between any two consecutive censuses.

An empirically determined population size for time t between two censuses T_1 and T_2 may be obtained as follows:

$$N_t = \frac{(\log N_{T_2} - \log N_{T_1})(T_1 - t)}{T_2 - T_1} + \log N_{T_2}$$

where $T_1 < t < T_2$, N_{T_1} and N_{T_2} are the population sizes at the census times T_1 and T_2, and N_t is the population size at time t.

The above procedure is applied to each cohort individually.

Estimation of seedling age

The ages of seedlings may be empirically determined for a given number of live seedlings. Again we assume a log-linear survivorship curve between consecutive censuses.

The computation begins at the time of germination, setting the age to $t = 0$, and $t = T_1$. N_{T_1} is the number of germinated seedlings; N_{T_2} is the number of live seedlings at the next census after germination. The time t is then increased in increments of 0.01 months. For every t, the corresponding number of live seedlings, N_t, is assessed. When the calculated value of N_t is equal to, or for the first time less than, the given number of live seedlings, t is the appropriate age.

As long as the given number remains less than the observed number of live seedlings at the census after germination, the computation continues. N_{T_1} and T_1, respectively, now refer to the number of live seedlings and the time at the next census after germination; N_{T_2} and T_2, respectively, refer to the number of live seedlings and the time of the subsequent census. The computation continues until the age is found.

The above procedure is described for one cohort. When several cohorts are to be considered together, the computation is performed for each cohort separately, and continued until the total number of live seedlings is equal to the given number. The calculated age thus reflects the average age for all cohorts involved.

Calculation of cohort half-life

Seedling half-life, the number of months in which 50 per cent of the individuals in a cohort die, can be calculated in two ways. If one assumes that the rate of mortality over time is constant, the number of seedlings decreases logarithmically with time, and the relationship between seedling number and time is as follows:

$$\log N_t = a + bt$$

where $a = \log N_{T_1}$, and $b = \dfrac{\log N_{T_2} - \log N_{T_1}}{t_2 - t_1}$

The half-life may then be computed as:

$$T_{1/2} = -\frac{\log 2}{b}$$

Half-life may also be calculated empirically using the estimated age of a given number of live seedlings. The computation begins at the time of germination, and continues until half the seedlings have died. This approach is more accurate, and may be preferable if data from intermediate censuses are available. The assumption of log-linearity applies between consecutive census dates but not necessarily over the entire period (Figure 12.3).

All half-life values reported here were determined empirically using the latter method.

When seedling mortality is log-linear, one may calculate not only the half-life, but successive half-lives – that is, the time necessary for 3/4, 7/8, 15/16 and 31/32 of the seedlings in a cohort to die. These fractional-lives were calculated empirically as described for half-life (Figure 12.4).

RESULTS

Characteristics of the physical features, forest vegetation, and seedling assemblages in each plot are summarized in Table 12.2.

From June 1983 through December 1984, a total of 6,403 seedlings were tagged in the forty-eight seedling transects. Of these seedlings, 1,581 (27.7 per cent) were present in the transects at the time of the first census and hence are of unknown age. The remaining 4,822 were new recruits recorded in the subsequent eight censuses. During the same eighteen-month period, 4,180 seedlings died, of which 771 were seedlings already present at the first census and 3,409 were recruits of known age. Figure 12.5 shows the standing crop, recruits and deaths in each plot over this period. A total of 1,921 additional seedlings died in the subsequent 4.5 years, leaving 302 seedlings, or 4.7 per cent of the total, alive in June 1989.

Of the 6,403 seedlings tagged, 6,281 were identified as belonging to 194 species. The remaining 140 (2.2 per cent of the total) were not identified; most of these died at very early stages before identification was possible. Trees were the most common life-form, represented by 81 per cent of the seedlings and 160 species. Lianas were next, with 14.5 per cent of the seedlings and twenty-eight species. Palms contributed 4.5 per cent of the seedlings and six species.

Cohort survivorship

Newly germinated seedlings were recorded at eight census dates, producing eight cohorts of known age. The mean half-life of these multi-species cohorts (all plots pooled) was 2.49 months (Table 12.2); the mean one-year survivorship rate of the cohorts was 0.14.

Seedling survivorship varied among plots (Figure 12.6). Cohorts from Plot 2 swamp had the shortest mean half-life, 1.73 months; cohorts from Plot 3 had

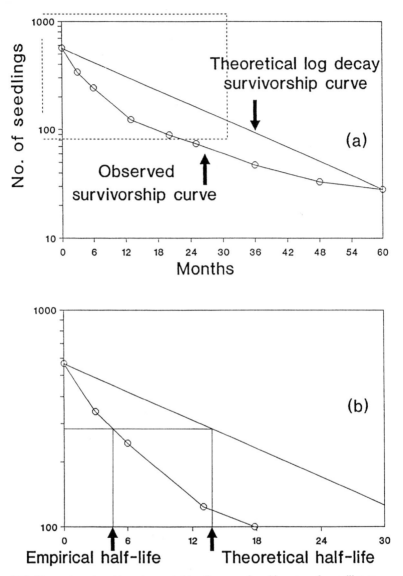

Figure 12.3 Observed survivorship and expected log-linear survivorship curve of a seedling co-hort of the understorey tree *Anaxagorea crassipetala*. (a) Comparison of the curves over a sixty-month period. (b) Detail over the first thirty months showing discrepancy in half-life estimates between empirical approach (log-linear between successive censuses) and theoretical approach (log-linear from first to last census)

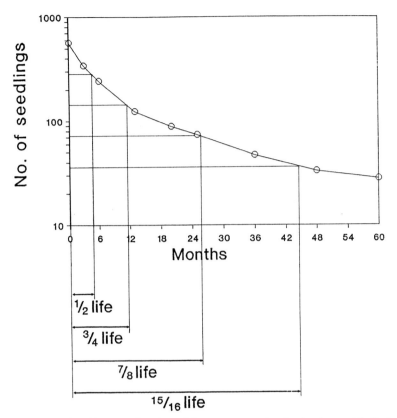

Figure 12.4 Survivorship curve of a cohort of *Anaxagorea crassipetala*, showing empirically determined fractional-life values, from half-life to 15/16-life, over the study period

the longest, 3.14 months. Cohorts from Plot 2 swamp have the poorest one-year survivorship rate (mean 0.07); cohorts from Plot 1, Plot 2 upland, and Plot 3 survived better during their first year with values of 0.18, 0.19, and 0.17 respectively (Table 12.2).

Mortality rates were much lower, and were rather similar among plots, in the uneven-aged, mixed-species seedling assemblage tagged at the time of the first census (Figure 12.7). These seedlings ($n = 1,581$) were of unknown age, and included some proportion of older, established seedlings; all, however, were less than 0.5 m in height when they were tagged. One year after the first census, 60.3 per cent of tagged seedlings in the upland plots (Plot 1, Plot 2 upland, and Plot 3) and 57.2 per cent of those in the Plot 2 swamp remained alive. After two years, the values were 37.9 per cent and 39.0 per cent, respectively. At the end of six years, 13.5 per cent and 11.2 per cent were still alive.

In all plots, survivorship was highest in cohorts germinating during comparatively wet periods, most notably in the wet season of July–August 1983.

Ecology of tropical forest tree seedlings

Table 12.2 Environmental features, forest structure and dynamics, and seedling demography in the La Selva permanent plots. Plot 2 is subdivided into swamp and upland areas for seedling studies. Forest data presented are from the 1982–83 plot inventory; carried out near the time the seedling transects were established

	Plot 1	Plot 2		Plot 3	Total
Environment					
Plot area (ha)	4.4	4.0		4.0	12.4
Parent material	Old alluvium	Old alluvium/colluvium		Basalt	
Topography	Plateau 90% Swamp 10%	Swamp 50% Rolling hills 50%		Steep hills 75% Plateau 25%	
Elevation (m)	34–48	32–45		33–71	
Stand characteristics (stems ≥10 cm dbh)					
Density (stems ha^{-1})	417.7	394.4		528.5	446.0
No. of species (total)	172	171		165	269
Species richness (ha^{-1})	91,92,93,95	79,94,95,100		95,102,103,107	95.5
Basal area (m^2 ha^{-1})	27.71	30.23		25.54	27.82
Annual mortality (1969–85) λ	1.85%	2.10%		2.26%	2.08%
		Plot 2 Swamp	Plot 2 Upland		
Seedlings					
No. of transects	15	11	7	15	48
Transect area (m^2)	75	55	35	75	240
No. of seedlings	1861	1788	1047	1707	6403
Tagged in Census 1	485	187	287	622	1581
Density (no. m^{-2})	6.47	3.40	8.20	8.29	6.59
Tagged in Censuses 2–9	1376	1601	760	1085	4822
Density (no. m^{-2})	18.34	29.11	21.71	14.46	20.09
No. of species (total)	110	87	82	121	194
Unidentified seedlings	48	40	20	32	140
Percentage unidentified	2.6%	2.2%	1.9%	1.9%	2.2%
1-year survivorship, even-aged cohorts, all species (±SE)	0.18±0.093	0.07±0.057	0.19±0.097	0.17±0.041	0.14±0.056
Half-life (months), even-aged cohorts, all species (±SE)	3.16±0.681	1.73±0.432	3.03±0.445	3.14±0.497	2.49±0.489

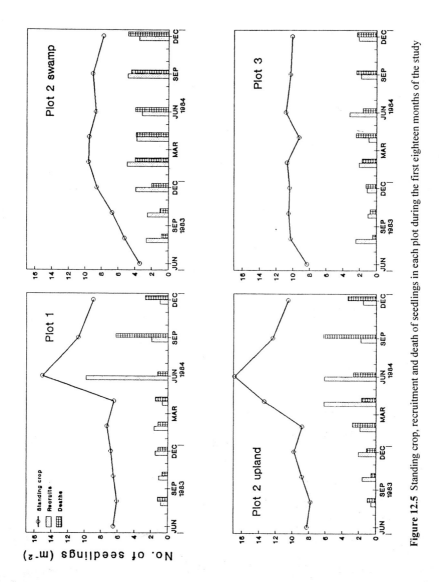

Figure 12.5 Standing crop, recruitment and death of seedlings in each plot during the first eighteen months of the study

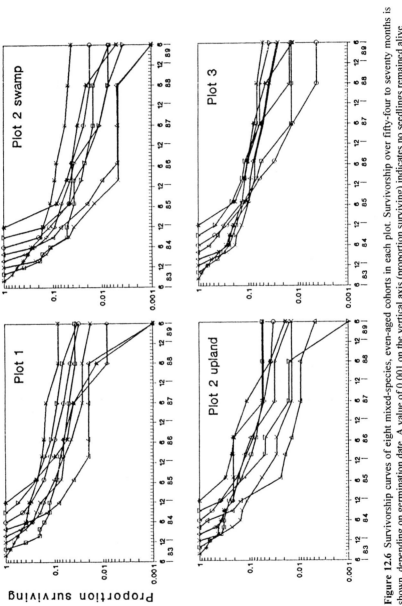

Figure 12.6 Survivorship curves of eight mixed-species, even-aged cohorts in each plot. Survivorship over fifty-four to seventy months is shown, depending on germination date. A value of 0.001 on the vertical axis (proportion surviving) indicates no seedlings remained alive

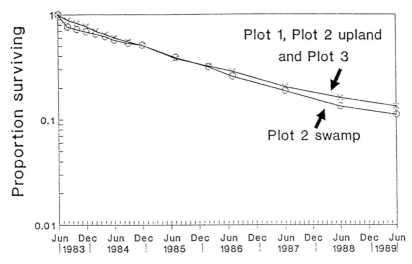

Figure 12.7 Survivorship over six years of seedlings tagged at the time of the first census. Seedlings are of unknown age, and all species are pooled. Upland plots (Plot 1, Plot 2 upland, and Plot 3) are separated from the Plot 2 swamp for analysis. Note much higher survivorship than in younger, even-aged cohorts

Species survivorship

The survivorship of cohorts varied both within and between species. The survivorship curves of the seventy-five most abundant species, presented in order of descending mean half-life, are given in the Appendix at the end of this chapter.

Variation in success of cohorts within species is more pronounced in some species than others. Consistently high survivorship was seen, for example, in cohorts of the palms *Socratea durissima* (thirty-two seedlings germinating in five cohorts) and *Welfia georgii* (sixty-seven in eight cohorts). Moderate survivorship was seen consistently in all cohorts of the palm *Euterpe macrospadix* (fifty-six in six cohorts). Survivorship was consistently very poor in cohorts of the canopy tree *Cespedesia macrophylla* (100 in four cohorts), the liana *Doliocarpus coriacea* (103 in eight cohorts), and the fast-growing, shade-intolerant trees *Cecropia obtusifolia* (954 in eight cohorts) and *C. insignis* (225 in six cohorts). In contrast, survivorship of several species varied widely among cohorts, including the understorey tree *Anaxagorea crassipetala* (681 in seven cohorts) and *Colubrina spinosa* (260 in three cohorts), the liana *Paragonia pyramidata* (219 in five cohorts), and the canopy tree *Pentaclethra macroloba* (198 in seven cohorts).

Table 12.3 lists the number of germinated seedlings of the seventy-five species and their half-life values. Half-life ranged from 40.70 months to 0.37 months, a difference of two orders of magnitude. The mean half-life among the species was 7.42 months.

Table 12.3 List of seventy-five species in which at least five seedlings germinated, in order of descending half-life. Total number of tagged seedlings of known age is shown for each species (all areas pooled)

	Species	Family	Number of seedlings	Half-life (months) (all cohorts included)
1	*Inga sapindoides*	Mimosaceae	5	40.70
2	*Protium pittieri*	Burseraceae	9	39.44
3	*Matayba* sp.	Sapindaceae	8	33.92
4	*Anomospermum* sp. "LS"	Menispermaceae	7	33.38
5	*Hernandia didymanthera*	Hernandiaceae	5	26.57
6	*Paullinia pinnata*	Sapindaceae	8	25.00
7	*Henriettella tuberculosa*	Melastomataceae	5	19.97
8	*Rinorea pubipes*	Violaceae	8	16.33
9	*Liana* sp. "cons."		5	15.91
10	*Casearia corymbosa*	Flacourtiaceae	21	15.32
11	*Socratea durissima*	Palmae	32	14.49
12	*Virola sebifera*	Myristicaceae	17	14.22
13	*Malpighiaceae* sp. "app."	Malpighiaceae	8	14.00
14	*Myrsinaceae* sp. 1	Myrsinaceae	5	13.91
15	*Ocotea leucoxylon*	Lauraceae	6	13.00
16	*Welfia georgii*	Palmae	67	11.98
17	*Paullinia* sp. "h.pel."	Sapindaceae	27	11.79
18	*Unident.* sp. "pel. c.s."		5	10.79
19	*Inga thibaudiana*	Mimosaceae	9	9.77
20	*Parathesis chrysophylla*	Myrsinaceae	14	9.67
21	*Sorocea pubivena*	Moraceae	5	7.92
22	*Cassipourea elliptica*	Rhizophoraceae	13	7.89
23	*Pterocarpus officinalis*	Fabaceae	6	7.78
24	*Protium panamense*	Burseraceae	6	7.52
25	*Pourouma aspera*	Moraceae	44	6.55
26	*Psychotria grandistipula*	Rubiaceae	149	5.42
27	*Neea amplifolia*	Nyctaginaceae	6	5.33
28	*Bignoniaceae* sp. "fr.b."	Bignoniaceae	38	4.98
29	*Brosimum lactescens*	Moraceae	6	4.87
30	*Anaxagorea crassipetala*	Annonaceae	681	4.77
31	*Euterpe macrospadix*	Palmae	56	4.70
32	*Perebea angustifolia*	Moraceae	32	4.54
33	*Rubiaceae* sp. 1	Rubiaceae	10	4.40
34	*Bignoniaceae* sp. 2	Bignoniaceae	18	4.32
35	*Chione costaricensis*	Rubiaceae	23	4.31
36	*Guatteria inuncta*	Annonaceae	29	4.06
37	*Xylosma hemsleyana*	Flacourtiaceae	6	4.01
38	*Hampea appendiculata*	Malvaceae	41	3.46
39	*Pterocarpus hayesii*	Fabaceae	11	3.41
40	*Cordia lasiocalyx*	Boraginaceae	5	3.30
41	*Dendropanax arboreus*	Araliaceae	30	3.27
42	*Neea laetevirens*	Nyctaginaceae	147	3.23
43	*Lauraceae* sp.1	Lauraceae	5	3.20
44	*Liana* sp. "cot.r."		0	3.00

continued

Table 12.3 continued

	Species	Family	Number of seedlings	Half-life (months) (all cohorts included)
45	*Dicranostyles ampla*	Convolvulaceae	32	2.98
46	*Bauhinia* sp. "m. l."	Caesalpiniaceae	19	2.83
47	*Paullinia* sp. "BEH1,0676"	Sapindaceae	6	2.81
48	*Paragonia pyramidata*	Bignoniaceae	219	2.74
49	*Colubrina spinosa*	Rhamnaceae	260	2.73
50	*Simarouba amara*	Simaroubaceae	15	2.73
51	*Pentaclethra macroloba*	Mimosaceae	198	2.59
52	*Casearia arborea*	Flacourtiaceae	39	2.31
53	*Doliocarpus multiflorus*	Dilleniaceae	29	2.17
54	*Warscewiczia coccinea*	Rubiaceae	67	2.08
55	*Vochysia ferruginea*	Vochysiaceae	31	2.08
56	*Veconcibea pleiostemona*	Euphorbiaceae	6	2.02
57	*Miconia multispicata*	Melastomataceae	227	1.75
58	*Machaerium seemanii*	Fabaceae	5	1.51
59	*Castilla elastica*	Moraceae	6	1.45
60	*Cordia bicolor*	Boraginaceae	16	1.35
61	*Vitex cooperi*	Verbenaceae	20	1.31
62	*Davilla* sp.	Dilleniaceae	5	1.25
63	*Laetia procera*	Flacourtiaceae	47	1.17
64	*Arrabidaea chica*	Bignoniaceae	30	1.15
65	*Cespedesia macrophylla*	Ochnaceae	100	1.11
66	*Luehea seemannii*	Tiliaceae	116	1.01
67	*Apeiba membranacea*	Tiliaceae	22	0.96
68	*Malpighiaceae* sp. 2	Malpighiaceae	6	0.93
69	*Terminalia amazonia*	Combretaceae	11	0.90
70	*Doliocarpus coriacea*	Dilleniaceae	103	0.86
71	*Cordia alliodora*	Boraginaceae	12	0.85
72	*Cecropia obtusifolia*	Moraceae	954	0.80
73	*Cecropia insignis*	Moraceae	225	0.64
74	*Goethalsia meiantha*	Tiliaceae	53	0.60
75	Unident. sp. "cot. em."		9	0.37

Does half-life predict future survivorship? To answer this question, we calculated the fractional-life values (3/4-life through 31/32-life) of species. Future survival, evaluated in terms of the time it takes for subsequent fractions of the cohort to die, is clearly related to half-life (Figure 12.8). In all cases, there was a significant correlation ($p < 0.01$) between fractional-life and initial half-life. Thus half-life values can be accepted as a good indicator of longer-term survivorship.

Survivorship changes little within species during the first few years of life, as seen by comparison of the four plots in Figure 12.8. Successive fractional-life periods increase at a generally constant rate in relation to initial half-life.

There is an inverse relationship between seedling half-life and abundance of seedlings that germinated during the eighteen-month period (Figure 12.9).

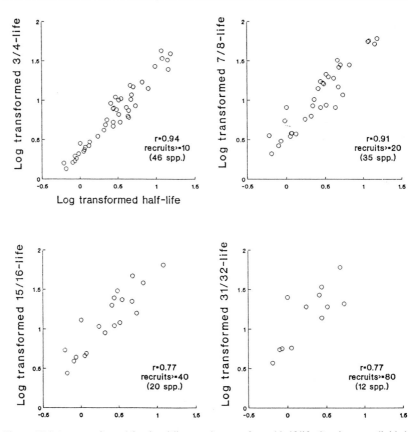

Figure 12.8 Log-transformed fractional-lives vs. log-transformed half-life. Species were divided into four groups based upon the number of recruits; for calculations of higher fractional lives, larger starting samples are required. In all four cases, subsequent fractional-life was significantly correlated ($p < 0.01$) with initial half-life

Species with the highest rates of seedling survivorship characteristically had relatively few recruits; the most abundant seedling species, in turn, had low survivorship. The relationship is rather loose, however; many species showed both low numbers and poor survivorship.

DISCUSSION

Recruitment patterns in swamp sites differed markedly from those in upland sites. The swamp had the lowest density of seedlings at the time of Census 1, with half (or less) the density of the other plots; the poorest half-life and one-year survivorship rate, less than half those of the other plots; and the highest rate of new germination. Regeneration in the swamp is thus characterized by ample germination followed by very heavy early losses.

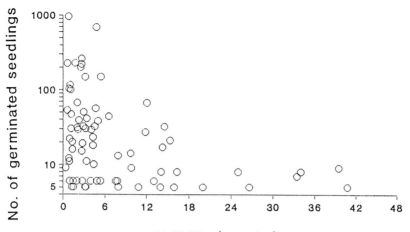

Figure 12.9 Relationship between seedling abundance and survivorship among the seventy-five most abundant species (five or more germinated seedlings). Longer half-lives are associated with lower seedling recruitment over the eighteen-month period

Suitable sites for seedling establishment are fewer in the Plot 2 swamp than elsewhere, due to a mosaic of imperfectly drained soils and areas of periodic inundation. The low density of established seedlings in the swamp mirrors the low density of adult trees in the stand. Diversity and species richness of adults are also markedly lower in the Plot 2 swamp than in upland areas, as a much smaller fraction of the available species pool appears able to tolerate edaphic conditions on the site (Lieberman et al., 1985c).

The foregoing sheds light on the low seedling density and poor rates of establishment in the swamp; why, however, does the swamp show much higher rates of new germination compared with the upland sites? Two possibilities may be considered. First, seed input may be higher in the swamp than elsewhere. This might occur if adult tree density were higher in the swamp (which it is not); if the mature assemblage included a disproportionate number of prolific species (which it does not); or if individual trees growing in the swamp set seed more abundantly than conspecifics growing elsewhere (about which we have no information). Second, alternatively, if seed rain is not higher in the swamp, the comparative abundance of newly-germinated seedlings in the swamp might instead reflect barriers to recruitment elsewhere, in sites which typically support a high standing crop of established seedlings. In the upland sites, competition for space or other limiting resources may reduce the probability that seeds arriving on the site germinate and survive long enough to be encountered and tagged. Detailed analyses of mortality in relation to both microsite features and density of previously tagged seedlings are needed to evaluate the two hypotheses.

The greatest attrition due to unsuitable habitat conditions apparently occurs early in the life of seedlings, as differences between plots in rates of survivorship had become negligible among the older, established seedling assemblage tagged in the first census. Based on their markedly higher survivorship rates, the seedlings tagged in Census 1 are presumed to be older, on average, than the oldest seedlings in our cohorts of known age. Thus, although all seedlings tagged in the first census were 50 cm or less in height, a sizeable proportion of them must have exceeded five or six years of age.

Differences among species in survivorship were tremendous; half-life varied by two orders of magnitude, from around 0.4 to over 40 months. There was a rather loose inverse relationship between recruitment rate and seedling half-life; no species showed both abundant germination and good survivorship. Other traits, such as seed size and size of the newly-germinated seedling, appear to vary with survivorship rate, although this has yet to be tested with large numbers of species. Palms, for example, comprise 25 per cent of adults in the stand (Lieberman et al., 1985c) but only 4.5 per cent of the seedlings, and showed rather high seedling survivorship in relation to their numbers. Palms as a group have large seeds with substantial energy reserves, and produce large, robust seedlings.

The most abundant seedling species, *Cecropia obtusifolia*, represented by 954 seedlings of known age, had exceptionally poor success, with a half-life of only 0.8 months. We wished to consider whether the calculated survivorship value of seedlings overall was unduly affected by this very abundant species. With all species considered, total mortality of tagged seedlings was 95.3 per cent as of June 1989. If *Cecropia obtusifolia* is omitted entirely from the calculation, the overall mortality was 94.5 per cent. Hence the influence of *Cecropia* on the analysis was rather small.

The correlation between half-life of species and their subsequent performance through longer fractional-life periods suggests that it may prove justifiable to apply short-term survivorship data as the basis for longer-term projections of cohort success. This finding should be of particular interest in the area of tropical forest management, where decisions must sometimes be made before long-term data can be accumulated. Implicit in any such projection, of course, is the assumption that conditions on the site remain unchanged.

While some cohort survivorship curves do appear to be log-linear, at least for short periods, others do not; thus we cannot say as a general rule that numbers decline logarithmically with time. As conditions change between seasons and years, mortality rates vary, altering the shape of the curve. Over short periods of time, however, or in the absence of evidence to the contrary, a log-linear model remains the most reasonable choice.

ACKNOWLEDGEMENTS

We thank Rodolfo Peralta and Gary Hartshorn for their collaboration. Seedling censuses were carried out with the assistance of Rodolfo Peralta, Ana Isabela Barquero, Manuel Víquez, Maria de los Angeles Molina and Victor Robles. We are especially grateful to Rodolfo Peralta for seedling identification. Meiqian Du assisted with data entry. Field facilities were provided by the Organization for Tropical Studies. This work was funded by National Science Foundation grants BSR-8117507 and BSR-8,414968, NASA grant NAGW-1033, Sigma Xi, and the UND Graduate School. We thank the Workshop organizers, Malcolm Hadley (UNESCO), M.D. Swaine (Aberdeen), and I. J. Alexander (Aberdeen), for supporting our participation.

REFERENCES

Bourgeois, W.W., Cole, D.W. Reikerk, H. and Gessel, S.P. (1972). Geology and soils of comparative ecosystem study area, Costa Rica. *University of Washington, Tropical Forestry Series Contribution* No. **11**.

Hartshorn, G.S. (1975). A matrix model of tree population dynamics. In Golley, F.B. and Medina, E. (eds.), *Tropical Ecological Systems*, pp. 41–51. Springer-Verlag, New York.

Hartshorn, G.S. (1978). Tree falls and tropical forest dynamics. In Tomlinson, P.B. and Zimmermann, M.H. (eds.), *Tropical Trees as Living Systems*, pp. 617–38. Cambridge University Press, Cambridge.

Hartshorn, G.S. (1983). Plants: introduction. In Janzen, D.H. (ed.), *Costa Rican Natural History*, pp. 118–57. Chicago, University of Chicago Press.

Holdridge, L.R. (1967). *Life Zone Ecology.* (Revised edn). Tropical Science Center, San Jose.

Holdridge, L.R., Grenke, W.C. Hatheway, W.H. Liang, T. and Tosi, J.A., Jr. (eds.) (1971). *Forest Environments in Tropical Life Zones: a Pilot Study*. Pergamon Press, Oxford.

Janos, D.P. (1975). Effects of vesicular–arbuscular mycorrhizae on lowland tropical rainforest trees. In Sanders, F. E. Mosse, B. and Tinker, P.B. (eds.), *Endomycorrhizas*, pp. 437–46. Academic Press, London.

Janos, D.P. (1980). Vesicular–arbuscular mycorrhizae affect tropical rain forest plant growth. *Ecology*, **61**, 151–62.

Li, M. (1990). *The Ecology of Neotropical Forest Tree Seedlings*. Ph.D. dissertation, University of North Dakota, Grand Forks.

Lieberman, D., Hartshorn, G.S. Lieberman, M. and Peralta. R. (1990). Forest dynamics at La Selva Biological Station, 1969–1985. In Gentry A.H. (ed.), *Four Neotropical Forests*, pp. 509–21. Yale University Press, New Haven.

Lieberman, D. and Lieberman, M. (1987). Forest tree growth and dynamics at La Selva, Costa Rica (1969–1982). *Journal of Tropical Ecology*, **3**, 347–58.

Lieberman, D., Lieberman, M. Hartshorn, G. and Peralta, R. (1985a). Growth rates and age-size relationships of tropical wet forest trees in Costa Rica. *Journal of Tropical Ecology*, **1**, 97–109.

Lieberman, D., Lieberman, M. Peralta, R. and Hartshorn, G.S. (1985b). Mortality patterns and stand turnover rates in a wet tropical forest in Costa Rica. *Journal of Ecology*, **73**, 915–24.

Lieberman, M., Lieberman, D. Hartshorn, G.S. and Peralta, R. (1985c). Small-scale altitudinal variation in lowland wet tropical forest vegetation. *Journal of Ecology*, **73**, 505–16.

Lieberman, M. and Lieberman, D. (1991). No matter how you slice it – a reply to Publicover and Vogt. *Ecology*, **72**, 1900–2.

Lieberman, M. and Lieberman, D. (1994). Patterns of density and dispersion of forest trees. In Bawa, K.S., Hartshorn, G.S., Hespenheide, H. and McDade, L. (eds.), *La Selva: Ecology and Natural History of a Neotropical Forest*, pp. 106–19. University of Chicago Press, Chicago.

Lieberman, M., Lieberman, D. and Peralta, R. (1989). Forests are not just Swiss cheese: the canopy stereogeometry of non-gaps in tropical forests. *Ecology*, **70**, 550–2.

Lieberman, M., Lieberman, D. and Vandermeer, J.H. (1988). Age–size relationships and growth behavior of the palm *Welfia georgii*. *Biotropica*, **20**, 270–3.

Parker, G.G. (1985). *Nutrient Loss and Recapture Following Felling of Tropical Hillslope Forests*. Ph.D. dissertation, University of Georgia, Athens.

Peralta, R., Hartshorn, G.S. Lieberman, D. and Lieberman, M. (1987). Reseña de estudios sobre composición florística y dinámica del bosque tropical en La Selva, Costa Rica. *Revista de Biologia Tropical*, **35** (Suppl. 1), 23–39.

Raich, J.W. (1980). *Carbon Budget of a Tropical Soil under Mature Wet Forest and Young Vegetation*. M.S. thesis, University of Florida, Gainesville.

APPENDIX

Survivorship curves of cohorts of seventy-five species, shown in order of descending half-life. Individuals from all plots are pooled. Species names are abbreviated, and the total number of tagged seedlings of known age is given in parentheses (see Table 12.3 for complete species names). Survivorship over fifty-four to seventy months is shown, depending on germination date. A value of 0.1 on the vertical axis signifies that all seedlings have died.

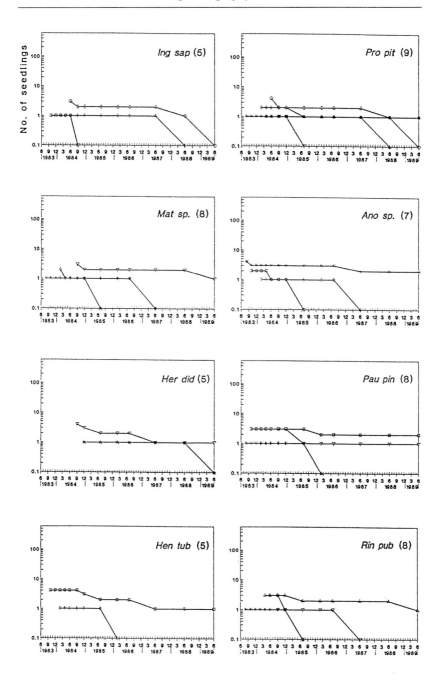

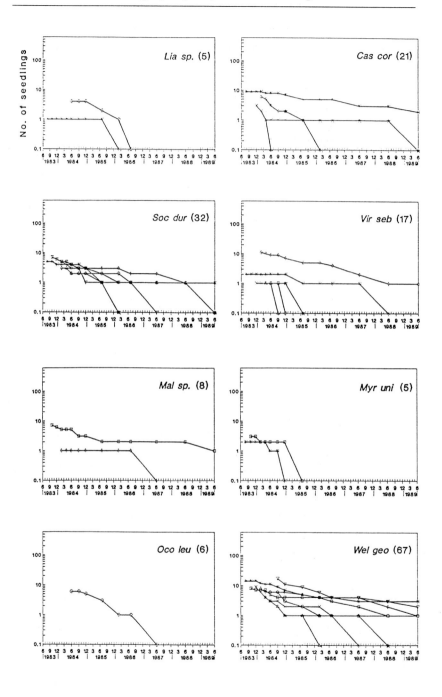

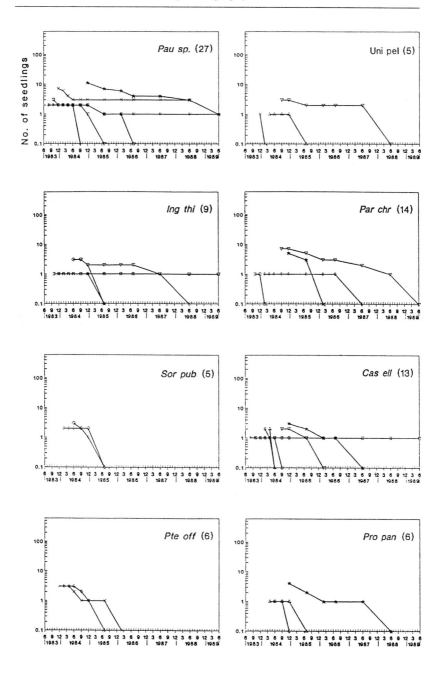

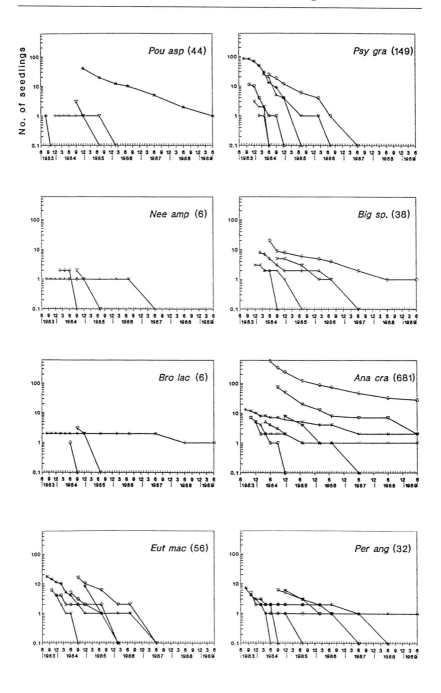

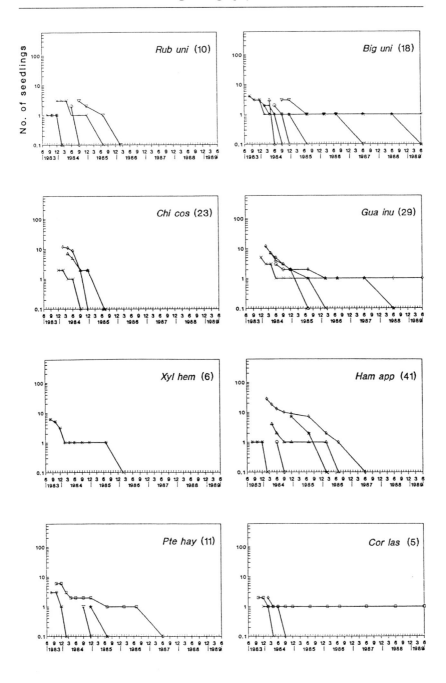

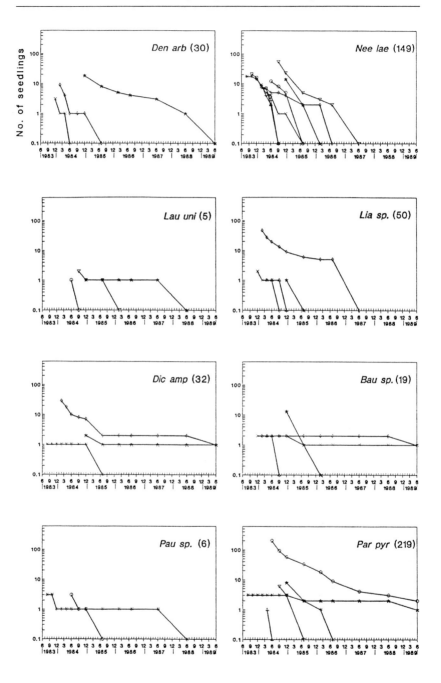

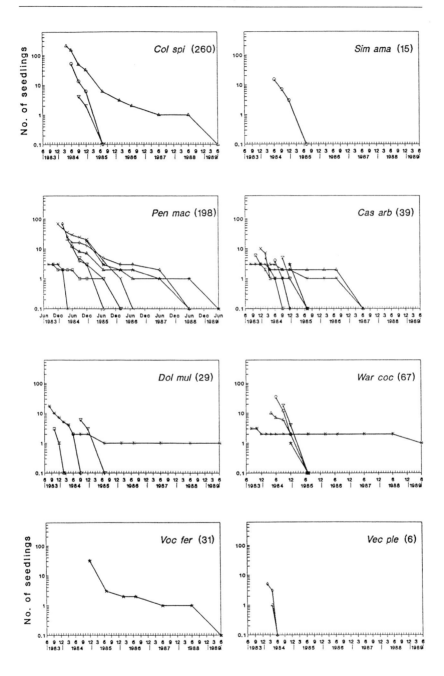

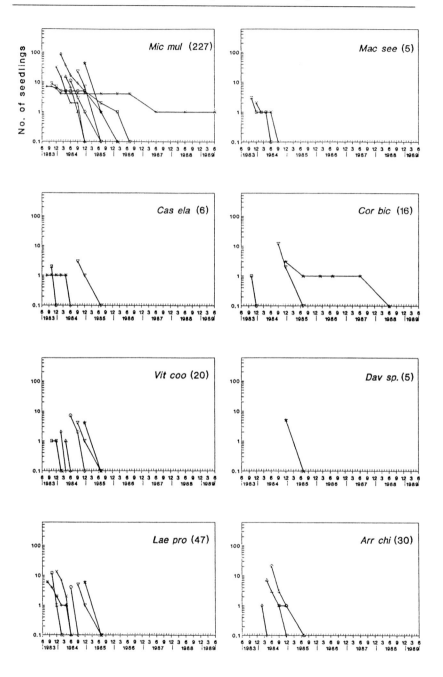

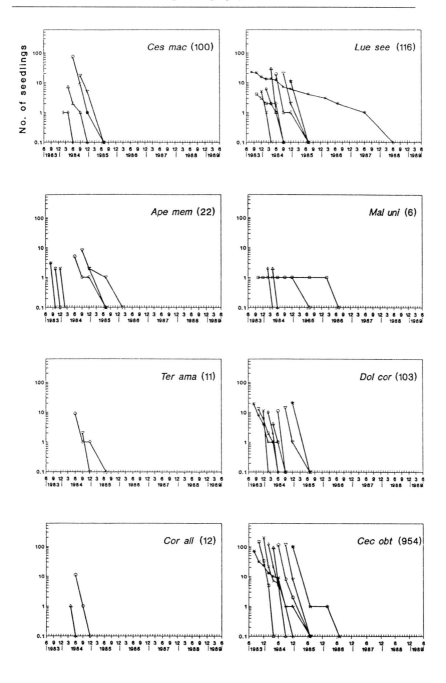

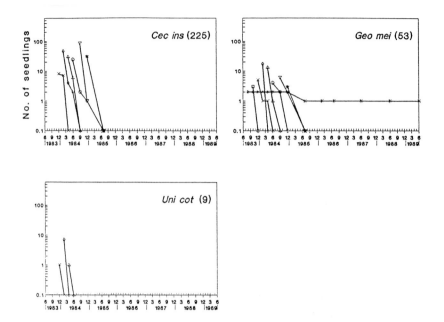

Manuscript received November 1992

CHAPTER 13

RATES OF MORTALITY AND GROWTH IN THREE GROUPS OF DIPTEROCARP SEEDLINGS IN SABAH, MALAYSIA

Margaret J. Still

INTRODUCTION

The most intense mortality in plants often occurs at the juvenile stage (Harper, 1977; Cook, 1979). In forests, the processes which shape future species composition may therefore operate strongly on seedlings and saplings. Differential rates of growth will also influence species composition and forest structure. Growth of the surviving seedlings requires increased light from canopy opening (Whitmore, 1984; Brokaw, 1985; Denslow, 1987), and tree species differ in the amount of light required for increased growth, or 'release' (Swaine and Whitmore, 1988). The need for study of the factors influencing seedling mortality and growth, and their rates in natural populations is often expressed (Richards, 1952; Garwood, 1983; Augspurger, 1984; Wyatt-Smith, 1987). Knowledge of these factors will lead to better understanding of the natural regeneration processes of trees, and has practical application in the management of forests to favour the regeneration of desired timber species.

The Dipterocarpaceae are exclusively non-pioneer, or climax trees (*sensu* Swaine and Whitmore, 1988) and most are large stature canopy or emergent trees. Dipterocarps dominate much of the rain forest of South-East Asia: distribution is centred in the Malesian rain forests, but the range extends to the seasonal forests of the Indian sub-continent. Borneo is the centre of diversity, with 287 species in nine genera, 59 per cent of which are endemic (Ashton, 1982). Two genera, *Shorea* and *Hopea*, are particularly species rich (Ashton, 1988). Dipterocarps in non-seasonal forests are well-known for mast-fruiting, thought to have evolved to satiate seed predators (Janzen, 1970). Fruiting occurs irregularly, but gregariously, usually two or three times per decade (Ashton, 1982). The one-seeded fruits have no dormancy, and most germinate in the shade within a few days of falling. Mortality can be very high immediately after germination, resulting in large fluctuations in seedling numbers over time (Fox, 1972; Whitmore, 1984). Growth rates in closed forest are very low (Fox, 1972), but seedlings can persist for many years (Wyatt-Smith, 1958; Fox, 1972), in some species forming 'seedling banks' of suppressed seedlings generally under 50 cm tall (Meijer and Wood, 1964; Harper, 1977).

Dipterocarps have been divided by foresters, on the basis of field experience and timber density, into the light hardwoods: fast growing species with strongly light-demanding seedlings; and heavy hardwoods: slow-growing species whose seedlings are more tolerant of long periods under closed forest (Meijer and Wood, 1964; Burgess, 1966; Wyatt-Smith, 1966), though there is likely to be a continuum of responses (Whitmore, 1984). The two groups are thus assumed to have differing requirements for regeneration: seedlings of shade-tolerant species can reputedly survive longer in closed forest and respond to smaller gaps with increased growth (release), while seedlings of the light-demanding species are less tolerant of long periods of suppression and require a larger gap for release, responding with faster growth rates. Wyatt-Smith (1958) suggested that the Red Merantis *Shorea leprosula* and *S. parvifolia* required a gap within ten years to commence growth, while other species were tolerant of longer periods of suppression. Responses to increased light following canopy opening are known to be especially strong in the light hardwood Red Meranti species (Nicholson, 1965; Liew and Wong, 1973; Whitmore, 1984). Thus a relatively wide range of response is found within the family.

The objective of this study was to investigate the rates of growth and mortality in natural populations of dipterocarp seedlings in undisturbed rain forest. This chapter focuses on variation in growth and mortality rates of seedlings in two Sections of *Shorea*, both emergent Red Merantis, and in seedlings of canopy species.

METHODS

The study site

The study site lies at the eastern edge of the Danum Valley Conservation Area, Sabah, Malaysia (4° 58′N, 117° 48′E), a 438 km^2 area of dipterocarp rain forest retained for conservation purposes by Yayasan Sabah and the Sabah Forest Department. The study area lies by the Segama River, around 70 km inland and 210 m above sea level. The region is to the south of the main monsoon belt, but is affected by it: strong squally winds are therefore rare, but there are seasonal trends in rainfall. Drier periods occur in April/May and in September between monsoons, and the north-east monsoon brings higher rainfall between November and March. Mean annual rainfall between 1985 and 1990 averaged 2,822 mm (Marsh and Greer, 1992). Within the forest, mean maximum and mean minimum temperatures were 28.4°C and 21.2°C (Brown, 1990). The topography in the study area is undulating, with occasional steep-sided gullies, and the soils are classified as orthic acrisols in the Bang Association, developed over Tertiary sandstones, mudstones and shales of the Kuamut Formation (Wright, 1975).

316

The forest around the study area is classified as Type A, *Parashorea malaanonan*, forest in Fox's (1972) classification of Sabah forest types. This is the dominant forest type on coastal areas in north-east and east Sabah and in the upper Segama catchment, and is characteristic of more fertile soils and areas of lower rainfall (Fox, 1972).

The study was carried out in two permanent enumeration plots (Newbery et al., 1992) in which the co-ordinates, girth and taxonomic identity were known for all trees ≥ 10 cm gbh (girth at breast height, 1.3 m). The family composition and structure of the 4-ha plots are described in detail in Newbery et al. (1992). Mean basal area of trees ≥ 10 cm gbh was $30.7\,\mathrm{m^2\,ha^{-1}}$ ($26.6\,\mathrm{m^2\,ha^{-1}}$ for trees ≥ 30 cm gbh). The plots were dominated by dipterocarps, which for trees ≥ 10 cm gbh contributed on average 9 per cent of tree density, and 13 per cent of the total basal area, rising to 66 per cent for trees ≥ 100 cm gbh. The Red Meranti species in this study contributed 39 per cent of the total basal area in Plot 1 (six species), and 29 per cent in Plot 2 (five species) (D.M. Newbery, unpublished data). Girth distributions show a linear relationship between the logarithms of girth and frequency, indicating a stable size distribution and suggesting no recent major disturbance (Newbery et al., 1992).

The species included in this study are six emergent (exceeding 50 m in height) *Shorea* species and two canopy species in two genera. The *Shorea* species in Section *Mutica*, the Light Red Merantis (LRM): *Shorea argentifolia* Sym., *S. leprosula* Miq., and *S. parvifolia* Dyer, are all large emergent trees, with strongly light-demanding, fast-growing saplings (Meijer and Wood, 1964; Fox, 1972; Ashton, 1982; Whitmore, 1984). The remaining three *Shorea* species are in Section *Brachypterae* and will be referred to as Dark Red Merantis (DRM): *S. johorensis* Foxw. and *S. pauciflora* King are also large emergent trees with light-demanding saplings, the latter generally with heavier timber than the LRM species (Meijer and Wood, 1964) while *S. fallax* Meijer is of smaller stature though still emergent, and is not an important timber species. *S. johorensis* is known to form a 'seedling bank', suggesting greater shade tolerance than the LRM species, although growth rates of the saplings are fast (Meijer and Wood, 1964). The two canopy species (rarely exceeding 30 m in height), *Hopea nervosa* King and *Vatica sarawakensis* Heim. are classified as medium hardwoods (Burgess, 1966).

Seedling enumeration

A seedling was defined as any individual less than 10 cm gbh, the minimum girth for inclusion in the tree enumeration. Seedlings were enumerated within a 2-ha area of Plot 1, and a 0.48-ha area of Plot 2, in which the species composition of dipterocarp trees was similar to that in Plot 1. Each dipterocarp seedling was identified, mapped with reference to the previously mapped trees, marked with a numbered tag, and height was measured. The first enumeration was between July and October, 1986. Subsequent enumerations were carried out in February 1987 (Plot 1 only) and June/July 1988 (both plots). If there was no sign of a seedling after a search of the vicinity it was recorded as dead, and deaths judged to be caused by falling debris were noted. Height of surviving seedlings was measured. Further details are given in Still (1993). Dipterocarp fruiting had not been recorded in the area for the previous three years: all seedlings were therefore assumed to be at least 3 years old at the first enumeration. There were no new recruits during the study period.

Mortality rates (m, % yr^{-1}) were described by the logarithmic model (Swaine and Lieberman, 1987):

$$m = 100 \, (\ln n_0 - \ln n_1) \, / \, t$$

where t is time in years between enumerations, n_0 is the number of individuals present at the beginning, and n_1 the number surviving to the next enumeration.

Seedling growth rates were calculated from the differences in heights (cm) measured at successive enumerations. Estimates of growth are therefore based on net height difference rather than actual growth. Relative Growth Rate (RGR, per cent yr^{-1}) is the change in height relative to initial height, allowing comparison of growth rates between individuals with different initial heights:

$$RGR = 100 \, (\ln H_2 - \ln H_1) \, / \, t$$

where H_1 is the original height, and H_2 the height after time t, the time elapsed in years. Annual absolute height increment, AHI, (cm yr^{-1}) was found from:

$$AHI = (H_2 - H_1) \, / \, t$$

RESULTS

Seedling number and height distribution

Total seedling densities of the Red Meranti *Shorea* species were 1,061 ha^{-1} in Plot 1 and 860 ha^{-1} in Plot 2 (which lacked *S. pauciflora*). Densities of LRM seedlings were 306 ha^{-1} and 360 ha^{-1} in Plots 1 and 2 respectively. Densities of the canopy species were 117 ha^{-1} in Plot 1 and 985 ha^{-1} in Plot 2; the difference was due to the greater number of *H. nervosa* seedlings in Plot 2.

Differences between groups in the proportions of small seedlings (<50 cm tall) may be related to ability to persist under closed canopy, leading to differential mortality. In both plots, DRMs had fewer small seedlings than both LRMs and canopy species (Figure 13.1). Proportions of small seedlings in the LRM and canopy groups were higher in Plot 2 than in Plot 1. Large seedlings (>2 m tall) must have either grown rapidly in response to canopy opening, or have succeeded in growing slowly under a closed canopy. In Plot 2, the proportions of large seedlings were similar in each group, while in Plot 1, LRMs

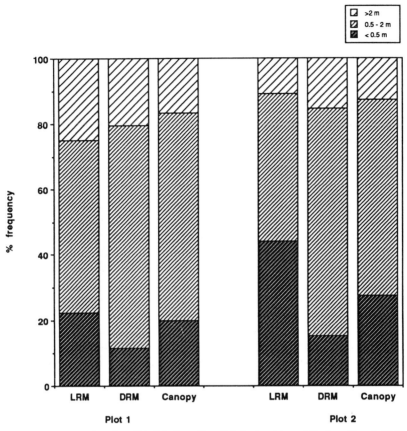

Figure 13.1 Frequencies of small (< 0.5 m), medium (0.5–2 m) and large (>2 m) seedlings in Light Red Merantis (LRM), Dark Red Merantis (DRM) and Canopy species groups in Plots 1 and 2

had significantly more large seedlings than the DRM and canopy groups. Proportions of large seedlings within groups differed between plots only in the LRMs (Figure 13.1).

Mortality of seedlings

Annual mortality rates for all eight species pooled were similar in both plots: 5.95 per cent in Plot 1 and 5.19 per cent in Plot 2 ($\chi^2 = 2.35$, df = 1, $p \geq 0.05$). In both plots, mortality rates in the three groups were ranked in the order LRM > DRM > canopy (Table 13.1). In Plot 1, the differences between groups were all highly significant (χ^2 tests, $p \geq 0.01$). In Plot 2, mortality of LRMs was very significantly higher than the other two groups (χ^2 tests, $p > 0.001$), while mortality rates of DRMs and canopy species were similar

Table 13.1 Seedling densities, and rates of mortality and growth in three groups of seedlings, Light Red Merantis (LRM), Dark Red Merantis (DRM) and canopy species in Plots 1 and 2. Mortality rates were compared with χ^2 tests, growth rates with Mann–Whitney tests: $*p < 0.05$; $**p < 0.01$; $***p < 0.001$; $p \geq 0.05$

Species group		Numbers per ha			Mortality (% yr^{-1})	Growth (% yr^{-1})
		Total	< 0.5 m	> 2 m		
Plot 1	LRM	306	61	67	10.00	5.4
	DRM	755	78	138	6.60	2.4
	Canopy	117	18	16	0.30	0.9
	LRM vs DRM				**	***
	DRM vs Canopy				***	NS
Plot 2	LRM	360	153	40	10.44	7.4
	DRM	500	73	73	3.12	5.0
	Canopy	985	259	90	1.73	3.5
	LRM vs DRM				***	**
	DRM vs Canopy				NS	*

($p \geq 0.05$). Mortality rates of the LRMs were almost identical in both plots at 10 per cent yr^{-1} ($\chi^2 = 0.01$, df = 1, $p \geq 0.05$), while mortality of DRM seedlings in Plot 1 was double the rate in Plot 2, a significant difference ($\chi^2 = 7.11$, df = 1, $p < 0.01$). There was no difference between plots in mortality of canopy species ($\chi^2 = 3.50$, df = 1, $p \geq 0.05$). Litterfall was estimated to account for a minimum of 11.1 per cent of all seedling deaths.

Annual mortality rates in individual species ranged from zero to 16 per cent. In Plot 1, mortality was highest in *S. argentifolia* (15.7 per cent yr^{-1}) and in Plot 2 in *S. parvifolia* (11.7 per cent yr^{-1}). Within each plot the DRM *S. fallax* had lower mortality than the LRMs. Mortality rates were lower in the canopy species: in Plot 1, no seedlings of *V. sarawakensis*, and only one seedling of *H. nervosa* died over the total period. In Plot 2, only one *V. sarawakensis* seedling died (0.9 per cent yr^{-1}), while next lowest mortality was in *H. nervosa*, with annual mortality of 2.0 per cent.

Mortality rates for two consecutive intervals were estimated only in Plot 1 populations. For each species, the null hypothesis was tested that mortality rates did not change over time, using the log model equation (which assumes constant mortality over time) to predict the number expected to die over the second interval given the observed rate over the first interval. Predicted number of deaths was compared with the observed number using a χ^2 goodness-of-fit test. Mortality rates were significantly higher over the second interval than over the first in two LRMs, *S. argentifolia* and *S. leprosula*, ($\chi^2 = 15.13$, $p < 0.01$; $\chi^2 = 4.31$, $p < 0.05$ respectively, df = 1) and in *S. johorensis* ($\chi^2 = 9.14$, df = 1, $p < 0.01$) (Figure 13.2). Mortality of LRMs as a group was significantly higher over the second interval ($\chi^2 = 6.81$, df = 1, $p < 0.01$),

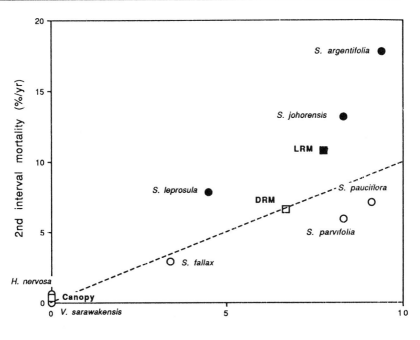

Figure 13.2 Comparison of mortality rates in the first and second interval for species and Light and Dark Red Meranti Groups (LRM. DRM) in Plot 1. Diagonal dashed line indicates equal mortality in the two intervals; filled symbols indicate the two rates were significantly different ($p < 0.05$)

increasing from 7.75 per cent to 10.74 per cent yr^{-1}. In contrast, mortality rates in DRM seedlings did not change ($\chi^2 = 0.02$, df = 1, $p \geq 0.05$).

Mortality and seedling size

The pattern of varying mortality rates with size differed between species (Figure 13.3). In the two species with highest rates (> 10 per cent yr^{-1}), *S. argentifolia* and *S. johorensis*, mortality was high in most height classes. In species with intermediate mortality rates (5–10 per cent yr^{-1}), *S. leprosula*, *S. parvifolia*, and *S. pauciflora*, there was a clear distinction in mortality between seedlings smaller and larger than 50 cm tall, with the smallest seedlings experiencing much higher mortality than larger seedlings. The contrast was greatest in *S. leprosula*, with mortality of 30 per cent yr^{-1} in seedlings under 50 cm tall, over five times higher than in the next larger size class. In *S. fallax*, mortality was similar, and low, in all height classes. Although in general, mortality was highest in smaller seedlings, several species showed secondary peaks in mortality in larger seedlings, between 1.5 and 2 m tall. Mortality

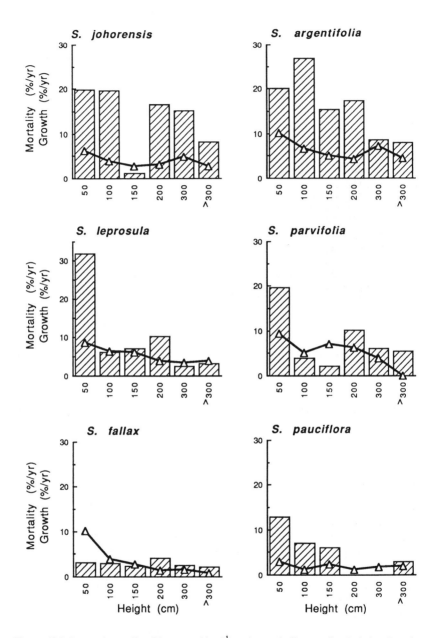

Figure 13.3 Rates of mortality (histogram, % yr^{-1}) and growth (line, median Relative Growth Rate, % yr^{-1}) in six height classes for Red Meranti species in Plot 1

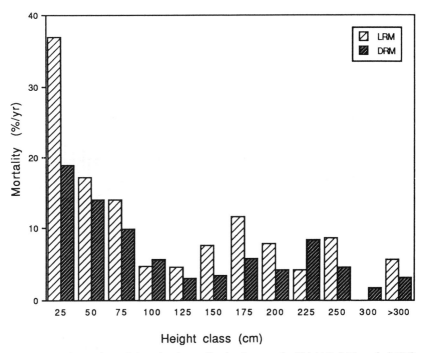

Figure 13.4 Comparison of size-related mortality (total per cent) of Light Red Merantis (LRM) and Dark Red Merantis (DRM) in Plot 1

rates in the LRMs were generally higher than in DRMs in most height classes (Figure 13.4). There was a secondary peak in mortality in larger seedlings of both LRM and DRM groups.

Growth of seedlings

In both plots, median growth rates of LRM seedlings were significantly higher than both DRM and canopy seedlings (Table 13.1). DRM seedlings grew faster than canopy seedlings in Plot 2, but there was no difference in Plot 1. In individual species, median RGR was highest in *S. argentifolia*, at 7.1 per cent yr^{-1} in Plot 1 and 11.1 per cent yr^{-1} in Plot 2. The equivalent absolute height increments were 5.6 cm yr^{-1} (Plot 1) and 7.7 cm yr^{-1} (Plot 2). The other LRMs had moderately high RGRs, ranging from 4.1 per cent yr^{-1} to 7.2 per cent yr^{-1}. Lowest growth rates were in the two canopy species, and in *S. pauciflora*, each with median height increments below 2 cm yr^{-1}.

A proportion of seedlings suffered net height loss between enumerations, mostly caused by falling debris breaking or bending over the stem, while many seedlings had net growth rates around zero. Seedlings were divided into

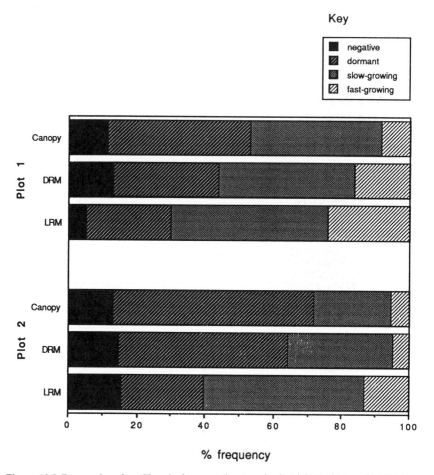

Figure 13.5 Frequencies of seedlings in four growth categories in Light Red Merantis (LRM), Dark Red Merantis (DRM) and Canopy species in Plots 1 and 2. Growth categories are based on net relative growth rate over twenty-two months: 'negative', < -4 per cent yr^{-1}; 'dormant', -4 to $+4$ per cent yr^{-1}; 'slow-growing', $> 4-16$ per cent yr^{-1}; 'fast-growing', > 16 per cent yr^{-1}

categories based on net relative growth rates: 'dormant' seedlings were defined as those with annual growth rates between -4 per cent and $+4$ per cent. The group with positive increments was subdivided into 'slow-growing' ($> 4-16$ per cent yr^{-1}) and 'fast-growing' (> 16 per cent yr^{-1}). 'Negative' increments were defined as those less than -4 per cent yr^{-1}.

The proportion of seedlings with positive growth rates decreased in the order LRM $>$ DRM $>$ canopy, while the proportion of dormant seedlings increased in the same order (Figure 13.5). A similar proportion of seedlings had negative increments in each group. Significantly more LRM seedlings than DRM and canopy seedlings had positive growth rates in both plots. In DRMs,

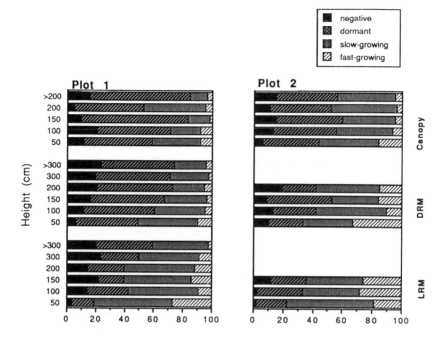

Figure 13.6 Frequencies of seedlings in four growth categories in different height classes in Light Red Merantis (LRM), Dark Red Merantis (DRM) and Canopy species in Plots 1 and 2. Height classes were combined if $n < 20$: thus largest height class for Plot 2 LRMs is seedlings > 150 cm tall, and for DRMs, > 200 cm tall. Growth categories are based on net relative growth rate over twenty-two months: 'negative', < -4 per cent yr^{-1}; 'dormant', -4 to $+4$ per cent yr^{-1}; 'slow-growing', > 4–16 per cent yr^{-1}; 'fast-growing', > 16 per cent yr^{-1}

the proportions of seedlings in each category were similar to those in canopy species in Plot 1, but differed in Plot 2. Although the pattern of variation between groups was similar in the two plots, the proportions of seedlings in the three growth categories differed significantly between plots in each of the three groups. In LRMs, Plot 2 had more positively-growing seedlings than Plot 1 ($\chi^2 = 10.29$, df = 2, $p < 0.01$ [the two positive growth categories were combined for testing]). In DRMs and canopy species ($\chi^2 = 33.49$, $\chi^2 = 17.84$ respectively, df = 2, $p < 0.001$ in both groups), Plot 2 again had more seedlings with positive increments and fewer dormant seedlings.

Growth category and seedling height

The proportion of positive growth rates was generally highest in small seedlings, and dropped to lower levels in larger size classes (Figure 13.6).

Frequency of negative increments increased with size in the DRMs, but in Plot 1 peaked in LRM seedlings around 2 m tall, decreasing in larger seedlings. Differences between the Meranti groups were most marked in small seedlings, especially in Plot 1: around half of DRM seedlings under 50 cm tall had zero or negative increments compared to only one-fifth of LRMs. In Plot 1, over half the LRM seedlings in all height classes except the largest had positive increments, compared to fewer than half the DRM seedlings in each height class; canopy species were more similar to DRMs, with up to 45 per cent of seedlings having positive increments in each height class. Differences between groups were less marked in Plot 2, where more seedlings in most height/species group combinations achieved positive growth rates (Figure 13.6).

Size-related variation in growth and mortality

If there are size classes in which mortality is high, but growth low, then because more time is spent in that height class, the risk of mortality is magnified. Conversely, size classes with the combination of high growth rates and low mortality rates may indicate enhanced performance. In species with seedlings tolerant of suppression, small seedlings may be expected to show low rates of both mortality and growth. In less tolerant species, small seedlings should show high mortality, but high growth rates of the survivors.

High rates of both mortality and growth occurred in small seedlings in all the *Shorea* species except *S. fallax* (Figure 13.3). The LRM species and *S. johorensis* (DRM) showed secondary peaks in growth and mortality in larger seedlings. In *S. argentifolia* and *S. leprosula*, the secondary growth peak coincided with relatively lower mortality in seedlings over 2 m tall, suggesting that 'release' may occur at this stage. The remaining two DRMs differed from each other in the pattern of size-related growth and mortality. In *S. pauciflora*, mortality generally decreased with increasing size, but growth was similar in all height classes. In contrast, mortality in *S. fallax* was constant with size, but growth rates were high in the smallest seedlings, paralleling the LRM pattern of growth.

Mortality and previous growth rate

In DRM seedlings, the risk of dying decreased steadily with increasing growth rate in the previous interval (Figure 13.7). In LRMs the pattern was less clear, and highest mortality was in seedlings with fast growth rates in the preceding interval. There was no difference between Meranti groups in subsequent mortality of seedlings with negative increments, suggesting that seedlings in both groups had similar abilities to survive stem damage. Dormant LRM seedlings were significantly more likely to die than dormant DRM

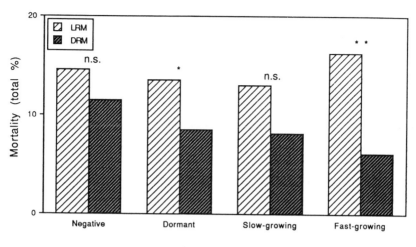

Figure 13.7 Comparison of total per cent mortality between Light Red Merantis (LRM) and Dark Red Merantis (DRM) with different growth rates in the preceding interval. Results of χ^2 test (df = 1) for differences between LRMs and DRMs are indicated: *, $p < 0.05$; **, $p < 0.01$; n.s., $p \geq 0.05$. Growth categories are based on net relative growth rate over 22 months: 'negative', < -4 per cent yr^{-1}; 'dormant', -4 to $+4$ per cent yr^{-1}; 'slow-growing', > 4–16 per cent yr^{-1}; 'fast-growing', > 16 per cent yr^{-1}

seedlings (χ^2 = 3.91, df = 1, $p < 0.05$), and LRM seedlings with positive growth rates were also significantly more likely to die than positively-growing DRM seedlings (χ^2 = 7.27, df = 1, $p < 0.01$). For seedlings which had grown rapidly over the first interval (over 16 per cent yr^{-1}), mortality of LRMs in the second interval was double that of DRMs (Figure 13.7).

Relationships between rates of mortality and growth, and population size

The observed differences between species in seedling growth and mortality rates might have an effect on population size. Numbers of seedlings in species with high mortality rates, for example the Light Red Merantis, are known to fluctuate over time as mast fruiting is followed by rapid die-off of small seedlings (Fox, 1972). In species with lower mortality rates, such as the DRMs and canopy species, seedlings may accumulate over time, leading to high population size. In species with few seedlings, low mortality may be necessary if numbers are to be maintained over time.

Rates of mortality and median growth over twenty-two months for the eight species in Plot 1 are plotted against initial population size (Figure 13.8). The species can be divided into three non-overlapping groups: species with intermediate numbers of seedlings, and high rates of growth and mortality; species with large seedling populations, low growth rates and low mortality;

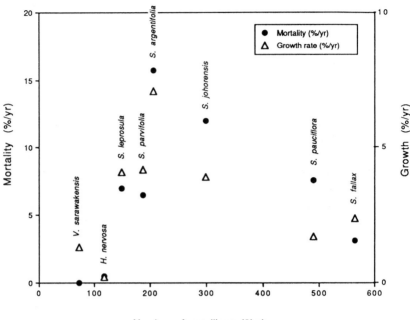

Figure 13.8 Relationship between rates of growth (median Relative Growth Rate, per cent yr^{-1}) and mortality (per cent yr^{-1}) and population size in individual species in Plot 1

and species with small seedling populations, and low growth and mortality rates. Group 1 comprises *S. johorensis* and the Light Red Merantis: *S. argentifolia*, *S. leprosula* and *S. parvifolia*. Group 2 includes the remaining Dark Red Merantis: *S. fallax* and *S. pauciflora*. The species of the main canopy, *H. nervosa*, and *V. sarawakensis* form Group 3. *S. johorensis* falls into Group 1, having similar rates of growth and mortality and population size to the three LRM species, despite its closer taxonomic affinity with the DRM species. Low rates of growth and mortality were found in species with both low and high population size. The high rates of mortality and growth in LRMs and *S. johorensis* suggest more dynamic seedling populations, with numbers likely to fluctuate more over time than the other species groups.

DISCUSSION

Seedling densities are lower than those reported for comparable areas of Sabah. Fox (1972) describes dipterocarp seedling densities of between 11,000 and 57,000 ha^{-1} as typical for Sabah forests, though the high spatial and temporal variation in seedling numbers is emphasized. The mean density of all dipterocarp seedlings at Danum was around 2,000 ha^{-1}: there may have been substantial mortality of the most recent recruits over the three years at least since the last mass fruiting event. Liew and Wong (1973) reported densities of *S. johorensis* in eastern Sabah of 390 to over 10,000 ha^{-1}, emphasizing the very high variation. The mean density for this species at Danum was 188 ha^{-1}.

Differences between groups or species in the proportions of small and large seedlings may reflect differences in shade tolerance and ability to grow in the understorey. High proportions of small seedlings were found in both relatively shade-tolerant canopy species (*H. nervosa* in Plot 2) and in strongly light-demanding species (*S. argentifolia* in both plots and *S. parvifolia* in Plot 2). The large proportion of small seedlings in *S. argentifolia* is surprising, given the high mortality rate in this species; these may be the result of particularly high recent recruitment. The mortality of smallest seedlings was higher in LRMs than in DRMs, and the difference in mortality of the smallest seedlings (<25 cm tall) versus taller seedlings was greater in LRMs than in DRMs, suggesting that there are differences in shade tolerance between the two Meranti groups.

Differences in the proportion of large seedlings may indicate different abilities to survive and grow slowly under low light levels. Alternatively, seedlings may be large because they are, or were, growing fast in a canopy opening. Thus, low mortality rates, or fast growth rates, could both lead to an accumulation of large saplings in the population. The evidence appears to point to both possibilities. High proportions of large seedlings occurred both in species with low mortality rates (*S. fallax* and *H. nervosa* in Plot 1), and those with high mortality and growth rates (*S. johorensis* and most of the LRMs). On the other hand, *V. sarawakensis*, with a very low mortality rate, had few large seedlings. There were clear differences between the LRM species in the proportions of both small and large seedlings (Still, 1993) despite their close taxonomic affinity and similar growth and mortality rates. Although there were significant differences between groups in mortality and growth rates, the proportions of small and large seedlings were quite similar in each group, and varied more between species within groups. In summary, there was no clear association between light-demanding status and the proportions of small and large seedlings in each group. The results suggest, however, that small LRM seedlings can persist for years in closed forest. The proportions of large seedlings in light-demanding species were no lower than in more shade-tolerant species, and the proportion of seedlings achieving fast growth rates was higher in the LRMs than in other groups, suggesting that light levels must be sufficiently high, or small canopy openings frequent enough, to allow growth of the light-demanding species in relatively closed canopy conditions (only 0.5 per cent of the forest in the plots was estimated to be gap, and mean gap size was only 23 m^2 (Newbery et al., 1992)).

Mortality rates in the three groups were ranked in the order LRM > DRM > canopy, and growth rates were ordered in the same way. Rates of both mortality and growth were consistently very significantly higher in LRMs than in

DRM and canopy seedlings in both plots. Differences between DRM and canopy seedlings were less consistent: DRM seedlings grew faster than canopy species in Plot 2, but not in Plot 1, while mortality of DRMs was higher than that of canopy species within Plot 1 but not Plot 2. Although the ranking of groups in terms of both growth and mortality rates was the same in both plots, there were some significant differences between plots in the absolute values within groups. Mortality of DRMs was significantly higher in Plot 1 than in Plot 2. In general, growth rates of all groups were faster in Plot 2 than in Plot 1: DRMs in Plot 2 grew as fast as LRMs in Plot 1, and the growth rate of canopy seedlings in Plot 2 was higher than that of both canopy and DRM seedlings in Plot 1. Examination of the growth categories shows that a greater proportion of seedlings in each group achieved fast growth rates (> 16 per cent yr^{-1}) in Plot 2. These observations suggest that light levels may be higher within the seedling study area of Plot 2 than in Plot 1. The higher relative growth rates recorded in Plot 2 may also be at least partly due to the higher density of small seedlings (< 50 cm tall: Plot 2, 485 ha^{-1}; Plot 1, 157 ha^{-1}), which have higher RGRs than larger seedlings. The fact that, in each plot, the ranking of groups in terms of growth and mortality rates, and significant differences between groups, are both maintained, suggests that there are clear differences between the groups in their inherent rates of growth and mortality, despite varying environmental conditions.

The ranking of the three groups in the same order for both mortality and growth rates suggests that there is a correlation between persistence (survival) and response to light (growth rate). In the DRMs, low mortality rates may have led to seedlings accumulating over time. In contrast, the LRMs appear to have more dynamic seedling populations, and higher mortality rates have resulted in population sizes which are currently lower than the DRMs.

ACKNOWLEDGEMENTS

The Malaysian Socio-Economic Research Council and the Danum Valley Management Committee granted permission to carry out this study. The Natural Environmental Research Council and the Royal Society South-East Asia Rain Forest Research Programme provided funding. E.J.F. Campbell, Y.F. Lee and C.R. Ridsdale assisted with taxonomic identification of the dipterocarps. I am grateful to D. McC. Newbery and M.D. Swaine for advice throughout the study and helpful comments on earlier drafts; and to S.F. Sutton-Jones for assistance with field-work.

REFERENCES

Ashton, P.S. (1982). Dipterocarpaceae. *Flora Malesiana*, Series. I, **9**, 237–552.

Ashton, P.S. (1988). Dipterocarp reproductive biology. In Leith, H. and Werger, M.A. (eds.), *Tropical Forest Ecosystems. B. Biogeographical and Ecological Studies*, pp. 219–40. Amsterdam, Elsevier.

Augspurger, C.K. (1984). Light requirements of neotropical tree seedlings: a comparative study of growth and survival. *Journal of Ecology*, **72**, 777–95.

Brokaw, N.V.L. (1985). Gap-phase regeneration in a tropical forest. *Ecology*, **66**, 682–7.

Brown, N. (1990). *Dipterocarp Regeneration in Tropical Rain Forest Gaps of Different Sizes*. Ph.D. Thesis, University of Oxford.

Burgess, P.F. (1966). Timbers of Sabah. *Sabah Forest Records* No. **6**. Forest Department, Sabah, Malaysia.

Cook, R.E. (1979). Patterns of juvenile mortality and recruitment in plants. In Solbrig, O.T., Jain, S., Johnson, G.B. and Raven, P.H. (eds.), *Topics in Plant Population Biology*, pp. 207-231. Columbia University Press, New York.

Denslow, J.S. (1987). Tropical rain forest gaps and tree diversity. *Annual Review of Ecology and Systematics*, **18**, 432–51.

Fox, E.D. (1972). *The Natural Vegetation of Sabah and Natural Regeneration of the Dipterocarp Forests*. Ph.D. thesis, University of Wales.

Garwood, N.C. (1983). Seed germination in a seasonal tropical forest in Panama: a community study. *Ecological Monographs*, **55**, 159–81.

Harper, J. (1977). *Population Biology of Plants*. Academic Press, New York.

Janzen, D.H. (1970). Herbivores and the number of tree species in tropical forests. *American Naturalist*, **104**, 501–28.

Liew, T.C. and Wong, F.O. (1973). Density, recruitment, mortality and growth of Dipterocarp seedlings in virgin and logged-over forests in Sabah. *Malaysian Forester*, **36**, 3–15.

Marsh, C.W. and Greer, A.G. (1992). Forest land-use in Sabah, Malaysia: an introduction to the Danum Valley. *Philosophical Transactions of the Royal Society, London*, Series B, **335**, 327–30.

Meijer, W. and Wood, G.H.S. (1964). Dipterocarps of Sabah (North Borneo). *Sabah Forest Record* No. **5**. Forest Department, Sandakan, Sabah, Malaysia.

Newbery, D. M., Campbell, E.F., Lee, Y.F., Ridsdale, C.E. and Still, M.J. (1992). Primary lowland dipterocarp forest at Danum Valley, Sabah, Malaysia: structure, relative abundance and family composition. *Philosophical Transactions of the Royal Society of London*, Series B, **335**, 341–56.

Nicholson, D.I. (1965). A review of natural regeneration in the Dipterocarp forests of Sabah. *Malayan Forester*, **28**, 4–24.

Richards, P.W. (1952). *The Tropical Rain Forest*. Cambridge University Press, Cambridge.

Still, M.J. (1993). *Population Dynamics and Spatial Patterns of Dipterocarp Seedlings in a Tropical Rain Forest*. Ph.D. thesis, University of Stirling.

Swaine, M.D. and Lieberman, D. (1987). Note on the calculation of mortality rates. *Journal of Tropical Ecology*, **3**, ii–iii.

Swaine, M.D. and Whitmore, T.C. (1988). On the definition of ecological species groups in tropical rain forests. *Vegetatio*, **75**, 81–6.

Whitmore, T.C. (1984). *Tropical Rain Forests of the Far East*. Second Edition. Oxford University Press, Oxford.

Wright, P.S. (1975). *The Soils of Sabah*. Vol 3, western parts of Tawau and Lahad Datu Districts. Land Resource Study 10. Ministry of Overseas Development, London.

Wyatt-Smith, J. (1958). Seedling/sapling survival of *Shorea leprosula, Shorea parvifolia* and *Koompassia malaccensis. Malayan Forester*, **21**, 185–93.

Wyatt-Smith, J. (1966). Ecological studies on Malayan forests. *Malayan Forestry Department Research Pamphlet 52*. Forest Research Institute, Kepong, Malaysia.

Wyatt-Smith, J. (1987). Foreword to Swaine, M.D. and Lieberman, D (eds.), The dynamics of tree populations in tropical forest. *Journal of Tropical Ecology*, **3**, iv.

Revised manuscript received December 1994

INDEX

Page numbers in **bold** type refer to figures, and those in *italics* to tables.